THE LUNG

CLINICAL PHYSIOLOGY *and*
PULMONARY FUNCTION TESTS

THE LUNG

CLINICAL PHYSIOLOGY
and PULMONARY FUNCTION TESTS

by

JULIUS H. COMROE, JR., M.D.
*Director, Cardiovascular Research Institute, and
Professor of Physiology, University of
California Medical Center, San Francisco*

ROBERT E. FORSTER, II, M.D.
*Professor of Physiology, Graduate School
of Medicine, University of Pennsylvania, Philadelphia*

ARTHUR B. DUBOIS, M.D.
*Professor of Physiology, Graduate School
of Medicine, University of Pennsylvania, Philadelphia*

WILLIAM A. BRISCOE, M.D.
*Associate Professor of Medicine, Columbia University
College of Physicians and Surgeons, New York*

ELIZABETH CARLSEN, Ph.D.
*Assistant Professor of Physiology, Columbia University
College of Physicians and Surgeons, New York*

SECOND EDITION

YEAR BOOK MEDICAL PUBLISHERS · INC.
35 EAST WACKER DRIVE · CHICAGO

Reprinted, August 1955
Reprinted, February 1956
Reprinted, May 1957
Lithoprinted, July 1959
Lithoprinted, February 1959
Lithoprinted, October 1959
Lithoprinted, August 1960
Second Edition, 1962
Reprinted, March, 1963

Translations of the First Edition have appeared in
French, Italian, Japanese and Spanish.

Library of Congress Catalog Card Number: 61-10997

PRINTED IN U.S.A.

Preface to the Second Edition

THE FIRST EDITION OF *The Lung* has been translated into Spanish, Japanese, French and Italian. Some wit then remarked, "It would be nice if someone translated it into English!" This second edition represents the "English translation." Practically all of the equations and their derivations have been moved to the Appendix and much of the original text has been rewritten with the intent of clarifying difficult concepts.

The most important change in this edition has been the addition of five chapters designed for the clinician. The first of these classifies pulmonary function tests into office, cardiopulmonary laboratory, or research procedures and indicates what can be learned from simple tests and when to ask for special, more complex studies. The second presents typical patterns of altered pulmonary function and cases illustrative of each. The third deals with special respiratory and pulmonary problems encountered by the anesthetist and surgeon and the fourth with the important questions of pulmonary disability and objective evaluation of pulmonary function in compensation cases. The fifth is a chapter on physiological therapy of pulmonary disease, which presents the rationale for treatment of acute and chronic respiratory and pulmonary disorders.

We wish to express our appreciation to reviewers of the first edition who pointed out the major omissions in it; we have followed their suggestions and hope that this second edition will be more useful to both clinicians and medical students.

—J. H. COMROE, JR.
—R. E. FORSTER, II
—A. B. DuBOIS
—W. A. BRISCOE
—E. CARLSEN

v

Preface to the First Edition

PULMONARY PHYSIOLOGISTS understand pulmonary physiology reasonably well. Many doctors and medical students do not. One reason is that most pulmonary physiologists, in their original and review articles, write for other pulmonary physiologists and not for doctors or medical students. This is *not* a book for pulmonary physiologists; it is written for doctors and medical students. Like the Beaumont Lecture* upon which it is based, it has only one purpose—to explain in simple words and diagrams those aspects of pulmonary physiology that are important to clinical medicine.

A few words of explanation:

1. This is not an illustrated book but a monograph constructed largely around illustrations. Most of the illustrations are schematic; artistic license has been used freely to achieve clarity.

2. Our monograph strives for understanding of physiological principles and broad concepts more than for technical completeness. Details of procedures have been presented in an earlier publication (*Methods in Medical Research* [Chicago: Year Book Publishers, Inc., 1950], Vol. 2).

3. Pulmonary physiology can be explained in words, pictures, or equations. Most physicians shudder at equations; therefore words and pictures predominate and the occasional equation is accompanied by a verbal explanation and full apology. However, all important equations are presented in an Appendix for the enjoyment of those who have difficulty with words and pictures.

4. There are no references in the text. This is not because we wish to slight pulmonary physiologists (including ourselves) but because doc-

---

* "The Physiological Diagnosis of Pulmonary Disease," delivered by J. H. Comroe, Jr., to the Wayne County Medical Society, Detroit, February 1, 1954.

umentation often breaks the continuity of thought. Selected references are given in the Appendix, but even these represent only a small fraction of important articles that have been written on this subject.

5. The case reports (Part II) have been presented deliberately with minimal clinical detail, and the reader is asked to accept that the diagnoses have been based on adequate clinical study.

6. This is not a primer; a primer would not enable the physician to cope with some of the more baffling concepts such as ventilation/blood flow ratios, diffusing capacity, physiological dead space, distribution, compliance, alveolar ventilation, or transpulmonary pressure. On the other hand, this is not an encyclopedia, and no attempt has been made to include all contributions in this small volume.

—J. H. COMROE, JR.
—R. E. FORSTER, II
—A. B. DUBOIS
—W. A. BRISCOE
—E. CARLSEN

Table of Contents

PART II

CLINICAL APPLICATIONS

PART III (Appendix)

PART ONE

CHAPTER 1

Introduction to Pulmonary Physiology

THE MAJOR FUNCTION of the cardiovascular and respiratory systems is to provide an adequate amount of *arterialized* blood at each moment to all of the tissues of the body. The lungs alone cannot accomplish this. Several processes are involved: First, mixed venous blood, low in O_2 and high in CO_2, is returned to the right atrium and ventricle to be pumped through the pulmonary circulation. Second, the mixed venous blood flowing through the pulmonary capillaries is arterialized, i.e., receives O_2 from the alveolar gas and gives off excess CO_2. Third, the arterialized blood is distributed to all of the tissues of the body according to their needs. Fourth, exchange of O_2 and CO_2 occurs between the blood in the tissue capillaries and the tissue cells themselves. The first, third and fourth of these processes are the major function of the cardiovascular system. The second process, the loading of mixed venous blood with enough O_2 at a high enough pressure and the unloading of excess CO_2, is the primary function of the lung; this monograph discusses only *pulmonary* function.

In the past two decades, a large number of physiologic tests has been developed for the qualitative and quantitative evaluation of pulmonary function in patients with suspected abnormalities of the cardiopulmonary system. These are now as important to the practice of medicine as are tests of hepatic, renal, cardiovascular and neuromuscular function, developed earlier. Tests of pulmonary function have proved to be of definite value both in diagnosis and in guiding therapy of patients with cardiopulmonary disorders. They have led to a better understanding of pulmonary physiology in healthy men and women of all age groups and to more precise knowledge of the pathologic physiology and natural course of pulmonary disease. They have aided in the early detection of pulmonary dysfunction in some patients considered to be normal on the basis of clinical and radiologic examination and have assisted in differential diagnosis in patients with a known disease in whom a specific diagnosis could not be made with certainty by other methods. They have been used for the objective evaluation of therapeutic measures such as the use of oxygen, helium-oxygen, pressure breathing, bronchodilators, cortisone, antibiotics, artificial respiration and surgical procedures and so have contributed to the development of more rational measures of treatment. Finally, they have been invaluable in securing physical, measurable data in patients who may or may not have pulmonary disability, and in determining, during the lifetime of the patient, the specific function of the lung that has been impaired.

The introduction of physiologic tests does not mean that these have supplanted other diagnostic procedures. Physiologic tests indicate only how disease has altered *function;* they cannot make an anatomic, a bacteriologic or a pathologic diagnosis. For example, function tests may reveal the existence of a right-to-left shunt but in themselves cannot locate it anatomically as being intracardiac or intrapulmonic. Again, physiologic tests may indicate that there is impairment of diffusion across the alveolo-capillary membranes but cannot differentiate interstitial edema from intra-alveolar edema, nor can they determine whether the intra-alveolar fluid is exudate or transudate. Furthermore, they do not reveal alterations in all types of pulmonary disease but do so only when the lesion disturbs *function* and disturbs it sufficiently that present tests can recognize with certainty the deviation from normal values. In general, they cannot detect slight reduction in functioning pulmonary tissue or the presence of small regions in the lungs that have neither ventilation nor blood flow. Results of physiologic tests will be normal in the presence of lesions such as fibrotic tuberculous cavities, cysts or carcinomatous nodules unless these lesions occupy so much space that they reduce the lung volume well below normal limits or are located so strategically that they disturb pulmonary function. Pulmonary function studies will not tell *where* the lesion is, *what* the lesion is or even that a lesion exists, if it does not interfere with the function of the lung. Therefore they supplement and do not replace a good history and physical examination, radiologic, bacteriologic, bronchoscopic and pathologic studies.

As in the case of physiologic tests of other systems, no *single* pulmonary function test yields all the information desired in any single patient.

The primary function of the lung is, as already stated, to arterialize the mixed venous blood. This involves the addition of adequate amounts of O_2 and the elimination of proper quantities of CO_2. This is achieved by pulmonary gas exchange which involves a number of processes (Fig. 1). The first of these is VENTILATION; this includes both *volume* and *distribution* of the air ventilating the alveoli. A large enough *volume* of inspired air must reach the alveoli each minute, and this air must be *distributed evenly* to the hundreds of millions of alveoli in the lungs; i.e., the volume of air going to each alveolus should be in proportion to the volume of that alveolus. The second of these is the process of DIFFUSION, by which O_2 and CO_2 pass across the alveolocapillary membranes. The third is PULMONARY CAPILLARY BLOOD FLOW; this must be adequate in *volume* and all of the mixed venous blood must be *distributed evenly* to all the ventilated alveoli.

This admittedly is an arbitrary division of the complex and inter-related functions of the lungs which have as their primary purpose the uptake of an adequate amount of O_2 and the elimination of excess CO_2. Furthermore, it ignores a matter of great importance, namely, that this gas exchange should be achieved with a minimal expenditure of energy by the respiratory and circulatory systems. The *work* involved in arteri-alizing the venous blood formerly was largely neglected. However, the *mechanical factors* in ventilation are of great importance, because in some patients adequate pulmonary gas exchange may be achieved only by a considerable increase in the work of the respiratory muscles; indeed, in patients with advanced pulmonary disease, the crucial factor in sur-vival may be whether the maximal effort available can produce adequate ventilation. Finally, the work required of the right ventricle in pumping blood through a restricted pulmonary vascular bed may also be of critical importance in survival. Figure 1, *5,* presents a schematic summary of some of the mechanical factors involved in gas exchange. The left side summarizes the processes involved in gas exchange between the alveoli and the pulmonary capillary bed; the right side illustrates that, for ade-quate inspiration, sufficient force must be applied to the lungs (by expan-sion of the thorax) to stretch elastic tissue components (coiled spring) and to overcome frictional resistance in the pulmonary tissues (shaded area in the coil) and in the airways (parallel lines). These mechanical factors in breathing are discussed in detail in Chapter 7.

The quantitative measurement of *all* of these processes requires a large number of physiologic tests. Not all of these tests are required in the management of each patient. Some of the tests are very simple and may

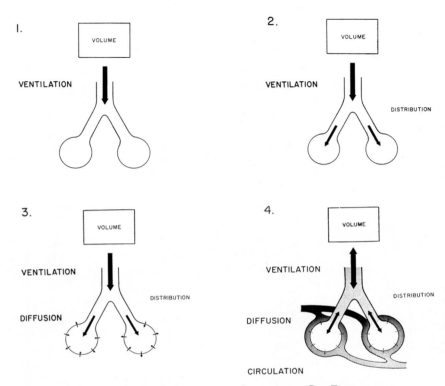

FIG. 1.—PROCESSES INVOLVED IN PULMONARY GAS EXCHANGE

The alveoli, where rapid gas exchange occurs, are represented by rounded areas; leading into these are tubes depicting the conducting airways or anatomic dead space (light gray in 4) in which no effective gas exchange occurs. Rectangular blocks indicate the minute volume of breathing. The two arrows entering the alveoli show distribution of total inspired gas (large arrow) to various alveoli. In 3 and 4, small arrows crossing alveolar walls designate the process of diffusion of O_2 out of the alveoli into the blood and of CO_2 from the blood into the alveoli. The shaded channel surrounding the alveoli in 4 represents pulmonary blood flow; it enters the capillary bed as mixed venous blood (dark) and emerges as arterialized blood (light). In 5, the left side is a summary of the processes of ventilation, diffusion and circulation. The right side represents the pulmonary "tissues" responsible for the mechanical properties of the lung: parallel lines in the conducting airways represent the fine airways responsible for airway resistance; the springlike coil surrounding the alveoli represents the elastic tissues of the lung, and stippled areas in the coil are the non-elastic tissues (see Chapter 7).

4

5.

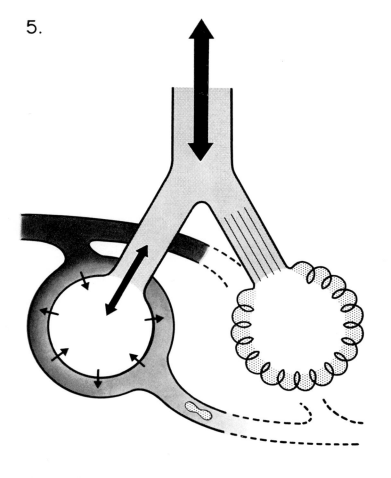

Gas Exchange   **Mechanical Factors**

FIG. 1 (*cont.*)

be carried out in a physician's office (p. 205); others require expensive apparatus or considerable technical experience and are normally carried out in a hospital cardiopulmonary laboratory; still others are research procedures and at present are available only in a few medical centers. However, some tests should now be performed on every patient with known or suspected cardiopulmonary disease, just as a hemoglobin determination, blood pressure measurement and urinalysis are performed routinely on all patients.

This monograph is divided into three parts. The first of these considers *separately* each of the components of pulmonary function (lung volumes, ventilation, pulmonary blood flow, diffusion and the mechanics of breathing). The second presents well-defined patterns of physiologic tests in patients with specific cardiopulmonary disorders, shows the usefulness and limitations of function tests by reference to cases, presents a logical approach to the practical use of physiologic tests, and discusses physiologic therapy of pulmonary disease. The third, the Appendix, includes information basic to the development of some tests of pulmonary function but not essential to their understanding.

CHAPTER 2

The Lung Volumes

FOR MANY YEARS, the only tests of pulmonary function were the measurements of the lung volumes (Fig. 2). Actually, these do not evaluate *function* since they are essentially anatomic measurements. Changes in the lung volumes, however, are often caused by alterations in physiologic processes, and for this reason it is important to know normal values and how to interpret deviations from these.

Because too many names had been applied to the same lung volumes, a group of American respiratory physiologists agreed in 1950 to use the terms and definitions in Table 1 in order to avoid confusion.

Normal values for lung volumes and subdivisions in recumbent men and women are given in Table 2. The standard deviations from the mean (see Table 28, p. 325) show that there is considerable variation even in a homogeneous group; consequently deviations from "normal" must be large to be significant in diagnosis.

A. VITAL CAPACITY AND ITS SUBDIVISIONS

The vital capacity and its subdivisions (inspiratory reserve volume, expiratory reserve volume and tidal volume) can be measured directly by the use of simple volume recorders such as bellows or spirometers. Approximate values are given in Table 2. The standard test is performed by asking the patient to inspire maximally and then expire completely into a bellows or spirometer.* In this test, no time limit is imposed on

---

* Some investigators also measure (*a*) the maximal volume *inspired* after a complete expiration or (*b*) the sum of the separately performed inspiratory capacity and expiratory reserve volume, and compare these with the standard measurement of vital capacity. Since some air may be "trapped" in alveoli by forced expiration beginning from the position of maximal inspiration, the test performed in the standard manner may yield lower values than (*a*) and (*b*) in patients with emphysema (see p. 197).

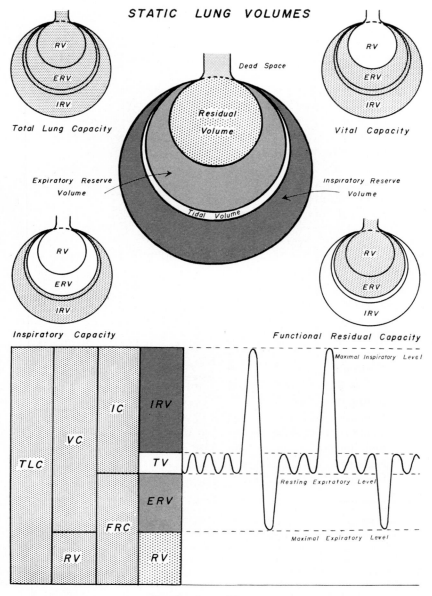

FIG. 2.—LUNG VOLUMES

TABLE 1.—The Lung Volumes and Capacities

A. Volumes.—There are four primary volumes which do not overlap (Fig. 2):

1. *Tidal Volume,* or the depth of breathing, is the volume of gas inspired or expired during each respiratory cycle.
2. *Inspiratory Reserve Volume* (formerly complemental or complementary air minus tidal volume) is the maximal amount of gas that can be inspired from the end-inspiratory position.
3. *Expiratory Reserve Volume* (formerly reserve or supplemental air) is the maximal volume of gas that can be expired from the end-expiratory level.
4. *Residual Volume* (formerly residual capacity or residual air) is the volume of gas remaining in the lungs at the end of a maximal expiration.

B. Capacities.—There are four capacities, each of which includes two or more of the primary *volumes* (Fig. 2):

1. *Total Lung Capacity* (formerly total lung volume) is the amount of gas contained in the lung at the end of a maximal inspiration.
2. *Vital Capacity* is the maximal volume of gas that can be *expelled* from the lungs by forceful effort following a maximal inspiration.
3. *Inspiratory Capacity* (formerly complemental or complementary air) is the maximal volume of gas that can be inspired from the resting expiratory level.
4. *Functional Residual Capacity* (formerly functional residual air, equilibrium capacity or mid-capacity), is the volume of gas remaining in the lungs at the resting expiratory level. The resting *end-expiratory* position is used here as a base line because it varies less than the end-inspiratory position.

◄———◄ Fig. 2.—*Above:* the large central diagram illustrates the four primary lung *volumes* and approximate magnitude. The outermost line indicates the greatest size to which the lung can expand; the innermost circle (residual volume), the volume that remains after all air has been voluntarily squeezed out of the lungs. Surrounding the central diagram are smaller ones; shaded areas in these represent the four lung *capacities*. The volume of dead space gas is included in residual volume, functional residual capacity and total lung capacity when these are measured by routine techniques. *Below:* lung volumes as they appear on a spirographic tracing; shading in vertical bar next to tracing corresponds to that in central diagram above.

TABLE 2.—LUNG VOLUMES IN HEALTHY RECUMBENT SUBJECTS
(Approximate values, in ml)

	MALE AGED 20–30 YR, 1.7 M²	MALE AGED 50–60 YR, 1.7 M²	FEMALE AGED 20–30 YR, 1.6 M²
Inspiratory capacity	3600	2600	2400
Expiratory reserve capacity..........	1200	1000	800
Vital capacity	4800	3600	3200
Residual volume	1200	2400	1000
Functional residual capacity.........	2400	3400	1800
Total lung capacity...............	6000	6000	4200
RV/TLC × 100	20%	40%	24%

the patient; he may expire as quickly or as slowly as he wishes. (Measurement of the *rate* of his complete, forced expiration is important in assessing the mechanical factors in expiration and is discussed on p. 196.)

SIGNIFICANCE OF CHANGES IN VITAL CAPACITY.—Physically, the vital capacity test measures a *volume* of gas, the maximum that can be expelled from the lungs by forceful effort after a maximal inspiration. The physician wishes to know whether this volume is normal for his particular patient. The values in Table 2 are only *typical* figures for a healthy recumbent subject. To be more precise, the physician may compare the measured vital capacity in his patient with tabulated data obtained for men and women in each decade (with consideration for any striking variation in height and weight of the individual, for the position in which the measurement was made, and for the rate at which the expiration was made), or he may compare it with predicted values derived from formulae in which surface area, height, weight and age are taken into consideration. The most useful formulae are:

For Males:

Vital capacity $= [27.63 - (0.112 \times age)] \times$ (height in cm)

For Females:

Vital capacity $= [21.78 - (0.101 \times age)] \times$ (height in cm)

(These formulae do not apply to children; separate formulae for them are included in the Appendix, Table 31, p. 327.)

The physician must still bear in mind several points: (1) The vital capacity of healthy individuals, even though they be of the same sex, height, weight and age, may vary as much as 20% from the average values. (2) The vital capacity may vary from time to time even in the same individual. For example, if the same individual were to repeat the same procedure a number of times, the vital capacity might vary as much as ±200 ml from the mean value. When the individual is lying down, his vital capacity may be 300 ml less than when standing, partly because of an increase in pulmonary blood volume and partly because of a shift headward in the position of the diaphragm.

For these reasons, a "low" vital capacity obtained during the first examination of a patient cannot be regarded as subnormal with certainty unless it is 20% less than the average or predicted value. Further, even a "normal" vital capacity may be low for a particular patient if his vital capacity before the onset of disease was much greater than the average for his age and height. *Changes* in vital capacity are often helpful in diagnosis. If daily or weekly measurements are made in the same patient, a change of only 250 ml or more is meaningful if the patient always performs the test in the same position and repeats the test several times so that a mean value can be obtained. (It is assumed that the patient comprehends the instructions and is willing and able to co-operate fully.)

Several examples illustrate these points. One patient's predicted vital capacity was 4500 ml and his actual measured vital capacity was 3800 ml. His measured vital capacity was, therefore, about 15% below the group average and could not on this basis be considered to be low. However, following therapy (to overcome bronchial obstruction), the vital capacity increased to 4200 ml. It is apparent that the initial value was actually low for this particular patient. Another patient, with a diffuse pulmonary interstitial disease, had a predicted vital capacity of 2900 ml, but her actual vital capacity was 3100 ml; two months later, during complete remission, vital capacity was 4030 ml, or 39% greater than the predicted "normal" value.

The physician can, by making serial measurements, follow the course of cardiopulmonary or respiratory disease, e.g., the degree of pulmonary congestion, the severity of respiratory muscle weakness in poliomyelitis, or the effectiveness of bronchodilator drugs in the treatment of asthma. In general, however, measurements of the *rate* of maximal air flow are of more value in assessing the severity of asthma. For example, patient W. T., a known asthmatic, was studied in the interval between attacks. His vital capacity was 5320 ml (114% of the predicted value); it increased only 50 ml following the subcutaneous administration of epinephrine, but maximal voluntary ventilation increased from 141 to 230 L/min after therapy. This probably represents an instance of narrowing of the lumen of bronchioles sufficient to cause increased resistance to air flow but not sufficient to block airways completely and so decrease vital capacity. On the other hand, in patient S. M., another asthmatic, *both* vital capacity and maximal voluntary ventilation increased after injection of epinephrine (from 2800 to 3640 ml and from 62 to 111 L/min); this suggests that initially some bronchioles were occluded completely and were opened by bronchodilator therapy. Such an increase in vital capacity is significant. The greater-than-normal daily variations in vital capacity often observed in patients with pulmonary emphysema are probably related to fluctuating obstruction of airways (see p. 220).

CHANGES IN VITAL CAPACITY CAUSED BY DISEASE.—Vital capacity may be reduced by a number of factors. In many instances, decrease in vital capacity is the result of an *absolute reduction in distensible lung tissue*. Examples of this are mass lesions of the lungs, occlusion of a major bronchus by bronchogenic carcinoma, bronchiolar obstruction, pulmonary edema, pneumonia, atelectasis, pulmonary restrictive disease, pulmonary congestion and surgical excision of pulmonary tissue.

Sometimes there is a decrease in vital capacity even though there is no disease of lung tissue or airways; examples of *non-pulmonary* causes of decrease in vital capacity are:

1. *Limitation to respiratory movements* because of depression of the respiratory centers or diseases of the neuromuscular system (such as poliomyelitis, peripheral neuritis, myasthenia gravis, and primary diseases of skeletal muscle).

2. *Limitation to thoracic expansion* imposed by certain bodily positions (such as a lateral position during thoracic surgery), tight strapping, scleroderma, body deformities (such as kyphoscoliosis) and thoracic pain (caused by fracture of a rib or by thoracic or upper abdominal incisions).

3. *Limitation to descent of the diaphragm* owing to pregnancy, ascites, abdominal tumor, pneumoperitoneum or paralysis of a phrenic nerve.

4. *Limitation to expansion of the lungs* caused by encroachment on the available intrathoracic space by pleural effusion, pneumothorax, diaphragmatic hernia, marked cardiac enlargement or large pericardial effusion.

Reduction in vital capacity may occur in so many diseases that it is not pathognomonic of any single disorder and indeed does not necessarily signify pulmonary disease at all. On the other hand, it is possible that a patient may have pulmonary disability even though his vital capacity is in the normal range; this is so commonly observed in emphysema that the simple volume measurement of vital capacity alone is notoriously unreliable in diagnosing this condition. Again, in patients who have disorders of the pulmonary circulation, vital capacity may be normal. Therefore one cannot rely on vital capacity for specific diagnosis, if used as an isolated test.

SIGNIFICANCE OF CHANGES IN INSPIRATORY CAPACITY AND EXPIRATORY RESERVE VOLUME.—As an approximate guide, the inspiratory capacity normally is 75% of the vital capacity and the expiratory reserve volume 25%. The expiratory reserve volume characteristically is subject to considerable variability even among members of a homogeneous group and indeed in the same individual. Position is an important factor; the expiratory reserve may decrease 600–900 ml on change from the erect to the supine position largely because of the elevation of the diaphragm. In general, changes in the expiratory reserve volume are difficult to interpret and are not diagnostically useful.

B. RESIDUAL VOLUME AND FUNCTIONAL RESIDUAL CAPACITY; THORACIC GAS VOLUME

RESIDUAL VOLUME AND FUNCTIONAL RESIDUAL CAPACITY.—These will be considered together since they are usually measured together. The residual volume, the volume of gas that remains in the lung at the end of a complete expiration, is the only one of the four lung *volumes* that cannot be measured by direct spirometry and must be determined by indirect means. (Normal values are given in Table 2, p. 10).

Residual volume and functional residual capacity are usually measured by either an open- or a closed-circuit method which estimates the volume of gas in the lungs in communication with the major airways at the time of the test. Each method requires that the measurements be made with relatively insoluble gases, i.e., gases that do not leave the alveolar gas readily to dissolve in blood or lung tissue.

The *open-circuit* method is based on the following principle (Fig. 3). The *volume* of gas in the patient's lungs is unknown. It *is* known, however, when the patient is breathing air, that this gas contains about 80% N_2. If the *amount* of N_2 in his lungs could be determined, the total volume of alveolar gas could be calculated easily. The amount of N_2 is determined by washing all the N_2 out of the lungs and measuring it. This is achieved by having the patient *inspire* O_2 (N_2-free) and then *expire* into a spirometer (previously flushed with O_2 so that it is N_2-free). He con-

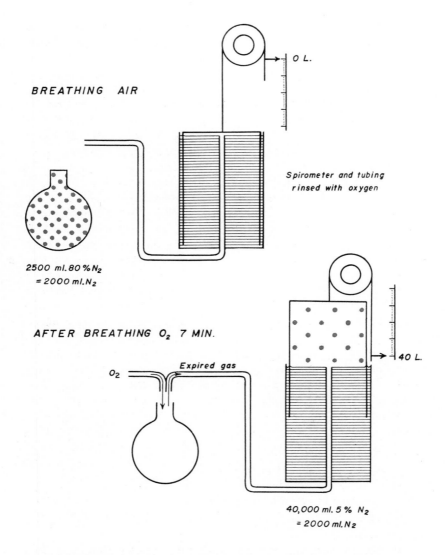

BREATHING AIR

Spirometer and tubing
rinsed with oxygen

2500 ml. 80 % N₂
= 2000 ml. N₂

0 L.

AFTER BREATHING O₂ 7 MIN.

O₂   Expired gas

40 L.

40,000 ml. 5 % N₂
= 2000 ml. N₂

MEASUREMENT OF FUNCTIONAL RESIDUAL CAPACITY
OPEN CIRCUIT METHOD

FIG. 3.—THE NITROGEN WASH-OUT METHOD

tinues to do this for some minutes. The expired gas is collected in the spirometer so that its volume and N_2 concentration can be measured.

At the beginning of the test all of the N_2 in the lung-spirometer system is in the lungs; at the end it is all in the spirometer (Fig. 3). In the example shown in Figure 3, at the end of the test the spirometer contains 40,000 ml of gas. The N_2 concentration of this gas is found to be 5%. Therefore the spirometer contains $0.05 \times 40,000 = 2000$ ml N_2, all of which came from the lungs; the other 38,000 ml of gas in the spirometer is mainly O_2, used to rinse the N_2 out of the lungs, plus some CO_2. Since the 2000 ml N_2 existed in the lungs as 80% N_2, then the total alveolar gas volume, at the moment at which the N_2 washout began, was 2000 ml. $\times \dfrac{100}{80} = 2500$ ml. Corrections must be made for small amounts of N_2 contained in "pure O_2" and for the amount of blood and tissue N_2 washed out as a result of lowering the alveolar PN_2.[†]

In healthy young subjects, the alveolar N_2 is washed out almost completely after O_2 has been breathed for about 2 min. However, in patients with asthma or emphysema, parts of whose lungs may be very poorly ventilated, a longer period of breathing O_2 (at least 7 min) is required; when there is a cyst which communicates poorly with the airway or very poorly ventilated regions (as in emphysematous lungs), an even longer period is required.

The principle of the closed-circuit method is shown in Figure 4. The bellows represents a spirometer, bellows or bag in the closed circuit. Helium (He) is usually used as the test gas. (In some laboratories, O_2 is breathed in a closed circuit and N_2 dilution is measured.) The initial concentration of He in the lungs is zero and in the bellows is precisely 10% (a known volume of He having been added to the bellows before starting the test). The initial volume of gas in the bellows is known; the initial volume of gas in the lungs is unknown. The subject then rebreathes from the bellows[‡] until mixing is complete; i.e., the concentration of He is the

[†] PN_2, PO_2, PCO_2, PH_2O, and PCO are symbols used to denote the *partial pressures* of N_2, O_2, CO_2, H_2O, and CO respectively. For a complete list of symbols used by pulmonary physiologists, see the Appendix, B. For a definition of partial pressure of a gas, see page 332.

[‡] O_2 is added and CO_2 is absorbed so that asphyxia does not develop.

Fig. 3.—Dots represent molecules of N_2. Initially, all are in the lungs (as 80% N_2). During the breathing of O_2 (N_2–free), the N_2 molecules are washed out of the lungs and, with the O_2 are collected as expired gas in the spirometer. The total amount of O_2 that was in the lungs is calculated from measurement of the volume and N_2 concentration of the expired gas.

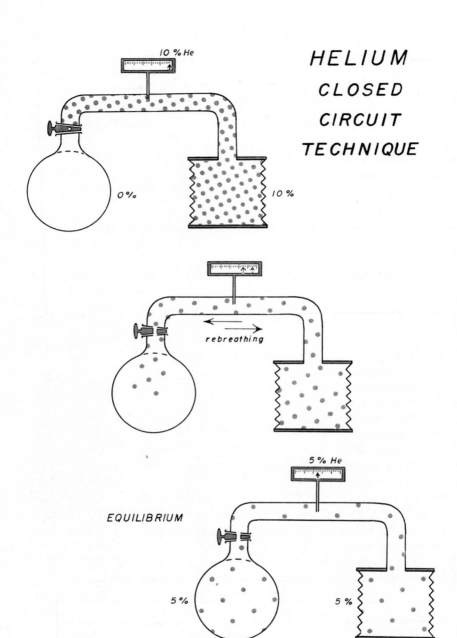

HELIUM
CLOSED
CIRCUIT
TECHNIQUE

10 % He

0 %

10 %

rebreathing

EQUILIBRIUM

5 % He

5 %

5 %

FIG. 4.—MEASUREMENT OF FUNCTIONAL RESIDUAL CAPACITY:
HELIUM CLOSED-CIRCUIT TECHNIQUE

16

CALCULATION OF FUNCTIONAL RESIDUAL CAPACITY
HELIUM CLOSED-CIRCUIT METHOD

AT BEGINNING OF TEST (BEFORE REBREATHING)	AT END OF TEST (AFTER REBREATHING)
Amt. He in lungs + Amt. He in bellows	= Amt. He in lungs + bellows
$V_L F_L + V_B F_B$	$= (V_L + V_B) (F_L \text{ or } B)$
$0 + (2000 \times 0.10)$	$= (V_L + 2000) (0.05)$
200	$= 0.05 V_L + 100$
2000	$= V_L$

V_L = Volume of gas in lungs	F_L = Fractional concentration of He in lungs
V_B = Volume of gas in bellows	F_B = Fractional concentration of He in bellows

same in both the lung and the bellows (see Fig. 21, p. 71). The initial volume of gas in the lung can then be computed.

The principle is the same as in the open-circuit method; i.e., the number of molecules of He is the same in the lung-bellows system at the end of the test as at the beginning (Fig. 4).

If the bellows at the beginning of the test contains 2000 ml of gas and its He concentration is 10% and if the lung contains no He, then the total amount of He present at the beginning of the test is 10% of 2000, or 200 ml (volume $\times$ concentration = amount). The same amount of He, 200 ml must be present in the mixed lung-bellows gas at the end of the test (assuming that an insignificant amount of the poorly soluble He enters tissues and blood). The equation and sample calculation (based on a final concentration of 5% He in both the lungs and bellows) are given in the tabulation.

In the open-circuit method, the volume of alveolar gas that is measured as the functional residual capacity (in a patient with unobstructed airways) is the volume contained in the lungs at the beginning of the

Fig. 4.—Dots indicate molecules of helium. Initially, all are in the bellows (as 10% helium) and none in the lungs. Rebreathing results in their redistribution until equilibrium occurs, at which time lung volume can be calculated (see text).

test.* If the test began precisely at the moment of *complete expiration,* the residual volume is measured. If it began at *full inspiration,* total lung capacity is measured. If it began at the *end of a normal expiration,* the functional residual capacity is measured. The last is the preferred starting point because the resting expiratory level is more constant than the point of either complete inspiration or complete expiration; the expiratory reserve volume is then measured and subtracted from the functional residual capacity to obtain the residual volume. However, the resting expiratory level may fluctuate by as much as 100 ml in healthy individuals and by as much as 400 ml in patients with emphysema. Since changes in this level lead to corresponding changes in functional residual capacity, duplicate determinations cannot be expected to agree precisely. Day-by-day variations also occur; these amount to about $\pm 5\%$ for residual volume in healthy individuals and more in some patients with pulmonary disease.

If gas in all of the alveoli were in free communication with the major airways and if all alveoli were reasonably well ventilated, the open- and closed-circuit methods just described would provide fairly accurate values for functional residual capacity and residual volume. However, in certain patients with pulmonary disease, some areas of the lungs are very poorly ventilated and some, at least at the time of the test, act as though they were almost totally obstructed. The N_2 in poorly ventilated areas may not be washed out over the conventional 7 min period of the test, or He may not be evenly distributed, and therefore the measured values for functional residual capacity and residual volume are less than the true values. Prolongation of the test period to 20 min or more provides a more accurate value. However, prolongation of the test period will not provide a true value when alveolar gas is *completely trapped* behind an occluded airway; this may occur in bullous emphysema, pulmonary cysts, lung tumors, asthma and even non-bullous emphysema. The volume of intrathoracic *"non-ventilated"* gas is termed "trapped gas"; it entered alveoli on some previous inspiration but was unable to leave them owing to mechanical reasons.†

---

* The functional residual capacity may change during the test. This does not affect the value obtained by the open-circuit method, but the closed-circuit method measures the volume of alveolar gas at the end of the test; allowance can be made for change in volume, since this is recorded on the spirometer record.

† There can, of course, be no gas-containing space in the lung that is *never* ventilated because the gas would be absorbed by the blood flowing around it. Obviously, "non-ventilated" areas with "trapped" gas must be replenished with inspired gas from time to time; however, there need not be any significant to-and-fro ventilation of these areas if the obstruction to expiratory flow is severe.

To obtain a true value for the volume of all of the gas in the lungs, whether well-ventilated, poorly ventilated or "non-ventilated," another method of measurement may be used—the pneumatometric or body plethysmographic (body-box) method for measuring *thoracic gas volume*.

THORACIC GAS VOLUME.—This is defined as the volume of gas in the thorax, whether in free communication with the airways or not.* The principle of its measurement in the body plethysmograph is based on Boyle's law, $PV = P'V'$, which states the relationship between changes in pressure and volume of a gas, if its temperature remains constant. The patient sits within the body plethysmograph and the air-tight door is closed. He breathes the air about him through a mouthpiece. At the desired point in the respiratory cycle (end-expiration, if one wishes to compare thoracic gas volume with functional residual capacity as measured by O_2 or He techniques), the mouthpiece is occluded by an electrically controlled shutter; the patient continues to breathe against this obstruction. Figure 5 shows schematically the events that occur before and during an inspiration. At end-expiration (left), we know that alveolar pressure, P, is equal to atmospheric pressure, because there is no gas flow; V, or thoracic gas volume, is unknown. The airway is then occluded. During the succeeding inspiration (right), the thorax enlarges and so decompresses the intrathoracic gas; this creates a new thoracic gas volume (V, original volume, plus ΔV, the increase in volume caused by decompression) and a new pressure, P'. The new pressure, P', is measured by the gauge in the airway between the patient's mouth and the occluded airway; under conditions of no flow, mouth pressure is assumed to equal alveolar gas pressure. The increase in thoracic gas volume (ΔV) is determined by noting the rise in plethysmographic pressure which is detected by a very sensitive electrical gauge (enlargement of the thorax compresses the air around the patient.). Knowing P, P' and ΔV, we can solve the equation of Boyle's law (since $V + \Delta V = V'$) and can calculate the unknown, V, the original thoracic gas volume.

The plethysmographic method is much more rapid than other methods used to measure functional residual capacity; five determinations can easily be made on one individual in 5 min; its major clinical usefulness, however, is in the determination of the true total lung capacity and of "non-ventilated" lung volume. Thoracic gas volume measured by the plethysmograph is the same as functional residual capacity measured by dilution methods in healthy individuals in whom there are no poorly or

---

* In patients with closed pneumothorax, the volume of gas in the pleural cavity will be measured along with pulmonary gas as "thoracic gas volume."

THORACIC GAS VOLUME

BOYLE'S LAW : P V = P'V'

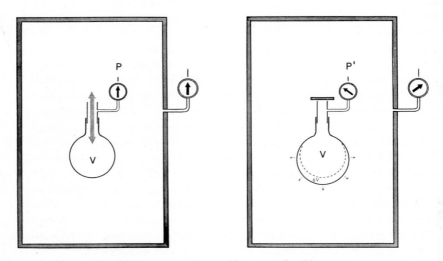

FIG. 5.—MEASUREMENT OF THORACIC GAS VOLUME:
BODY PLETHYSMOGRAPH TECHNIQUE

The rectangle represents the air-tight body plethysmograph. The patient (as he often appears to a pulmonary physiologist) is represented simply as his alveoli and conducting airway; V is the gas volume to be measured, and ΔV (right side) is the increase of volume when the patient inspires with airway occluded. The two circles with pointers represent pressure gauges—one measuring airway pressure and the other, plethysmographic pressure. (See text.) P' is the pressure corresponding to the new volume, V', which is V + ΔV.

non-ventilated areas. Thoracic gas volume, however, exceeds functional residual capacity, measured by gas dilution, in many patients, and the difference between them provides a quantitative measure of "non-ventilated" lung volume. For example, in some patients with non-cystic pulmonary emphysema, the thoracic gas volume at full inspiration may be 1–3 liters more than is estimated by conventional tests which depend on N_2 washout or He dilution. Prolongation of the "dilution" or "washout" tests to 20 or 30 min usually gives a true value for thoracic gas volume, but the plethysmographic method is much easier and quicker to perform.

This provides a truer picture of the lung volumes in many patients with emphysema, whose total lung capacity is often far greater than suspected because of the existence of large areas that are "non-ventilated," at least temporarily.

In the future we may expect that both methods (gas dilution and plethysmographic) will be used in order to measure both total gas volume and "washout volume" and so determine the volume of "non-ventilated" gas.

SIGNIFICANCE OF INCREASE IN FUNCTIONAL RESIDUAL CAPACITY.— This is usually assumed to represent structural emphysematous changes in the lungs. Actually it represents *hyperinflation* rather than emphysema.* Hyperinflation may result from (1) structural changes such as occur in emphysema, whether this be due to disease or to a natural process of aging, (2) partial obstruction to the airway, predominantly expiratory, as in asthma or peribronchiolar fibrosis (see Fig. 50, p. 188), (3) compensatory overinflation of the lung following surgical removal of lung tissue, or (4) deformity of the thorax.

It is not generally recognized that hyperinflation of the lung does not in itself produce pulmonary disability. Elderly individuals with an increased functional residual capacity may have little or no pulmonary incapacity. This is simply because the *ventilation* of the lung (see Chapter 3) is more important to good function than the alveolar *volume*. In order to ensure adequate oxygenation of the blood, the alveolar Po_2 must be maintained at the proper level, usually about 100 mm Hg. This depends only upon whether ventilation supplies as much O_2 each minute to the alveoli as the pulmonary capillary blood removes. If the pulmonary capillary blood removes 250 ml of O_2/min, only 250 ml O_2 must be added to alveolar gas by the process of ventilation; this is true whether the functional residual capacity is 2000 ml or 4000 ml.

An analogy may be helpful here: If 250 ml of O_2 were absorbed chemically each minute in a *small* air-tight box containing air, and simultaneously 250 ml of O_2 were piped into the box each minute, the O_2 concentration in the box would remain constant; if 250 ml of O_2 were absorbed chemically each minute in a *large* air-tight room containing air, and simultaneously 250 ml of O_2 were piped into the room, the O_2 concentration of the large room would again remain constant. Assuming rapid and uniform distribution in both the small box and the large room,

---

* There are many concepts and definitions of emphysema. To avoid confusion, the term emphysema will be used in this monograph to describe a pathologic condition of the lung characterized by reduction or loss of elastic fibers, ruptured alveolar septa and decrease in the pulmonary capillary bed, regardless of etiologic factors. The usual functional changes noted in emphysema are described on pages 227 and 274.

the volume of the container therefore is unimportant in determining the O_2 concentration and partial pressure.

Actually a *very small* functional residual capacity would be disadvantageous because alveolar P_{O_2} would fluctuate widely throughout the respiratory cycle, coming closer to mixed venous P_{O_2} during expiration (since expiration is, in a sense, equivalent to breath-holding) and closer to the inspired P_{O_2} during inspiration (see Fig. 6, p. 26). This would lead to uneven ventilation and to slight anoxemia (p. 74).

On the other hand, though a large functional residual capacity acts as a buffer against wide fluctuations in alveolar P_{O_2} and P_{CO_2}, it is a disadvantage when a rapid *change* in alveolar gas *composition* is necessary. For example, if a patient is given 100% O_2 to breathe instead of air, he will achieve a high alveolar O_2 concentration more slowly if his functional residual capacity is large than if this capacity is small. Again, if it is desired to anesthetize a patient with N_2O or cyclopropane, or to cause hyperpnea by inhalation of 10% CO_2, it will take longer to achieve the desired alveolar concentration of the gas if the functional residual capacity is large (other things being equal).* Again, an analogy using small and large closed spaces may be helpful: if a man were to smoke in an air-tight phone booth, the smoke concentration would rise much more rapidly than if he were to smoke in a large room.

An increase in functional residual capacity is also a disadvantage because the thorax is always larger than normal; because of this abnormal position, some muscular inefficiency and mechanical disadvantage may result. Certainly, a great enlargement of the functional residual capacity must lead to a reduction in inspiratory capacity (if the total lung capacity is not enlarged), and this usually limits the patient's ability to increase his ventilation on demand. The anatomic (respiratory) dead space is also larger when the lungs are hyperinflated (see Fig. 13, p. 42). The *mechanical* factors which result in an enlarged functional residual capacity are discussed on page 186.

SIGNIFICANCE OF INCREASE IN RESIDUAL VOLUME.—An increase in functional residual capacity means that the lung is hyperinflated during quiet breathing. An increase in residual volume means that the lung is still hyperinflated even after *maximal* expiratory effort; i.e., the patient cannot, by voluntary effort, force his thorax and lungs back to a normal size. This signifies that certain changes have developed in the thoracic

---

* But even here alveolar ventilation, and the degree of uneven ventilation, are more important than alveolar volume in determining the rate of change of alveolar concentration.

cage, in the respiratory muscles or in the pulmonary tissues; these changes may be reversible in certain patients with partial bronchial obstruction, as in young asthmatics, but appear to be irreversible in patients with emphysema with loss of elasticity of alveolar or airway tissues or in patients with persistent bronchial obstruction caused by secretions, congestion, edema, inflammation, or other tissue change.

Residual volume and functional residual capacity usually increase together. In some instances, residual volume may be increased without increase in functional residual capacity (if expiratory reserve volume decreases sufficiently). An increase in residual volume occurring without increase in total lung volume must mean that the vital capacity is reduced. However, the ability to *ventilate* is not necessarily reduced on this account since the full vital capacity is rarely used even for maximal ventilation, except in patients with paralysis or weakness of the respiratory muscles (as in poliomyelitis), where the vital capacity and tidal volume may be equal.

Residual volume may be decreased in diffuse pulmonary restrictive disease of many types and in a number of diseases in which alveoli are occluded in many portions of the lung.

SIGNIFICANCE OF CHANGES IN RESIDUAL VOLUME/TOTAL LUNG CAPACITY RATIO.—Values for healthy young adults lie between 20 and 35%. However, an increase in this ratio does not necessarily signify that the absolute value for residual volume is also greater than normal. The fraction, $\frac{\text{residual volume}}{\text{total lung capacity}}$, can increase if either the absolute residual volume is increased (as in asthma or emphysema) or the total lung capacity is decreased (as in pulmonary restrictive disease or congestion). Thus use of the ratio *alone* tends to obscure the actual values for these lung volumes. Again, it must be emphasized that a residual volume greater than 35% of total lung capacity does not signify pulmonary insufficiency or disability since older people may have values as high as 50% with few or no symptoms referable to the cardiopulmonary system.

C. TOTAL LUNG CAPACITY

Normal figures are presented in Table 2 (p. 10). Total lung capacity is usually determined by measuring the functional residual capacity and adding the inspiratory capacity. It may be *estimated* from calculated normal vital capacity by dividing vital capacity by 0.8 for the age group 15–34 years, by 0.75 for 35–49 years and by 0.65 for the group over 50.

Total capacity may vary from the estimated normal by ± 15 to 20% in healthy subjects.

Radiologists have attempted to measure residual lung volume and total lung capacity from planimetric tracings of films of the chest taken in several planes. Good approximations may be obtained in normal individuals who have no pulmonary disease, since radiologic chest volume (minus cardiac volume) is closely related to the pulmonary gas volume. However, in patients with parenchymal lung disease or vascular congestion, correlation is poor. It is possible that better correlation will be obtained between radiologic chest volume and thoracic gas volume, measured by the use of the body plethysmograph.

The total lung capacity is decreased in patients who have extensive pulmonary disease (restrictive disease, edema, exudate, atelectasis, neoplasms) or have pulmonary tissue compressed (by congestion, pneumothorax, hydrothorax) in such a manner as to prohibit compensatory overdistention of other parts of the lungs. It is also reduced when there is non-pulmonary limitation to full expansion of the thorax (see p. 238). Total lung capacity may be normal in the presence of large cysts with open airways. It may be low if these are closed and the total lung capacity has been measured by conventional gas dilution methods rather than by the body plethysmograph. It may remain normal in the presence of restrictive disease if the latter is of the bronchiolar type which leads to hyperinflation. Total lung capacity is usually normal or increased in emphysema; this is because there is no fibrotic process tending to restrict the expansion of the lung. However, coalescence of several alveoli into one (by tearing of septa) reduces the surface for gas exchange even though the alveolar volume may increase.

Therefore normal or increased total lung capacity does not imply that ventilation is normal or that the total lung surface for diffusion is normal in quantity or in its properties.

SUMMARY

The vital capacity, inspiratory capacity and expiratory reserve volume are relatively easy to measure by using simple volume recorders. Since there is always a residual volume of gas in the lungs that cannot be expelled by maximal expiration, this volume (and also the functional residual capacity and total lung capacity, which include the residual volume) must be measured indirectly. Gas dilution methods measure the volume of the lung with open airways, and the body plethysmograph method measures all gas in the lung whether it is in well-ventilated, poorly ventilated or "non-ventilated" regions.

The interpretation of measured lung volumes requires basic knowledge of pulmonary physiopathology because (1) there may be no changes in lung volume in certain types of serious lung disease, (2) the variation in a homogeneous healthy group is so great that the interpretation of small changes is difficult, (3) even marked changes may be caused by extra-pulmonary disorders, and (4) changes in lung volumes usually have less significance with respect to function than do changes in ventilation, diffusion and circulation.

Nevertheless, routine, serial determinations of the lung volumes can help the physician in many problems related to diagnosis, therapy and progression of pulmonary disease.

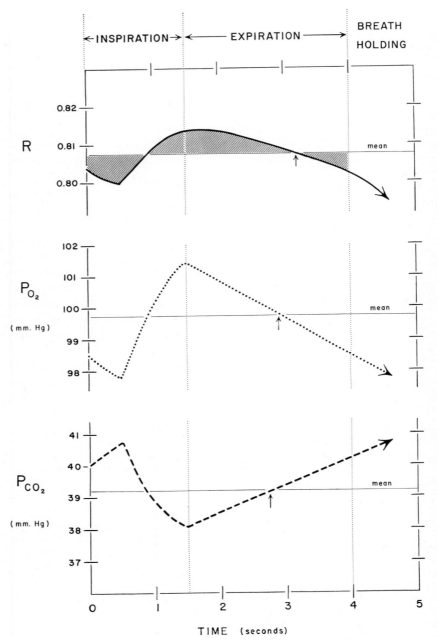

FIG. 6.—ALVEOLAR GAS TENSIONS DURING A RESPIRATORY CYCLE

26

CHAPTER 3

Pulmonary Ventilation

THE MAJOR FUNCTION of the *cardiovascular system* is to supply to the capillary bed of each tissue of the body a *volume* of blood that is adequate at each moment for the metabolic needs of each tissue. The cardiovascular system is well designed to increase or decrease *total* blood flow, according to over-all demands, and to distribute more blood to metabolically active tissues and less to relatively inactive tissues. However, it has no control over the *composition* of the blood—how much glucose, amino acids, hormones, O_2 or CO_2 the blood contains.

The major function of the *respiratory system* is to maintain at optimal levels the partial pressure of O_2 and CO_2 in the pulmonary alveoli and

<hr>

◄━━◼ FIG. 6.—During *inspiration,* one would expect that alveolar Po_2 would rise because fresh air ($Po_2 = 149$ mm Hg when saturated with water vapor at $37°C$) is added to the alveolar gas ($Po_2 = 98.5$ mm Hg at end-expiration). During *expiration,* one would expect that alveolar Po_2 would decrease and alveolar Pco_2 would increase; this is because expiration is essentially breath-holding (with lung volume decreasing throughout the expiration), and blood continues to flow through the pulmonary capillaries and continues to remove O_2 and add CO_2.

NOTE: At the beginning of inspiration, alveolar Po_2 continues to fall (instead of rising) and alveolar Pco_2 continues to rise (instead of falling). This is because the first gas to enter the alveoli during inspiration is alveolar gas that filled the anatomic dead space at the end of the previous expiration; it does not alter the composition of gas in the alveoli, and exchange of O_2 and CO_2 continues as it did during expiration. After the dead space gas is drawn in, and alveolar Po_2 rises sharply because *fresh inspired air* now adds O_2 to the alveoli far more rapidly than it is absorbed.

The top graph shows the variation in R values throughout the cycle; R is the gas exchange ratio and equals $\dfrac{CO_2 \text{ eliminated}}{O_2 \text{ absorbed}}$ at any moment.

It is obvious that a "spot sample" of expired alveolar gas is not representative of alveolar gas at all times during the respiratory cycle.

27

in the arterial blood. This it does by *ventilation,* a cyclic process of inspiration and expiration (Fig. 6) in which fresh air enters the alveoli and then an equal volume* of alveolar gas leaves them.

So far, we have discussed only the *static* lung volumes (Chap. 2). Ventilation is a *dynamic* process. During inspiration, active muscular contraction enlarges the thorax; this further lowers intrathoracic pressure (normally subatmospheric at end-expiration) and causes pulmonary or alveolar gas pressure (normally atmospheric at end-expiration) to become subatmospheric. Fresh air, at atmospheric pressure, then enters the airway and alveoli, where the pressure is lower.

Certain principles are fundamental to an understanding of this cyclic process of ventilation:

1. Let us begin at end-expiration. The partial pressures of O_2 and CO_2 in alveolar gas of a healthy individual are approximately equal to those in pulmonary capillary blood (P_{O_2}, 100 mm Hg; P_{CO_2}, 40 mm Hg). If a patient were to inspire gas of precisely the same chemical composition as that of his alveolar gas, this inspired tidal volume would enlarge his functional residual capacity but it would not raise the alveolar P_{O_2} nor lower the alveolar P_{CO_2} (see Fig. 6). Oxygen uptake would not stop on this account (any more than it would during breath-holding) because alveolar gas, even though not enriched by additional O_2, would still have a higher P_{O_2} than *mixed venous blood.* Continued removal of O_2 by the pulmonary capillary blood each minute without the addition of an equal amount of O_2 to the alveoli would result in arterial anoxemia (see p. 48). Simultaneously there would be CO_2 retention and respiratory acidosis.

2. The respiratory tract is composed of the conducting airway (nose, mouth, pharynx, larynx, trachea, bronchi and bronchioles) and the alveoli. Rapid exchange of O_2 and CO_2 between gas and blood occurs only in the alveoli, and not in the conducting airway.

The conducting airway, at the end of a normal expiration (pre-inspiration), is filled with *alveolar* gas (Fig. 7). This alveolar gas is

---

* This statement is only approximately true. As a rule, more O_2 is *absorbed* from the alveoli than CO_2 is *added;* for example, O_2 uptake may be 250 ml/min and CO_2 elimination only 200 ml/min. In this case, the alveolar gas volume "shrinks" by 50 ml/min, or 3–5 ml/breath. Thus, whenever the CO_2 output/O_2 uptake ratio (respiratory exchange ratio, R) is less than 1.0, the *expired* tidal volume is slightly less than the *inspired* tidal volume; the difference between these two volumes leaves the alveoli by way of the blood instead of through the bronchioles. Another mechanism leading to a smaller expired gas volume, at least over short periods, is bronchial obstruction of a type which allows gas to enter but not to leave alveoli; this type of mechanical disturbance is sometimes termed "air trapping" (p. 197).

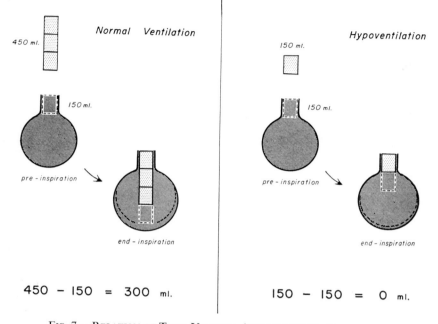

FIG. 7.—RELATION OF TIDAL VOLUME, ANATOMIC DEAD SPACE AND
ALVEOLAR VENTILATION

Circular part represents the alveoli, where rapid exchange of O_2 and CO_2 occurs;
the tube leading to the alveoli represents all of the conducting airways.

Left (normal ventilation): At the end of a normal expiration (pre-inspiration),
the dead space is filled with 150 ml of alveolar gas. In this example, tidal volume
during inspiration will be 450 ml (3 blocks of 150 ml each). During inspiration, 450
ml of gas enters the alveoli (dotted line indicates pre-inspiratory alveolar volume).
However, 150 ml is alveolar gas that had filled the dead space at the end of the last
expiration; this, having the same *composition* as alveolar gas, does not raise alveolar
Po_2 or lower alveolar Pco_2. Two blocks (300 ml) of the *inspired* gas do reach the
alveoli and do raise alveolar Po_2 and lower alveolar Pco_2. The remaining block of
inspired gas (150 ml) is left in the dead space at end-inspiration and is flushed out on
the next expiration, thus never entering into gas exchange.

Right (hypoventilation): During inspiration, 150 ml of dead space gas enters the
alveoli and the 150 ml of inspired air remains in the dead space, so that alveolar
ventilation should be zero. This schematic representation is, however, inaccurate
when tidal volume is low (see Fig. 9, p. 32).

29

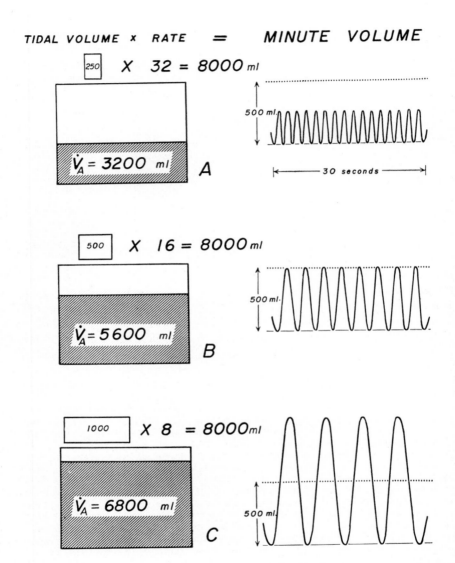

TIDAL VOLUME × RATE = MINUTE VOLUME

250 X 32 = 8000 ml

$\dot{V}_A$ = 3200 ml   A

500 ml.

|←——— 30 seconds ———→|

500 X 16 = 8000 ml

$\dot{V}_A$ = 5600 ml   B

500 ml.

1000 X 8 = 8000ml

$\dot{V}_A$ = 6800 ml   C

500 ml.

(T.V. − D.S.) × RATE = ALVEOLAR VENTILATION ($\dot{V}_A$)

FIG. 8.—TIDAL VOLUME, DEAD SPACE AND ALVEOLAR VENTILATION AT
DIFFERENT TIDAL VOLUMES AND RATES OF BREATHING

30

drawn back into the alveoli during the early part of the next inspiration. It does not raise alveolar P_{O_2} nor lower alveolar P_{CO_2}. Only the fresh air that goes beyond the conducting airway into the alveoli raises alveolar P_{O_2} and lowers alveolar P_{CO_2}. In Figure 7, at end-expiration only 300 ml of 450 ml of inspired fresh air has entered alveoli; the remainder (150 ml) has stayed in the conducting airway and is washed out during the next expiration (see also Fig. 14, p. 43). This latter portion of the tidal volume is wasted, useless or ineffective as far as alveolar ventilation is concerned and is called "dead space" ventilation.

In this particular breath:

Tidal volume (V_T)	$= 450$ ml
Anatomic dead space ventilation (V_D)	$= 150$ ml
Alveolar ventilation ($V_T - V_D$)	$= 300$ ml

Alveolar ventilation then refers not to the volume of *gas* entering the alveoli, but the volume of *fresh air* entering them.

3. Deep breathing causes a greater fraction of the tidal volume to enter the alveoli; shallow breathing causes a smaller fraction of the tidal volume to enter the alveoli. Figure 8 illustrates this. Assume that the volume of the conducting airway is 150 ml. In *A*, $(250 - 150)/250$ or 0.4 of the tidal volume results in alveolar ventilation; in *B*, $(500 - 150)/500$ or 0.7 of the tidal volume enters the alveoli; in *C*, $(1000 - 150)/1000$ or 0.85 of the tidal volume enters the alveoli.[†]

4. Since the major function of ventilation is to arterialize the mixed

---

[†]From this and Figure 7 (*right*) we would conclude that, when the tidal volume was decreased so that it exactly equals the volume of the conducting airway, alveolar ventilation would become zero. However, this is not true because inspired gas travels through the airways not as a block with a square front (as pictured in Fig. 9, *A*) but rather with a spike or cone front (as pictured in Fig. 9, *B*). Thus some inspired gas *does* reach the alveoli even though the tidal volume is less than the volume of the conducting airway; it has been shown that a few ml of inspired gas enter the alveoli when the tidal volume is only 60–70 ml and the volume of the conducting airway is 150 ml. The equation (alveolar ventilation/breath = tidal volume — anatomic dead space) therefore is not accurate when the tidal volume is abnormally low.

◄━━◀ FIG. 8.—Area of each small block represents tidal volume (250, 500, or 1000 ml). Total area of each large block (shaded + unshaded areas) = *minute* volume of ventilation; in each case it is 8000 ml. Shaded area of each block represents volume of *alveolar* ventilation per minute; this varies in each case since Alveolar Ventilation/min = (Tidal Volume — Dead Space) × Frequency. A dead space of 150 ml is assumed in each case, although actually the dead space would increase somewhat with increasing tidal volume. *Right*, spirographic tracings.

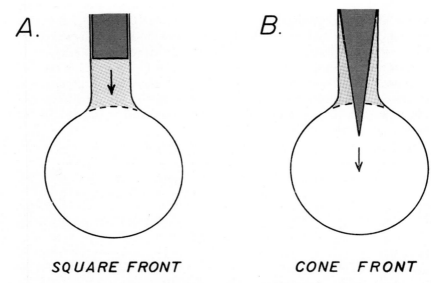

SQUARE FRONT   CONE FRONT

Fig. 9.—Movement of Inspired Air Through Conducting Airways

Gas moves through the conducting airways as a cone front (B), not as a square
front (A).

venous blood, it must supply each minute to the alveoli and pulmonary
capillary blood a volume of O_2 equal to that used by the body and must
remove a volume of CO_2 approximately equal to that formed by the
metabolic activity of tissues. The *supply* of O_2 each minute must equal
the *requirements* each minute. Therefore, *minute* ventilation or *minute*
volume of ventilation is a more important measurement than tidal volume
or rate. However, *minute alveolar* ventilation is far more important than
the over-all minute volume of breathing since the latter is uncorrected for
the amount of ventilation of the anatomic dead space. Figure 8 (p. 30)
shows that for equal, *un*corrected minute volumes of breathing, *alveolar*
ventilation may be too little (A), adequate (B) or too much (C).

Therefore, one cannot give precise "normal values" for *minute volume*
of breathing because the useful part of this (the alveolar ventilation) depends on the pattern of breathing (tidal volume and frequency of respiration) and on the volume of the conducting airway. (See pp. 327 and 328
for approximate predicted values.)

5. "Normal" values for *alveolar* ventilation per minute must be related to the metabolic activity of the patient. If he is exercising or if he has fever or hyperthyroidism, "normal" values for alveolar ventilation will be higher than if he were basal, hypothermic or hypothyroid.

In a healthy basal 150 lb adult male with an O_2 consumption of 250 ml/min, about 4.3 liters of *alveolar* ventilation per minute is adequate to arterialize his mixed venous blood. Alveolar *hypo*ventilation occurs when ventilation is too little; alveolar *hyper*ventilation, when it is too great (see pp. 44 and 49).

6. Later in this chapter (p. 74), we shall emphasize that even when the minute *volume* of alveolar ventilation, calculated as [(tidal volume — anatomic dead space) × (rate)], is normal or increased, this may be inadequate to arterialize his venous blood *if ventilation is not uniform.* In Chapter 4, we shall explain that the volume of alveolar ventilation (similarly calculated) may be normal or increased and still be inadequate *if pulmonary capillary blood flow is not uniform.* In Chapter 5, we shall learn that the volume of alveolar ventilation may be normal or increased and still be inadequate to oxygenate the blood *if there is a decrease in the diffusing capacity of the lung.*

Does this mean that no measurements of ventilation are useful except the most elegant ones made in research laboratories? No. If the patient's tidal volume is decreased or if his rate is very slow or very rapid, his alveolar ventilation may be abnormally low and these simple measurements of tidal volume and rate have provided information of diagnostic value. If his uncorrected minute ventilation or calculated alveolar ventilation per minute is decreased (with respect to his level of metabolic activity), he surely is suffering from alveolar hypoventilation, and simple methods have established at least part of the diagnosis. *Normal or high values,* however, must not be accepted as adequate until defects in distribution of gas and blood and in diffusion have been ruled out.

In the remainder of this section we shall assume, unless specified otherwise, *that alveolar ventilation and pulmonary capillary blood flow are uniform and that the diffusing capacity is normal;* i.e., we shall consider only the volume of alveolar ventilation and its component parts (frequency, tidal volume, and anatomical dead space volume) and discuss (*a*) how to measure these, (*b*) the causes and effects of alveolar hypoventilation, and (*c*) the physiological mechanisms regulating ventilation.

I. Volume of Pulmonary Ventilation

A. FREQUENCY (RATE) OF BREATHING

This is the only respiratory measurement made routinely in most hospitals. The average frequency of breathing is about 11–14/min in healthy individuals under basal conditions. Deviations from the normal rate are helpful clinically in calling attention to respiratory or pulmonary disorders. However, the rate of breathing is not very valuable as an index of useful ventilation because either rapid or slow rates may be associated with either hyper- or hypoventilation, depending on other factors (see Fig. 8, p. 30).

B. TIDAL VOLUME (DEPTH OF BREATHING)

The physician should train himself to think in terms of *both* tidal volume and rate. He can, by inspection, note whether the chest appears to be moving uniformly and adequately; by auscultation, determine whether breath sounds indicate reasonably adequate alveolar expansion, by use of a tape, measure the expansion of the chest, and by percussion, determine the excursion of the diaphragms. The surgeon or anesthesiologist can estimate the excursions of the anesthesia bag. A fluoroscopist can be trained to look for hypoventilation and, further, to decide whether it is due to involvement of the costal or of the diaphragmatic component.

However, although all of these may give useful *impressions,* they are not *quantitative* so far as volumes are concerned and may be misleading. For example, some patients with pulmonary disease appear to be ventilating normally or excessively as judged by external movements of the chest and abdomen, but actually are breathing too little air. This is because the respiratory *effort* is great and quite prominent but mechanical factors have prevented adequate movement of air. This is a common observation in patients with asthma, extensive bronchopneumonia and massive collapse of the lung. Hypoventilation occurs frequently in patients under general anesthesia because the anesthesiologist overestimates the excursions of the rebreathing bag or underestimates the minute volume required by the anesthetized patient. Occasionally a patient in a body respirator may be hypoventilated even though the excursions of the pump are maximal. This may occur in a completely apneic patient or in one who is still breathing spontaneously, though inadequately. In the first instance, the patient may be hypoventilated because of mucus in his airway or because of increased stiffness of his lungs or thorax. In the second instance, an additional factor may be present; namely, the pump may be in the inspiratory phase when the patient is making his expiratory effort, or vice versa. For example, we have measured the tidal volume of a patient in a body respirator and found it to vary between 100 and 800 ml, depending on whether the respirator was assisting or opposing the patient's spontaneous respiratory efforts. In another patient, who was breathing spontaneously, his minute volume was 5.2 L/min before he was placed in the respirator but only 4.3 L/min while being ventilated by a body respirator.

Whenever there is any question about the adequacy of ventilation, quantitative measurements should be made. These can be made easily even in a sick patient by several methods: (1) An ordinary basal metabolism (closed-circuit) apparatus may be used. It is preferable to fill the bell or bellows with air rather than with O_2 because inhalation of O_2 by an anoxemic patient may remove reflexes caused by anoxemia and so result in a marked decrease in tidal volume and frequency. The apparatus, filled with air, may be used as a closed system with rebreathing for a few breaths (without causing significant anoxemia or CO_2 retention). It may also be used as an open system if valves are so arranged that the patient breathes either from or into the bell or bellows; since the capacity of the bell or bellows is usually only 4.5–6.0 liters, a continuous record can be obtained for only 30–60 sec. (2) A "bag in a box" system can be used for much longer periods; this apparatus consists of a 50–100 liter thin rubber bag sealed in an air-tight box, so arranged with valves that the patient inspires from the bag and expires into the box around the bag. (3) If none of these is available, the patient's expired gas can be directed by valves into a large rubber or plastic bag (Douglas bag or meteorological balloon) and its volume measured later by pushing the collected gas through a gas meter. From this measurement of volume of gas breathed per minute (minute volume) and a count of respiratory frequency at the time of the gas collection, average tidal volume can be computed.

Average values for tidal volume in healthy basal males are approximately 450–600 ml, but there is considerable deviation from these figures. Considered alone, tidal volume is not useful as an index of alveolar ventilation because either increased or decreased tidal volume may be associated with hyper- or hypoventilation, depending on other factors (Fig. 8, p. 30). However, when tidal volume is considered along with frequency, it is often possible to diagnose hypoventilation, without the necessity of other tests. Unfortunately from the point of view of

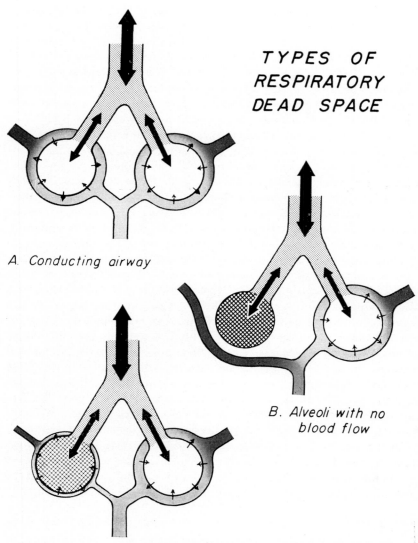

TYPES OF
RESPIRATORY
DEAD SPACE

A. Conducting airway

B. Alveoli with no
blood flow

C. Ventilation in excess of blood flow

Fig. 10.—Anatomic and "Physiologic" Dead Space

simple diagnosis, many patients with pulmonary disease have increased, rather than decreased, tidal volume.

C. RESPIRATORY DEAD SPACE

ANATOMIC DEAD SPACE.—The terms used to describe different types of respiratory dead space ("anatomic," "physiologic," "alveolar," "parallel," "series," etc.) are confusing even to experts. One type (Fig. 10, *A*) is simply the internal volume of the conducting airway from the nose and mouth down to the alveoli. This volume is usually called the "anatomic dead space" because, physically, it is the internal volume of a series of anatomic tubes. Its estimation during life must be based on the concept of a conducting airway (where *no* gas exchange occurs) leading abruptly to gas sacs or alveoli (where *rapid* gas exchange occurs). Measurement of *anatomic* dead space is usually based on Bohr's equation, which states simply that the gas *expired* from the lungs is a mixture of gas from the *dead space* and gas from the *alveoli;* if we can measure two of these (the *expired* and the *alveolar* gas) we can calculate the third (the *dead space* gas) (see Fig. 14 and p. 335). It is difficult to obtain a representative sample of alveolar gas (see Fig. 6, p. 26). However, for measurement of anatomic dead space, the proper sample is that part of the alveolar gas which has just washed out the dead space, and this value can be obtained with accuracy by use of continuous, rapid electrical gas analyzers. Present values for the anatomic dead space are those obtained by Fowler, who made such continuous analyses using the nitrogen meter (Fig. 11, p. 38); they confirm the data obtained many years ago by Krogh. Figure 12 (p. 40) illustrates the procedure and the principle involved. A N_2 meter is used for the continuous and almost instantaneous analysis of the N_2 concentration of gas entering or leaving the subject's mouth. The subject, who previously had been breathing room air, inspires a single breath of pure O_2; a N_2 meter records 0% N_2 (pure O_2) during inspiration. At end-inspiration, the dead space is filled with O_2 which has

---

◄━━━◄ FIG. 10.—Circular parts represent the alveoli, where rapid gas exchange occurs. Arrows in the conducting airways signify the tidal volume entering and leaving the whole lung and its distribution to different regions (see Fig. 1). Width of the blood channel surrounding the alveoli indicates the volume of blood flow to each region; dark gray designates mixed venous blood entering and light gray indicates well oxygenated blood leaving the pulmonary capillaries. Anatomical dead space is stippled. Physiological dead space includes this and some (C) or all (B) of the gas volumes ventilating crosshatched areas.

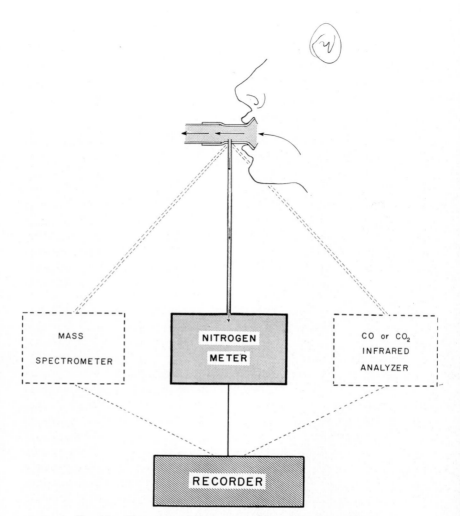

FIG. 11.—ELECTRICAL METHODS FOR RAPID MEASUREMENT OF
GAS CONCENTRATION

A small sample of gas, entering or leaving the subject's mouth, is drawn continuously by a vacuum pump through electrical gas analyzers which measure gas concentration and send a signal to the recorder. CO or CO_2 may be analyzed by infrared absorption, N_2 by emission spectroscopy and a great variety of gases by mass spectrometry. If the tubing conducting gas to the analyzers has a small dead space and the sampling rate is fast, the apparatus can sample, analyze and record 90% of an abrupt change in gas concentrations in 0.05–0.08 sec. For a specific single-breath analysis, see Figure 12.

just been inspired. At the beginning of expiration, the first gas to issue from the mouth is pure O_2 (Fig. 12, phase A) which has entered and left the dead space without *any* mixture with alveolar gas; therefore, the N_2 meter continues to record 0% N_2. Toward mid-expiration, pure alveolar gas is exhaled, uncontaminated with dead space gas (phase C); its concentration here is recorded as 40% N_2, indicating that the inspired O_2 diluted the alveolar N_2 to half of its original concentration. (The actual concentration depends on the volume of O_2 inspired and the volume of the functional residual capacity just before inspiration). Between phases A and C is phase B. In this phase, the N_2 concentration of the expired gas rises rapidly; this represents the remainder of the dead space gas (pure O_2) being washed out by alveolar gas, which has a N_2 concentration of 40%. The concentration of N_2 in the alveolar gas at the very beginning of phase C is used in Bohr's equation, for the calculation of anatomic dead space. (A sample record and calculation is given in Figure 60 and on p. 336.)

Normal values for anatomic dead space are illustrated in Figure 13. This shows that values for females are usually smaller than those for males and that values are usually larger for older men, for individuals with increased tidal volume caused by exercise or by pulmonary disease, and for patients with a large functional residual capacity. The anatomic dead space is decreased by pneumonectomy because of the removal of some of the conducting airway (although that for the remaining lung becomes proportionately increased because of hyperinflation of remaining alveoli and airways) and by tracheotomy; tracheotomy has been performed occasionally as a therapeutic measure to improve alveolar ventilation in patients who have a very low, fixed tidal volume such as may occur in cases of advanced emphysema, although its advisability has been questioned because it decreases the efficacy of coughing (see p. 283). Anatomic dead space may be reduced in asthma (as a result of bronchial obstruction) or increased by disease such as bronchiectasis.

It is difficult to measure anatomic dead space as a routine test in most laboratories, and in general it is permissible to use the values shown in Figure 13 if one takes into account factors such as age, sex, functional residual capacity, and tidal volume. In adults, Radford has noted that anatomic dead space (ml) = weight of patient (lb), as an approximate value.

A case report of a patient in whom measurements of anatomic dead space aided in diagnosis is presented on page 215.

"PHYSIOLOGIC" DEAD SPACE.—That portion of the inspired air which

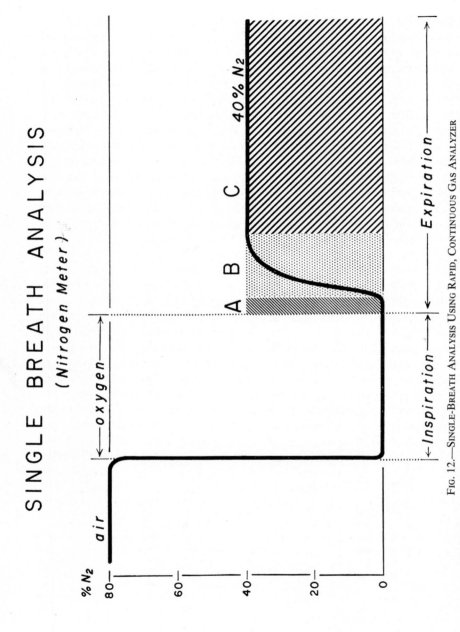

FIG. 12.—SINGLE-BREATH ANALYSIS USING RAPID, CONTINUOUS GAS ANALYZER

traverses the conducting airway and enters alveoli is called *alveolar ventilation*. In some patients, not all of this alveolar ventilation is equally effective in arterializing mixed venous blood; Figure 10, *B* (p. 36) shows ventilated areas of the lung which have no pulmonary capillary blood flow. The inspired air which enters these areas is wasted; the patient must expend energy to move this gas back and forth, but this accomplishes no respiratory function. Such gas is sometimes called "dead space" or "alveolar dead space." The volume of this "dead space" gas, however, is *not the volume of all of these alveoli* that have no blood flow but only *the volume of inspired gas that enters these alveoli on each breath.* It therefore fills no physical or anatomic space as does the gas in the conducting airway and cannot be called "anatomic dead space." It (plus the anatomic dead space) has been called part of the "physiologic dead space"; however, it is not physiologic but pathologic, and its only claim to the name is that it is usually measured by physiologists!

Figure 10, *C,* illustrates a similar condition varying only in degree; here, instead of *no* pulmonary capillary blood flow, there is reduced blood flow to alveoli pictured on the left. Ventilation is far in excess of that required to bring arterial blood Po_2 and Pco_2 to physiologic levels, and so a *portion* of the inspired gas entering these alveoli is wasted. This also has been designated "alveolar dead space" or part of the "physiologic dead space," but again is neither "physiologic" nor "space," nor "dead."

The terms dead space, anatomic dead space and physiologic dead space are so entrenched that we shall probably continue to use them. Physiologically, it is simpler to think of a volume of inspired gas which is not useful or effective in arterializing the venous blood—in one case because it never reached alveoli (Fig. 10, *A*), in another because it reached alveoli with no blood flow (Fig. 10, *B*), and in a third because too much reached the alveoli in proportion to their capillary blood flow

---

◄━━━◀ Fig. 12.—The N_2 meter samples, analyzes, and records continuously the N_2 concentration of gas being inspired or expired. During inhalation of air *(left)* the N_2 meter records 79–80% N_2 in inspired and expired gas. The subject is then requested to take a deep breath of O_2 and breathe out slowly and evenly. During inspiration, the N_2 meter records 0% N_2. At the beginning of expiration, about 50 ml of pure O_2 (0% N_2) is expired (phase *A*); this is followed by about 200–300 ml of gas of rapidly rising N_2 concentration (phase *B*), which represents the washout of the remainder of the dead space gas by alveolar gas, and then by pure alveolar gas (phase *C*). This is an idealized presentation of events that would follow inhalation of O_2 if functional residual capacity (including dead space gas) were 2000 ml, volume of inspired O_2 2150 ml, dead space 150 ml, and distribution of O_2 to the alveoli perfectly uniform.

ANATOMIC DEAD SPACE

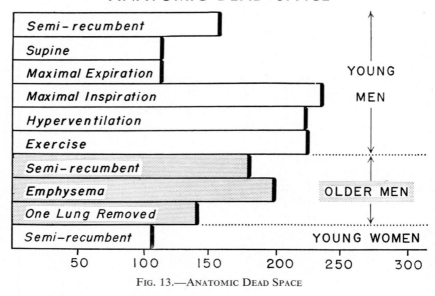

FIG. 13.—ANATOMIC DEAD SPACE

(Fig. 10, C). This relationship between alveolar ventilation and pulmonary capillary blood flow will be considered in detail in Chapter 4, page 87.

D. ALVEOLAR VENTILATION PER MINUTE

1. CALCULATED ON THE BASIS OF TIDAL VOLUME, ANATOMIC DEAD SPACE AND FREQUENCY OF BREATHING.—This has been discussed on pages 28–33 and illustrated in Figures 7 and 8 (pp. 29 and 30). This calculated volume represents only the volume of fresh air reaching the alveoli per minute; it is wholly effective in arterializing venous blood only when the distribution of inspired gas is uniform in relation to pulmonary capillary blood flow. If distribution is not uniform, some of this alveolar ventilation is wasted or ineffective and even if the calculated volume is "normal," more inspired air must be delivered to the alveoli each minute to arterialize the blood.

2. CALCULATED ON THE BASIS OF CO_2 ELIMINATION.—Carbon dioxide is formed in the tissues and is carried in the venous blood to the pulmonary capillaries where it enters the alveoli. On expiration, it is exhaled

ALVEOLAR   VENTILATION

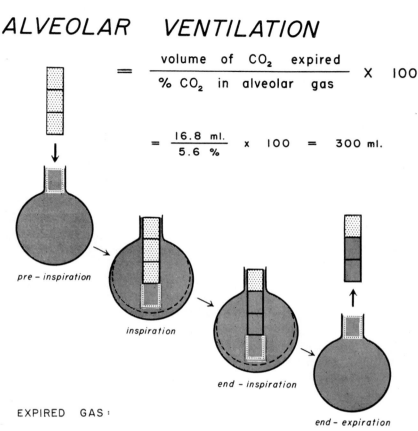

$$= \frac{\text{volume of } CO_2 \text{ expired}}{\% \; CO_2 \text{ in alveolar gas}} \times 100$$

$$= \frac{16.8 \text{ ml.}}{5.6 \%} \times 100 = 300 \text{ ml.}$$

pre – inspiration

inspiration

end – inspiration

end – expiration

EXPIRED   GAS :

Alveolar   components

| 5.6 % | of | 150 ml. | = | 8.4 ml. CO_2 |
| 5.6 % | of | 150 ml. | = | 8.4 ml. CO_2 |

Dead space component

| 0.0 % | of | 150 ml. | = | 0.0 ml. CO_2 |
| | | | | 16.8 ml. CO_2 |

FIG. 14.—ALVEOLAR VENTILATION CALCULATED ON BASIS OF EXPIRED CO_2

Each block represents 150 ml of gas. Dotted blocks represent inspired air (0.04% CO_2); shaded blocks represent alveolar gas (5.6% CO_2). During inspiration, 150 ml of dead space gas + 300 ml of inspired air enter the alveoli; dotted lines show pre-inspiratory lung volume. Almost instantly (end-inspiration) the inspired air mixes with alveolar gas and becomes part of it. During expiration, 450 ml of gas leaves the alveoli; 150 ml remains in the respiratory dead space, and 300 ml leaves as expired gas along with the 150 ml of dead space gas. Alveolar ventilation and volume of CO_2 expired for the breath are expressed as ml, corrected to BTPS (body temperature, ambient pressure, saturated with water vapor).

as part of the expired gas (Fig. 14). Because inspired air contains practically no CO_2 (0.04%), all of the CO_2 in the expired gas must have come from the alveoli. Furthermore, it must have come from alveoli with pulmonary capillary blood flow. If one measures the *amount* of CO_2 in *expired* gas and the *per cent* of CO_2 in *alveolar* gas (see p. 51), then the *volume* of gas coming from the alveoli—i.e., the effective alveolar ventilation—can be measured (see Appendix, p. 341).

In an individual with uniform distribution of inspired gas and pulmonary capillary blood flow, alveolar ventilation calculated in these two ways should be equal; in healthy young men, Severinghaus made measurements of alveolar ventilation per breath by both methods and they differed by only 2–3% of the tidal volume. When there is non-uniform distribution, the calculation based on CO_2 elimination will yield lower values for alveolar ventilation because it measures the useful or effective alveolar ventilation and not the wasted or ineffective parts.

E. HYPOVENTILATION OF THE LUNGS

CAUSES OF HYPOVENTILATION.—Hypoventilation exists when an insufficient volume of fresh air enters the alveoli each minute relative to the metabolic activity of the body. Recently, the term "hypoventilation syndrome" or "alveolar hypoventilation syndrome" has been used widely, although originally it was applied specifically to a small group of obese individuals ("Pickwickian") who were anoxemic because of insufficient ventilation rather than because of uneven distribution or impairment of diffusion. We believe that the term "hypoventilation syndrome" is as unnecessary as the term "anemia syndrome." Indeed, we believe it is improper to use the term because, if a patient is hypoventilating, a detailed study should be made to determine the cause. As a rule, hypoventilation in ambulatory patients with cardiopulmonary disease is due to mechanical factors limiting thoracic or pulmonary movements, but Table 3 shows clearly that hypoventilation is not one specific disease but can be caused in many ways. A reading of Chapter 7 will make it clear that the different mechanisms causing hypoventilation can be identified. For example, if the critical factor limiting ventilation is a "stiffer" lung or organic obstruction of the airways, contraction of the respiratory muscles can still exert considerable force on the lungs, and this can be measured as a change of intra-esophageal pressure (reflecting a change of intrathoracic pressure); on the other hand, if the critical limiting factor is neuromuscular weakness or paralysis or thoracic immobility, the muscles

TABLE 3.—CAUSES OF HYPOVENTILATION

1. *Depression of respiratory centers* by general anesthesia, excessive doses of morphine or barbiturates, cerebral trauma, increased intracranial pressure, prolonged anoxia or cerebral ischemia, high concentration of CO_2 or electrocution.
2. *Interference with neural conduction or with neuromuscular transmission to the respiratory muscles* by traumatic spinal cord lesions, infections such as poliomyelitis, peripheral neuritis or neuromuscular block produced by curare, decamethonium, succinylcholine, nerve gases, myasthenia gravis, botulinus or nicotine poisoning.
3. *Diseases of respiratory muscles.*
4. *Limitation of movement of thorax* by arthritis, scleroderma, emphysema, thoracic deformity or elevation of the diaphragm.
5. *Limitation of movement of lungs* by pleural effusion or pneumothorax.
6. *Pulmonary diseases*
   a) decrease in functioning lung tissue caused by disorders such as atelectasis, tumor or pneumonia;
   b) decreased distensibility of lung tissue as in restrictive disease and congestion;
   c) obstructive lesions in the upper or lower respiratory tract.

can exert little force on the lungs and the intra-esophageal pressure changes will be relatively minor.

EFFECTS OF HYPOVENTILATION ON BLOOD GASES.—Since, by definition, hypoventilation supplies inadequate amounts of fresh air, it must lead to anoxemia, CO_2 retention and respiratory acidosis (Table 4; Fig. 15). The sequence of events is as follows: Each minute, less O_2 is added to the alveoli by ventilation than is removed by the pulmonary capillary blood. Alveolar Po_2 falls, and arterial Po_2, O_2 content and per cent saturation of hemoglobin decrease, resulting in anoxemia. Simultaneously, alveolar Pco_2 rises, because inadequate alveolar ventilation cannot remove the volume of CO_2 that is added to the alveoli by the pulmonary capillary blood. Since the Pco_2 of the blood at the end of the pulmonary capillaries (which has just left the alveoli) is in equilibrium with alveolar Pco_2 (see p. 136), end-pulmonary capillary and systemic arterial Pco_2 must also rise. A rise in arterial Pco_2 causes a fall in pH (respiratory acidosis, see Chapter 6).

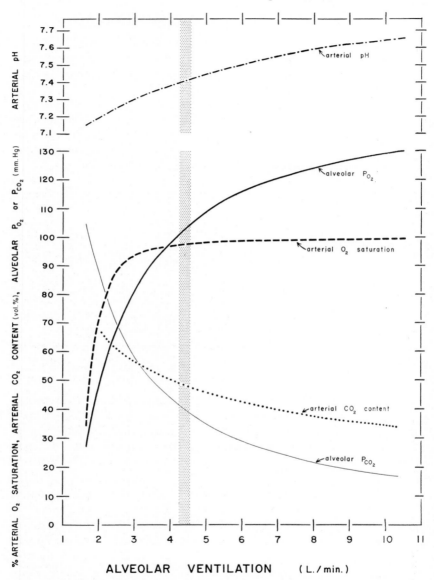

O₂ consumption = 250 ml./min.

FIG. 15.—THE EFFECT OF CHANGING ALVEOLAR VENTILATION ON ALVEOLAR GAS
AND ARTERIAL BLOOD O₂, CO₂ AND pH

46

TABLE 4.—EFFECT OF NORMAL, INCREASED AND DECREASED
ALVEOLAR VENTILATION ON ARTERIAL BLOOD

TYPE OF VENTILATION	ALVEOLAR VENTILATION, L/MIN	ALV. & ART. GAS TENSIONS*		ART. BLOOD GAS CONTENTS		ART. PH, UNITS
		O_2 mm Hg	CO_2 mm Hg	O_2 % sat.	CO_2 mM/L	
Hypoventilation	2.50	67	69	88.5	27.2	7.24
Normal	4.27	104	40	97.4	21.9	7.40
Hyperventilation	7.50	122	23	98.8	17.5	7.56

* In each case, respiratory exchange ratio of 0.8 and O_2 consumption of 250 ml/min are assumed, and the values are calculated from the CO_2–O_2 diagram of Rahn and Fenn. It is also assumed that arterial and alveolar O_2 tensions are the same, although this would not be true in example 2 in which the alveolar P_{O_2} is low (see p 129).

Hypoventilation always results in anoxemia and CO_2 retention when the patient is breathing air (see Table 5). This is shown graphically in Figure 15; the failure of arterial O_2 saturation to fall to the same extent as alveolar O_2 pressure is due to the shape of the O_2 dissociation curve (see p. 142).

It is important to realize that, when the patient is breathing O_2, hypoventilation rarely leads to anoxemia, but always leads to CO_2 retention. The simple mathematical calculation in Table 5 makes this clear.

The arterial blood can be well-oxygenated despite severe hypoventilation, if a high concentration O_2 is breathed; however, CO_2 cannot be eliminated properly without an adequate volume of alveolar ventilation.

◄━━◄ FIG. 15.—Vertical hatched line represents values in a "normal" man with alveolar ventilation of 4.27 L/min, O_2 consumption of 250 ml/min and R (gas exchange ratio) of 0.8 (see "Normal," Table 4, above). NOTE: (1) When alveolar ventilation exceeds this value, alveolar and arterial P_{O_2} rise, but there is little increase in arterial O_2 saturation because Hb is almost maximally saturated at the P_{O_2} achieved by "normal" alveolar ventilation. (2) When alveolar ventilation decreases to less than 3 L/min, arterial O_2 saturation falls sharply because of the steep slope of the O_2 dissociation curve at this P_{O_2} (see also Fig. 41, p. 142). (3) The line for blood CO_2 content, unlike that for arterial O_2 saturation, shows no abrupt inflection and is not flat until very high ventilations are achieved. Thus an increase in ventilation which is ineffective in increasing the O_2 saturation is effective in decreasing the CO_2 content.

This chart applies approximately in a great variety of conditions. The lines apply exactly when (1) barometric pressure is 760 mm Hg, (2) O_2 consumption is 250 ml/min, (3) R is 0.8 and (4) gas tensions are the same in all alveoli and in the arterial blood. Figure 62 (p. 348) provides similar data for various values of R, alveolar ventilation and O_2 consumption.

TABLE 5.—EFFECTS OF HYPOVENTILATION
(Patient breathing air or O_2)

Let us assume that the frequency of breathing is 20/min and that hypoventilation is so extreme that alveolar ventilation is only 100 ml instead of 350 ml/breath. During the first of these small tidal volumes the following exchange of O_2 would occur:

BREATHING AIR

O_2 added to alveoli/breath (O_2 inspired minus O_2 expired)
100 ml inspired air (20.93% O_2) contains	20.93 ml O_2
100 ml expired alveolar gas (14% O_2) contains	14.00 ml O_2
	= 6.93 ml O_2/breath

O_2 removed from alveoli/breath
(O_2 consumption, 240 ml/min) = 12.00 ml O_2/breath
Volume of O_2 removed exceeds volume of O_2 added; alveolar and arterial O_2 tensions must fall.

BREATHING OXYGEN

O_2 added to alveoli/breath (O_2 inspired minus O_2 expired)
100 ml inspired O_2 (100% O_2) contains	100 ml O_2
100 ml expired alveolar gas (18% O_2*) contains	18 ml O_2
	= 82 ml O_2/breath

O_2 removed from alveoli/breath
(O_2 consumption, 240 ml/min) = 12 ml O_2/breath
Volume of O_2 added exceeds volume of O_2 removed; alveolar and arterial O_2 tensions must rise.

However, *no matter whether air or O_2 is breathed, hypoventilation always leads to an accumulation of CO_2.* The following calculations make this clear.

BREATHING AIR OR OXYGEN

CO_2 eliminated from alveoli/breath (CO_2 expired minus CO_2 inspired)
100 ml expired alveolar gas (5.6% CO_2) contains	5.6 ml CO_2
100 ml inspired air (0.04% CO_2) contains	0.0 ml CO_2
	= 5.6 ml CO_2/breath

CO_2 added to alveoli/breath
(CO_2 production, 200 ml/min) = 10.0 ml CO_2/breath
Volume of CO_2 added exceeds volume of CO_2 eliminated; alveolar and arterial tensions must rise.

---

* A single breath of 100 ml O_2 will instantaneously raise the O_2 concentration of alveolar gas from 14 to about 18%.

For example, a patient had marked depression of respiration because of a brain tumor. His arterial saturation was normal because he was given 100% O_2 to breathe; however, his arterial Pco_2 was 166 mm Hg (normal, 40 mm Hg) and arterial blood pH was 6.86. Similarly, many patients receiving general anesthesia have definite respiratory depression; if the inspired mixture is rich in O_2, their arterial blood will be well-oxygenated but will, nevertheless, contain excessive amounts of CO_2.

Compensatory mechanisms which attempt to maintain normal arterial blood pH are discussed in Chapter 6.

F. HYPERVENTILATION OF THE LUNGS

The term "hyperventilation" refers to an increase in ventilation in excess of that required to maintain normal arterial blood Po_2 and Pco_2.

CAUSES OF HYPERVENTILATION.—As in the case of hypoventilation, it is important to determine the cause of hyperventilation.

1. *Anxiety.*—This may be acute (reaction to the physician, the hospital or the pulmonary function equipment) or chronic, as in the "hyperventilation syndrome."

2. *Neurocirculatory asthenia.*

3. *Lesions in the central nervous system.*—These include certain types of meningitis, encephalitis, cerebral hemorrhage and trauma believed to excite the central respiratory mechanisms, and lesions (possibly in the pons) which may destroy respiratory inhibitory regions.

4. *Hormones and drugs.*—Epinephrine (to a lesser extent, norepinephrine) and some female sex hormones (e.g., progesterone) stimulate breathing, presumably by excitation of central mechanisms. Analeptic drugs stimulate respiration only when given in very large doses. Excessive doses of salicylates produce centrally induced hyperventilation.

5. *Increased metabolism.*—Hyperthyroidism and fever may sometimes increase ventilation out of proportion to the increase in metabolic rate. Hot baths may cause hyperventilation and respiratory alkalosis. Certain types of gram-negative bacteremia cause hyperventilation, but this may occur even without fever.

6. *Hypoxia.*—A decrease in arterial Po_2 causes hyperventilation when neuromuscular mechanisms permit it and there are no serious mechanical limitations to increased ventilation. There is great individual variability in the ventilatory response to a decrease in the Po_2 of arterial blood (see p. 53).

7. *Acidosis.*—Metabolic acidosis usually increases alveolar ventilation (see p. 56).

8. *Pulmonary reflexes.*—Collapse of alveoli (pneumothorax, atelectasis), irritation of "deflation receptors," pulmonary hypertension and irritation of receptors in the lower respiratory tract (as by ether vapor) may cause reflex hyperventilation.

9. *Hypotension.*—Low blood pressure causes hyperventilation either reflexly through carotid and aortic presso-receptor mechanisms or centrally by decreasing cerebral blood flow and permitting medullary tissue P_{CO_2} to rise.

10. *Mechanical overventilation.*—Excessive ventilation can occur when respiration is controlled by the anesthesiologist manually (pressure on the rebreathing bag) or by mechanical respirators.

11. *Pain.*—Pain, especially somatic pain, can lead to hyperventilation.

EFFECTS OF HYPERVENTILATION ON BLOOD GASES.—Hyperventilation leads to a decrease in alveolar CO_2 tension and a rise in alveolar O_2 tension (Fig. 15, p. 46, and Table 4, p. 47). The decrease in alveolar P_{CO_2} leads to a decrease in arterial blood CO_2 tension and content and to respiratory alkalosis, *but the increase in alveolar* P_{O_2} *produces only an insignificant increase in arterial* O_2 *saturation of normal individuals living at sea level.* Examination of the dissociation curves for CO_2 and O_2 (pp. 142 and 154) shows why the effect of hyperventilation differs with respect to blood CO_2 and O_2. The CO_2 content of the blood is influenced equally (though in opposite directions) by an increase or decrease in the arterial P_{CO_2}, and this holds true over the whole physiologic range of the CO_2 dissociation curve. However, the O_2 content and saturation of blood are *not* influenced in a *linear* manner by an increase or decrease in arterial P_{O_2}; arterial blood is almost completely saturated with O_2 at the arterial P_{O_2} present during quiet breathing of room air, and a further increase in arterial P_{O_2} caused by hyperventilation can add very little O_2 to the blood (see Fig. 15, p. 46). On the other hand, when the arterial P_{O_2} and saturation are low, hyperventilation both lowers arterial P_{CO_2} and *increases* arterial P_{O_2} and saturation.

When hyperventilation is chronic (as in residents at high altitude), compensatory mechanisms usually restore the blood pH to or toward normal and minimize the effects of hyperventilation on the body (p. 158).

G. DIAGNOSIS OF HYPO- AND HYPERVENTILATION

Because ventilation cannot be called inadequate or excessive unless related to the metabolic rate of the body, in the final analysis the adequacy of ventilation is measured by its ability to maintain normal levels of arterial blood P_{O_2} and P_{CO_2}. Since the level of arterial P_{O_2} may be influenced markedly by impaired alveolar-capillary diffusion but arterial P_{CO_2} is not, the level of arterial P_{CO_2} is a more trustworthy guide in the diagnosis of alveolar hypoventilation. Arterial blood P_{CO_2} may be *measured* by bubble equilibration techniques or by the CO_2 electrode devised by Severinghaus; it may be *calculated* from data on arterial blood CO_2 content and pH. Its upper limit may be inferred from analysis of end-expired alveolar gas samples; the P_{CO_2} of these usually exceeds arterial P_{CO_2} but cannot, of course, be greater than the P_{CO_2} of mixed venous blood. There are many inexpensive devices for measuring quickly the concentration of CO_2 in gas samples. If repeated or continuous monitoring of end-expired CO_2 concentration is desired, the infra-red CO_2 analyzer is useful if proper precautions are taken.

SUMMARY.—*Hypo*ventilation with *air* leads to anoxemia, CO_2 retention and respiratory acidosis. *Hypo*ventilation with *oxygen* usually leads only to CO_2 retention and to respiratory acidosis. *Hyper*ventilation with air "blows off" CO_2 and produces respiratory alkalosis but adds little to the oxygenation of the blood (unless the alveoli were *hypo*ventilated at the outset).

H. THE O_2–CO_2 DIAGRAM

The "O_2–CO_2 diagram," or "alveolar air diagram," of Fenn and Rahn is employed by some pulmonary physiologists to convey an accurate, quantitative picture of the inter-relationships among alveolar gas tensions, blood gas contents, alveolar ventilation and pulmonary blood flow. This graph is invaluable to those who prefer graphs to equations, models, schemas or words; once its use is mastered, it will permit quick solution of complex problems, without the use of any equations. However, since most physicians are not accustomed to think in terms of graphic representations, we have decided to use explanations in words in this text. The O_2–CO_2 diagram is included in the Appendix as an introduction to the work of Rahn, Fenn and Riley for those who wish to study it (see p. 346).

I. REGULATION OF VENTILATION

The body has mechanisms available to sense inadequate alveolar ventilation and to correct it. Since hypoventilation with air leads to anoxemia,

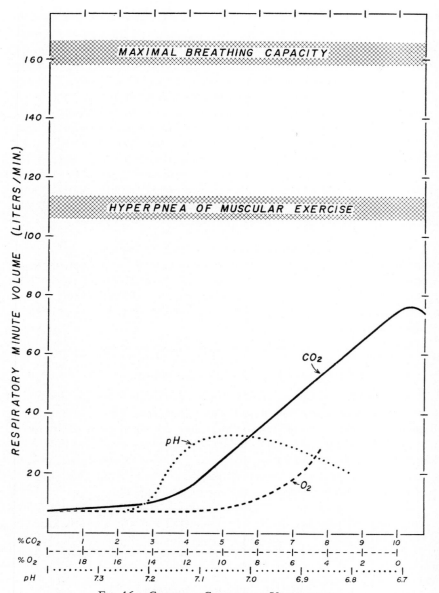

FIG. 16.—CHEMICAL CONTROL OF VENTILATION

TABLE 6.—Pulmonary Ventilation in Response to CO_2 Excess and O_2 Lack*

Conc. of CO_2 or O_2 in Inspired Air, %	TV, ML	Frequency Breaths/Min	Min Vol, L/Min	Alv. Vent., L/Min
	Effects of CO_2 Inhalation on Ventilation (More than 20 normal subjects studied at each concentration of CO_2)			
0.03	440	16	7	4.6
1.0	500	16	8	5.6
2.0	560	16	9	6.6
4.0	823	17	14	11.3
5.0	1300	20	26	22.5
7.6	2100	28	52	47.9
10.4	2500	35	76	69.0
	Effects of Brief Anoxemia (8–10 min) on Ventilation (9–36 subjects studied at each concentration of O_2)			
20.93	500	14	7	4.9
18.0	500	14	7	4.9
16.0	536	14	7.5	5.4
12.0	536	14	7.5	5.4
10.0	593	14	8.3	6.2
8.0	812	16	13.	10.4
6.0	—	—	18.	—
5.2	—	—	22.	—
4.2	933	30	28.	23.2

* All data are mean values and the same as in Figure 16; alveolar ventilation was calculated using predicted anatomic dead space, taking into account increases in tidal volume.

CO_2 retention and respiratory acidosis, one would suppose that compensatory mechanisms would be activated by a decrease in O_2, an increase in CO_2 or a decrease in pH. Figure 16 shows that all three of these can increase pulmonary ventilation, though the relative sensitivities of these mechanisms differ considerably. It is also of interest that the useful compensatory mechanisms are those that increase primarily the tidal volume and therefore increase alveolar ventilation (see Table 6).

EFFECT OF ANOXEMIA.—The characteristic respiratory stimulation produced by anoxemia is an increase in tidal volume, with some accelera-

◀——◀ Fig. 16.—Hyperpneas produced in normal man by breathing low O_2 and high CO_2 mixtures and in patients with acidosis or contrasted with maximal possible hyperpnea (maximal breathing capacity) and with minute volume attained during severe muscular exercise. (Data from Am. J. Physiol. 130:777, 1940; 137:256, 1942; 138:659, 1943; 149:277, 1947; J. Indust. Hyg. 11:293, 1929; and J. Clin. Invest. 27:500, 1948.)

tion of the frequency of breathing. This is due to reflexes initiated in the chemoreceptors of the carotid and aortic bodies by a decrease in arterial Po_2. These bodies are attached directly to large arteries, the ascending aorta and the external carotid, and "sample" the arterial blood as it flows through them very rapidly. If these structures are removed or inactivated, little or no hyperpnea occurs in response to a lowered arterial Po_2. It is important to emphasize that the "low O_2 stimulus" is *not* decreased O_2 *content* or *saturation* of the arterial blood, but decrease in the *partial pressure* or *tension* of O_2 (Po_2). In anemia, CO poisoning or sulf- or methemoglobinemia, the defect is solely a reduction in active hemoglobin; the O_2 content of arterial blood may be reduced greatly with no appreciable change in arterial Po_2. In these conditions there is no anoxic stimulus to the chemoreceptors and no increased ventilation.

Although it would be reasonable to suppose that these O_2 receptors would be exquisitely sensitive to slight changes in arterial Po_2, actually they are not. It is true that some of the chemoreceptor units are activated by the Po_2 of normal arterial blood, but most of these appear to function as emergency mechanisms to increase ventilation when anoxemia becomes severe. When normal men are subjected for short periods of time to increasing degrees of uncomplicated O_2 lack by the inhalation of 21, 18, 16, 14, 12 and 10% O_2, there is no significant increase in respiration until 16% O_2 is breathed. When men are subjected to somewhat more severe anoxemia for a period of several weeks, somewhat greater hyperpnea occurs. There is no doubt that anoxemia is capable of increasing respiration in man, but it appears that anoxemia greater than that seen in most patients with chronic pulmonary disease is required before breathing is stimulated conspicuously in most individuals. However, the chemoreceptor mechanism is a rugged one and functions even during deep anesthesia or moderately severe depression of the central nervous system. It is of interest that the hyperpnea of anoxemia becomes well defined in most individuals at approximately the arterial Po_2 that marks the beginning of the steep slope of the O_2 dissociation curve (see Fig. 41, p. 142).

One can determine readily the extent to which anoxemia is responsible for increasing or maintaining a patient's ventilation by measuring ventilation when the patient is breathing air and again when O_2 is substituted for air. In healthy individuals with normal arterial Po_2 and saturation, inhalation of O_2 decreases minute ventilation only slightly and only for a few minutes; after this, if inhalation of O_2 is continued, ventilation increases to about 10% greater than normal. In patients with serious depression of the respiratory center, inhalation of O_2, by removal of anoxemic reflexes, which are now far more important than in normal individuals, may decrease ventilation markedly. Thus, in a patient suffering from emphysema and pulmonary insufficiency (arterial O_2 saturation 69%), inhalation of O_2 was followed by a decrease in minute volume from 4.6 to 2.2 L/min; his arterial blood became well saturated with O_2 (because of the high Po_2 in the inspired gas) but arterial Pco_2 rose to 150 mm Hg and pH decreased to 7.06. This type of reaction occurs only seldom during O_2 therapy; however, it is important to recognize that it *can* occur and to be prepared to combat the hypoventilation by mechanical aids (see p. 285).

EFFECT OF AN INCREASE IN ARTERIAL Pco_2. The normal respiratory center is exquisitely sensitive to a rise in arterial Pco_2 and responds promptly with an increase in tidal volume and alveolar ventilation; with a further increase in arterial Pco_2, frequency of breathing is also increased (see Table 6, p. 53). Hypoventilation leads to a rise in arterial Pco_2; the latter, by stimulation of the respiratory center, usually increases ventilation and restores arterial Pco_2 to normal levels. However, this mechanism is readily depressed by anesthesia, drugs, severe anoxemia, cerebral injury or by high, narcotic concentrations of CO_2 itself. Under these conditions, ventilation does not increase and the arterial Pco_2 remains at a high level. Arterial Pco_2 may also rise when there is mechanical limitation to ventilation, so that even a sensitive respiratory center cannot cause hyperventilation. It is sometimes useful to measure the ventilatory response of the patient to the inhalation of 7.5% CO_2 in air. A poor response indicates that the sensitivity of the respiratory center is decreased, *if* mechanical limitation to breathing is not present. For example, a patient had no mechanical limitation to breathing (maximal voluntary ventilation was 190 L/min) but had an unusually sluggish response to the inhalation of 7.5% CO_2 in air. This clue led to the diagnosis of a lesion in the region of his medullary respiratory center. Since CO_2 excess, acting on the medullary respiratory center, causes the latter to bombard the respiratory muscles with a larger number of nerve impulses, a specific test of the state of the respiratory center would be the measurement of the electrical activity of (*a*) the center, (*b*) its efferent nerves or (*c*) the respiratory muscles. This is difficult to do. A normally functioning center will increase the force of respiratory muscle contraction and lower and raise intrathoracic pressure even though there may be mechanical limitation to movement of the lung; this may be used as an indication of the activity of the center *if the thorax is free to move and there is no neuromuscular disorder.*

Patients with pulmonary emphysema may have a diminished response to inhalation of CO_2 for *several* reasons: (*a*) There may be mechanical limitation to movement of the *thorax*. (*b*) There may be mechanical limitation to movement of the *lung* (airway obstruction and "air trapping"). (*c*) There may be depression of the respiratory center owing to the effects of chronic anoxemia, chronic CO_2 retention ("CO_2 narcosis") or both. (*d*) Removal of anoxemic reflexes may occur *if the inhaled CO_2 was mixed with high concentrations of O_2 instead of with 20.93% O_2.* (*e*) The existing high level of buffer base (increased hemoglobin and bicarbonate) may prevent arterial Pco_2 from rising abruptly. (*f*) Cerebral edema or an increase in cerebrospinal fluid pressure (presumably caused by cerebral vasodilatation produced by the increased arterial Pco_2 and decreased arterial Po_2) may depress the respiratory center.

The respiratory response to inhalations of CO_2 mixtures may be used to determine the depth of narcosis in a patient with morphine or barbiturate poisoning: a patient who responds with vigorous hyperpnea cannot have serious central depression and usually recovers if given good medical and nursing care.

In some patients with cardiopulmonary disease, such as congestive heart failure and pulmonary restrictive disease, the arterial Pco_2 may be low. If the arterial Pco_2 is low, the patient must be *hyper*ventilating, but the hyperventilation must be caused by mechanisms other than a rise in Pco_2; these other respiratory drives may be initiated by acidosis, anoxemia or vagal stretch reflexes (Hering-Breuer).

EFFECT OF ACIDOSIS.—A decrease in pH can lead to an increase in tidal volume and alveolar ventilation. The Kussmaul type of breathing in diabetic or renal acidosis is an example of this. Probably both central and reflex chemoreceptor mechanisms are involved. There is little quantitative information about the sensitivity of these mechanisms in man; the data in Figure 16 (p. 52) were obtained from the study of a small group of patients with diabetic acidosis.

OTHER FACTORS INFLUENCING PULMONARY VENTILATION.

1. *Protective reflexes.*—A *cough reflex* produces forceful expiratory effort when foreign, irritating materials enter the lower respiratory tract. An *upper respiratory reflex* causes apnea, closure of the glottis and bronchial constriction when irritant materials enter the upper airway. A *swallowing reflex* results in closure of the glottis and inhibition of inspiration, when food is passing from the mouth to the esophagus. A *submersion reflex* causes apnea and bradycardia when water enters the upper respiratory tract; this is especially well developed in diving animals.

2. *Pulmonary stretch (Hering-Breuer) reflexes.*—The best-known of these is the "inflation" or "inhibito-inspiratory" reflex, which checks res-

piration when the lungs have been inflated to a certain volume or degree of stretch. The afferent nerve fibers run in the vagus nerves; the very slow, deep breathing that follows experimental section of both cervical nerves is due to loss of this check mechanism so that each inspiration becomes maximal. A less well-known member of this group is the "deflation" or "excito-inspiratory" reflex which causes earlier and more rapid inspiration and acceleration of respiratory frequency; it is initiated by deflation or collapse of portions of the lungs.

A third stretch reflex produces a maximal inspiration following a greater-than-normal inspiration and presumably provides a mechanism for reinforcing deep inspiration when this is required.

3. *Thoracic chemoreflexes (Von Bezold; Bezold-Jarisch reflexes).*— These include the coronary and pulmonary chemoreflexes. Stimulation results in reflex apnea, bradycardia and hypotension. This response is produced by the injection or inhalation of minute amounts of a wide variety of chemical substances (such as the veratrum alkaloids, antihistaminic drugs and serotonin) so that they reach either the pulmonary or the coronary circulation; afferent impulses travel in the vagus nerves. The effects in experimental animals are dramatic and sometimes catastrophic, but effects may vary in different species and the physiologic or pathologic significance of these reflex effects in man is still obscure.

4. *Circulatory factors.*—Increase or decrease of pressure in the carotid sinus and aortic arch leads to increase or decrease in the number of impulses from these vascular receptors (pressure-, baro- or stretch receptors) to the respiratory center. Since these baroreceptor impulses are inhibitory, increase in arterial blood pressure reflexly diminishes pulmonary ventilation and decrease in blood pressure augments it.

Serious hypotension also appears to result reflexly in constriction of the arterioles supplying the carotid and aortic bodies so that ischemia of these structures may occur and cause intense respiratory stimulation (the metabolic activity of the chemoreceptor tissue, though slight, exceeds the supply of O_2 when blood flow is very sharply curtailed and then local Po_2 and pH decrease and Pco_2 rises to stimulant levels).

A decrease in cerebral blood flow may also permit the accumulation of stimulant materials such as CO_2 in the cells of the respiratory center and augment respiratory activity; an increase in cerebral blood flow may produce the reverse effect.

5. *Reflexes from joints.*—Back and forth motion of a limb produces afferent impulses which reflexly increase the rate and occasionally the depth of breathing.

6. *Pain receptors.*—Pain may cause either respiratory stimulation or

inhibition, depending on the character, origin (visceral or somatic), and intensity.

7. *Temperature.*—Increase in body temperature increases pulmonary ventilation, sometimes so tremendously that overventilation and tetany follow. The effects result in part from warming the medullary centers by the blood and in part from warming the chemoreceptors.

8. *Supramedullary regulation.*—Supramedullary areas exert important effects on the medullary respiratory center; these include the pontine pneumotaxic center and cortical areas.

J. PULMONARY VENTILATION DURING EXERCISE

The cardiopulmonary system of a healthy young adult at rest need supply only about 250 ml of O_2 to the body tissues each minute; during the most vigorous muscular exercise, it must supply very much more (the maximum recorded is 5500 ml/min—a 22-fold increase). It accomplishes this by a great increase in cardiac output per minute and by a tremendous increase in alveolar ventilation; the latter maintains alveolar and arterial Po_2 at normal levels despite the considerable increase in blood flowing past the alveoli each minute and the very huge quantities of O_2 that must be added to each ml of blood. (Increased activity of skeletal muscle lowers tissue Po_2, raises tissue Pco_2, increases tissue temperature and lowers tissue pH; all of these favor dissociation of HbO_2 and delivery of O_2 to the tissues and therefore lower the venous O_2 content far below the familiar levels given for the resting individual—see p. 145).

Figure 16 (p. 52) shows that the minute volume of breathing during maximal, but brief, exercise in healthy young men may exceed 100 L/min. This is about 50 L/min *less* than that attainable by maximal *voluntary* hyperventilation but very much more than the ventilation forced on the same men by inhalation of high concentrations of CO_2 or of low concentrations of O_2 or by a decrease in pH.

Actually, during moderate muscular exercise in a healthy individual, there is no significant change in arterial Po_2, Pco_2, or pH, so that an increased "chemical drive," acting centrally or reflexly on systemic arterial chemoreceptors, does not exist and cannot be held responsible for the increase in ventilation.* Many different theories have been proposed to

---

* In exhausting muscular exercise, arterial Po_2 and pH may decrease and Pco_2 rise; in moderate exercise, they usually do not. In patients who have a limitation to ventilation, *mild* exercise may produce these same chemical changes; this is because their ventilation cannot keep pace with the demands for O_2 uptake and CO_2 elimination.

explain this hyperpnea in the face of normal arterial P_{O_2}, P_{CO_2} and pH. These include (a) increased "sensitivity" of the medullary respiratory center to normal arterial P_{CO_2} levels, possibly caused in part by liberation of epinephrine; (b) bombardment of the respiratory center by impulses from the motor cortex en route to the exercising muscles; (c) an unidentified X-substance formed during muscle contraction and acting on the respiratory center; (d) a rise in blood temperature; (e) reflexes from the exercising muscles, originating in either stretch- or chemoreceptors; (f) conditioned reflexes; (g) reflexes originating from receptors in the central venous system or pulmonary circulation. No single theory proposed to date is adequate, and it is likely that multiple factors are responsible.

Exercise tests are often used in the evaluation of pulmonary function, even though the cause of the respiratory response is known only incompletely. Some of the measurements made are:

1. Rate, tidal volume, minute volume, anatomic dead space and alveolar ventilation during mild, moderate or maximal exercise (treadmill, stationary bicycle or steps) and again in the recovery period.

2. Oxygen consumption during exercise and in the recovery period following exercise.

3. Pulse rate and blood pressure during and after exercise.

4. Arterial O_2 saturation, P_{O_2}, P_{CO_2}, pH and diffusing capacity during exercise.

There are still gaps in our knowledge that must be filled before we can utilize fully the data from exercise tests. First, it is perplexing to decide what normal data should be used as a basis for comparison. Those listed in (1), (2) and (3) differ in trained athletes, healthy non-athletes and probably again in older men and women, and in sedentary or convalescent individuals—all without pulmonary disease. Many patients with pulmonary disease have voluntarily restricted their activity for long periods because of dyspnea; the data obtained in this group may overestimate the pulmonary factors because of the changes that have occurred in the cardiovascular system and in the limb (and respiratory) muscles. Second, a very mild exercise that overtaxes some patients with severe pulmonary disease might not be sufficient to test the capacity of other patients; for this reason, there is no single standard test that can be applied to everyone. Third, brief exercise (1 min step test) does not permit a "steady state" to develop, but some ill patients cannot exercise longer than 1 min. Fourth, exercise pushed beyond certain limits—to determine the capacity of the pulmonary system—may be dangerous in some patients because arterial O_2 saturation may decrease at the very time that cardiac work increases.

Certain measurements are helpful at the present time: (1) The relationship between O_2 consumption and the O_2 supplied by pulmonary ventilation helps to determine whether the patient is hyper- or hypoventilating in response to the need for O_2. Healthy men require about 1.7 liters of alveolar ventilation to supply 100 ml of O_2 to the tissues (see Table 4, p. 47). If, after allowance is made for reasonable errors in using a predicted value for anatomic dead space, the volume of ventilation is too small, there is definite *hypo*ventilation. If the ventilation is too much, the patient is bringing more inspired air to his alveoli per minute than would be needed to oxygenate the venous blood, *if* distribution and diffusion were normal. Determination that such overventilation exists does not solve the problem of its cause—i.e., whether it is due to uneven distribution of gas and blood, impairment of diffusion or to the hyperventilation syndrome. (2) The degree of exercise, level of minute ventilation and amount of respiratory work at which dyspnea occurs provide base-line data on which to gauge improvement or worsening of the patient's condition.

SUMMARY.—We know a great deal about the average ventilatory response of healthy subjects to specific stimuli to respiration, such as decrease in arterial P_{O_2}, increase in arterial P_{CO_2}, decrease in arterial pH, increase in blood temperature, passive movements of joints and muscular exercise. Unfortunately these average data are not helpful in evaluating any one patient's ventilatory response to chemical or nervous stimuli because: (1) there is considerable individual variability even within a homogeneous group of individuals, (2) there is considerable variability in the sensitivity of the respiratory center of patients receiving drugs, and finally (3) there is great variability in the mechanical ability to ventilate the lungs. Nevertheless, important diagnostic information can sometimes be obtained by analysis of the patient's ventilatory response to one or more of these stimuli (see Case 1, p. 215).

II. Uniformity of Alveolar Ventilation

The lung is often regarded as a uniform structure in which each alveolus has the same volume, the same distensibility, the same ventilation, the same blood flow and the same facility for diffusion of gases across its alveolar-capillary membranes. If this were so, and all the fresh air inspired into the alveoli were distributed uniformly to alveoli of equal volume and with equal blood flow, then ventilation would be maximally effective in arterializing the mixed venous blood. The real lung is not uniform. We know that differences exist between the ventilation and blood flow of different parts of the lungs, even in healthy subjects. In the remainder of this chapter and in Chapter 4, we will discuss in some detail the concept of uneven distribution of gas and blood and its effect on function.

In the very simplest of lungs (Fig. 17, *left*) the organ consists of a single chamber with pulmonary capillaries in its walls; in such a lung, ventilation is almost certain to be uniform throughout. As the lung becomes more complex, septa develop to a greater and greater extent. This increases greatly the surface for gas exchange but also increases the opportunity for *uneven* ventilation. The human lung, with an estimated

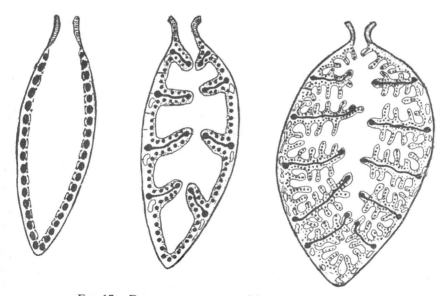

FIG. 17.—DEVELOPMENT OF THE MULTI-ALVEOLAR LUNG

Left, uni-alveolar lung of Proteus. *Center,* multi-alveolar lung of Siren with simple septa. *Right,* multi-alveolar lung of Rana with complex septa. Black dots in walls and septa represent pulmonary capillaries. (From Krogh, A.: *The Comparative Physiology of Respiratory Mechanisms* [Philadelphia: University of Pennsylvania Press, 1941].)

DISTRIBUTION OF INSPIRED GAS

UNIFORM DISTRIBUTION

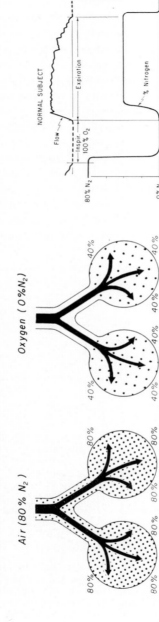

Air (80% N₂) Oxygen (0% N₂)

NON-UNIFORM DISTRIBUTION

Air (80% N₂) Oxygen (0% N₂)

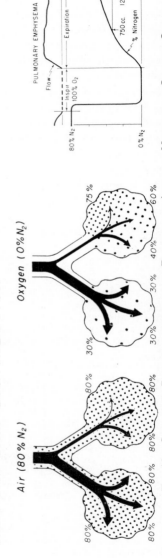

Fig. 18.—Schematic Representation of the Dilution of Alveolar Nitrogen by Inspired Oxygen

300,000,000 alveoli, is too complex to picture. In such a lung, even though healthy, alveolar ventilation is not absolutely uniform. In a very large percentage of patients with chronic pulmonary disease, alveolar ventilation may be decidedly uneven; in the same individual, poorly ventilated and hyperventilated areas may coexist side by side.

Every physician is familiar with uneven ventilation in the form of diminished or absent breath sounds regionally; every radiologist is familiar with the fact that some sections of the lungs "light up" more than others during breathing,§ and every anesthesiologist and thoracic surgeon has witnessed directly uneven lung movement during operations with the thorax open. It is not generally known, however, that *uneven* or *non-uniform* ventilation can lead to pulmonary insufficiency even though the minute volume of breathing and the alveolar ventilation (calculated from tidal volume, anatomic dead space and frequency) be normal or increased.‖ Knowledge of the existence, magnitude and effects of uneven ventilation is therefore essential for the complete evaluation of pulmonary function.

Recently the physiologist has become interested in the quantitative aspects of uneven ventilation. Figure 18 shows schematically a physiol-

---

§ Variations in radiolucence in different areas of the lungs are seen best when there is gross, regional uneven ventilation, and when the patient makes a rapid, forced expiration.

‖ The volume and distribution of alveolar ventilation and of pulmonary capillary blood flow are inextricably linked to one another in the process of arterializing the venous blood. This problem is discussed in detail in Chapter 4. In this section we shall discuss only *uneven or non-uniform distribution of inspired gas,* because this is easier to measure and to understand.

◄——◄ Fig. 18.—In each case, the same volume of gas (air or O_2) is inspired, distribution being uniform in one case (*above*) and non-uniform in the other (*below*). N_2 molecules are represented by black dots. *Left,* schematic representation of alveolar N_2 during breathing of air; *center,* schematic representation of alveolar N_2 immediately after a single breath of O_2; *right,* actual records of N_2 concentration and gas flow during the next expiration.

NOTE: Even when distribution of inspired *air* to the alveoli is non-uniform, it would be undetected owing to lack of sensitivity of the N_2 meter to small changes in % N_2. In the illustration, both air and alveolar gas (*left*) are pictured as containing 80% N_2. Actually, air contains 79.03% N_2 and alveolar gas about 80–81% N_2. However, even if *all* the air went to *half* the alveoli, it would lower alveolar N_2 from 80 or 81% to 79.5 or 80.5% and the N_2 meter would not be able to detect such small changes with accuracy. The breathing of any N_2-free gas, such as O_2, dilutes the N_2, the degree of dilution depending upon the fraction of inspired O_2 distributed to the various regions of the lungs. Thus, when there is non-uniform distribution, inhalation of O_2 magnifies the effect of this in the different areas.

ogist's concept of even and of uneven ventilation. Let us assume that when an individual is breathing air, his lungs contain 2000 ml of gas which has a N_2 concentration of approximately 80%.¶ If he inspires 2000 ml of O_2 into his *alveoli* and this O_2 is distributed evenly to each of the millions of alveoli in the lungs (in relation to its pre-inspiratory volume), each alveolus will now contain 40% N_2 (Fig. 18, *above*). On the other hand, if the 2000 ml of O_2 is distributed *unevenly,* some alveoli may get less than their share (hypoventilation) and others may get more than their share (hyperventilation); in this case the composition of alveolar gas will be decidedly *non-uniform* at end-inspiration (Fig. 18, *below*).

It is impossible to put sampling needles into thousands of alveoli to determine whether gas composition is uniform or not, but it is possible to sample and to analyze the gas that leaves the alveoli on the expiration immediately after the inhalation of O_2. Figure 18 shows such records obtained with the N_2 meter. We are already familiar with the first parts of this record (see Fig. 12, p. 40, in which phase *A* represents pure dead space gas and phase *B* represents a mixture of alveolar and dead space gas). Here, the important part is the last phase, *C,* which is expired alveolar gas. If the inspired O_2 were distributed evenly to all the alveoli so that each now contained 40% N_2 instead of 80%, it is obvious that the first, middle and last parts of the expired *alveolar* gas must all contain 40% N_2; therefore, the N_2 meter record of the alveolar gas would appear as in Figure 18 (*above*); i.e., it would be a perfectly horizontal record. On the other hand, if the inspired O_2 were distributed unevenly to the various alveoli, the end-inspiratory N_2 concentrations would vary in different parts of the lungs and the N_2 meter record of expired alveolar gas would be far from a horizontal line; the first gas expired usually has a low N_2 concentration (since it ordinarily comes from the hyperventilated parts which received a larger share of the inspired O_2) and the last gas expired usually has a higher N_2 concentration (since it generally comes from a hypoventilated region which received little O_2).

This record (Fig. 18, *below right*) emphasizes the difficulties that result from considering a *spot* sample of "alveolar gas" to be truly representative of *all* alveolar gas. It is obvious that the first part of expired

---

¶ Inspired air contains 79.03% N_2. Since N_2 is not utilized by body tissues, alveolar gas should contain exactly the same per cent of N_2 as inspired gas. It does when the blood adds to alveolar gas a volume of CO_2 exactly equal to the volume of O_2 removed. The blood usually removes a little more O_2 than it adds in the form of CO_2, and this shrinkage of the alveolar gas volume raises the N_2 concentration to 80% or a little higher. This is known as the respiratory quotient (RQ) effect.

alveolar gas may differ markedly in gas composition from the last, and it requires little imagination to realize that the alveolar gas remaining in the unexpired residual gas may have yet a different composition.

A. TESTS OF UNEVEN DISTRIBUTION* OF INSPIRED GAS

These tests measure only the distribution of inspired gas to the alveoli just as though the lungs were an impermeable bag or bellows and the processes of diffusion and circulation did not exist. They require the use of gases such as N_2, H_2 or helium which are so poorly soluble that they do not pass in great quantity from the alveolar gas into the blood or pulmonary tissues.

SINGLE-BREATH TECHNIQUE: OPEN CIRCUIT.—This has just been described to illustrate graphically the problem of distribution. The patient inspires a single breath of O_2 and then expires slowly and evenly into a spirometer or flow meter while the N_2 meter records continuously N_2 concentration. No measurements are made on the first 750 ml of expired gas because in some patients the last part of this may contain some dead space gas. However, the increase in N_2 concentration is measured over the next 500 ml of expired gas, which is certain to be alveolar gas. In healthy young adults, distribution is not perfectly uniform, but the N_2 concentration does not rise more than 1.5% throughout the expiration of this 500 ml of alveolar gas.† In older healthy individuals, the N_2 concentration rises more (Table 7). However, in patients with severe emphysema, the N_2 concentration may rise as much as 16%. This increase depends on uneven distribution of the gas *during inspiration* and also on *unequal rates of gas flow* from different regions of the lungs *during expiration*. If all regions emptied synchronously during expiration, the N_2 meter record would be horizontal even though the concentration of N_2 varied in different parts of the lung at end-inspiration.

---

* The nomenclature used in discussing distribution is, like the lung, non-uniform! "Uneven ventilation" = "non-uniform ventilation" = "uneven" or "non-uniform distribution of inspired gas" = "non-homogeneous ventilation or distribution" = "poor mixing." The problem of "non-uniformity" appears to be one of uneven *distribution* to different air sacs, lobules or lobes rather than the slow *mixing within an alveolus* (either by mechanical mass flow or by interdiffusion of gases); it has been shown that interdiffusion of gases within an alveolus is 80% complete in only 0.002 sec if the diffusion distance is 0.5 mm, or in 0.38 sec if the diffusion distance is 7 mm.

† If the expiration is very slow, the functional residual capacity very small and the arterial blood O_2 saturation quite low, a slight change in N_2 concentration may occur between the 750 and 1250 ml samples because the O_2 uptake greatly exceeds the simultaneous CO_2 elimination when 100% O_2 is inhaled.

This test has many advantages. It is rapid, requires only a single breath of O_2 and very little co-operation from the patient and is very well adapted to use as a screening test, particularly in younger age groups. Further, it is not influenced by the magnitude of the tidal volume, minute volume, functional residual capacity or by the rate of N_2 washout from the body and blood. Its only drawback is that it requires the use of a special instrument, such as the N_2 meter.

MULTIPLE-BREATH TECHNIQUES: OPEN CIRCUIT.—Some of these tests are quantitative but difficult and laborious; others are simple but give

TABLE 7.—INCREASE IN N_2 CONCENTRATION DURING SINGLE-BREATH TEST PERFORMED ON 51 NORMAL INDIVIDUALS AND 104 PATIENTS WITH PULMONARY DISORDERS*

	NO. OF SUBJECTS †	MEAN INCREASE	RANGE
Normal, young	26	0.7% ± 0.3	0.0– 1.5
Normal, old	25	1.8% ± 1.1	0.0– 4.5
Asthma	24 (5)	3.8	0.5– 8.5
Emphysema	17 (14)	6.9	3.0–12.0
Bronchiectasis	9 (1)	4.6	1.0– 8.0
Sarcoid	9 (2)	3.4	1.0– 6.0
Congestive heart failure........	14 (5)	3.0	0.5– 8.5
Pulmonary carcinoma	7 (7)	5.1	3.0– 6.5
Postpneumonectomy	5 (5)	4.2	2.0– 7.5
Miscellaneous	19 (5)	2.7	0.5– 8.5

* From Comroe, J. H., Jr., and Fowler, W. S.: Am. J. Med. 10:408-413, 1951.
† Numbers in parenthesis refer to patients more than 50 years of age.

only approximate values. All are based on the rate of washout of pulmonary N_2‡ when O_2 is breathed (Fig. 19). The simplest of these tests, the "pulmonary N_2 emptying rate," requires only that the patient breathe O_2, usually for 7 min, and then, by forced expiration, deliver a sample of alveolar gas at the end of the 7 min period. If the inspired O_2 is distributed evenly to all alveoli during the 7 min period, the N_2 will be washed out of these evenly and the final alveolar gas sample will contain less than 2.5% N_2. However, if some areas are markedly *hypo*ventilated during normal breathing, they will still have a high N_2 concentration at the end of 7 min

‡ As the concentration of pulmonary N_2 is reduced, some N_2 dissolved in the tissues and blood will enter the alveoli because the pressure of N_2 in blood and tissues is now higher than the alveolar P_{N_2}, and gases, like liquids, move from a region of higher partial pressure to a region of lower pressure. This N_2 can be corrected for, approximately, and need not concern us here.

NITROGEN ELIMINATION BY INHALATION OF O_2

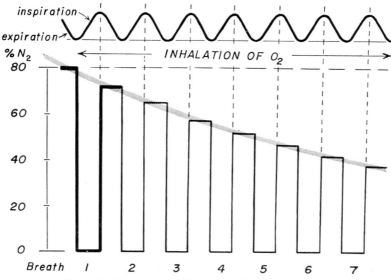

FIG. 19.—PULMONARY NITROGEN WASHOUT CURVE

A subject with uniform distribution of inspired gas breathes O_2 at constant tidal volume; N_2 concentration of respired gas is followed continuously with a N_2 meter. The N_2 record for the first breath (broad line) is similar to the N_2 meter record of the single-breath test in Figure 12 (p. 40), except that here the record is greatly compressed. Each plateau represents the N_2 concentration of expired *alveolar* gas. The resulting N_2 washout curve is a single exponential curve (see text). The data correspond to those in Table 8, alveolar N_2 concentration for each breath being that immediately preceding each inspiration.

TABLE 8 (see Fig. 19)

	% ALV. N_2 AT BEGINNING OF EACH INSPIRATION	% DILUTION OF ALVEOLAR GAS ON EACH BREATH	RESULTING DECREASE IN % ALV. N_2 IN EACH BREATH	% ALV. N_2 AT END OF EACH INSPIRATION
Breath 1	80%	10%	$10 \times 80 = 8.0\%$	$80 - 8.0 = 72\%$
Breath 2	72%	10%	$10 \times 72 = 7.2\%$	$72 - 7.2 = 64.8\%$
Breath 3	64.8%	10%	$10 \times 64.8 = 6.48\%$	$64.8 - 6.48 = 58.3\%$
Breath 4	58.3%	10%	$10 \times 58.3 = 5.83\%$	$58.3 - 5.83 = 52.5\%$
Breath 5	52.5%	10%	$10 \times 52.5 = 5.25\%$	$52.5 - 5.25 = 47.3\%$
Breath 6	47.3%	10%	$10 \times 47.3 = 4.73\%$	$47.3 - 4.73 = 42.6\%$
Breath 7	42.6%	10%	$10 \times 42.6 = 4.26\%$	$42.6 - 4.26 = 38.3\%$

67

and the alveolar gas sample, obtained by forced expiration, will empty these so that the N_2 concentration of this gas is more than 2.5%. For the sake of simplicity, no measurements of functional residual capacity, tidal volume, frequency of breathing or dead space are made. However, the completeness of N_2 washout during the 7 min period does depend, among other things, on these factors. For example, patients with pulmonary disease may hyperventilate even at rest, and this tends to reduce alveolar N_2 to normal values at the end of a 7 min period even though some areas are poorly ventilated. This was demonstrated in a patient who had a large emphysematous bulla (later removed surgically) and decidedly uneven ventilation by the single-breath N_2 meter test (7% increase in expired alveolar N_2 concentration over a 500 ml volume); his 7 min "pulmonary N_2 emptying rate" was normal, because his minute volume of breathing was 16.5 L/min during the test—i.e., about three times normal ventilation.

A more difficult but quantitative test is one in which the stepwise decrease in the alveolar P_{N_2} which occurs is followed continuously, breath by breath, by rapid electrical analyzers. The *actual* measurements of alveolar P_{N_2} breath by breath can then be compared with *theoretical* values that one would expect breath by breath if the inspired O_2 were distributed *evenly* to all the alveoli, i.e., if the lungs were a perfect, single mixing chamber. These theoretical values depend on the volume of gas in the alveoli being washed out (the functional residual capacity), tidal volume, dead space and frequency of breathing.

An example of the calculation and measurements necessary for obtaining the theoretically perfect data follows. At the beginning of the test, the volume of alveolar gas is measured and is found to be 2550 ml. The anatomic dead space is 150 ml. The first breath of O_2 is 450 ml. However, only 300 ml of O_2 plus 150 ml of dead space gas (the latter having the same composition as alveolar gas) enter the alveoli (Fig. 14, p. 43). There is now 2550 + 150 ml, or 2700 ml, of alveolar gas with a concentration of 80% N_2 in the alveoli; this contains 2160 ml of N_2. However, this volume of N_2 is now in a volume of 3000 ml (300 ml of O_2 having been added), and so its new concentration is $\frac{2160}{3000} \times 100$ or 72% (see Fig. 19, p. 67). Similarly, the theoretical N_2 concentration at the end of the second breath can be calculated, assuming that alveolar N_2 concentration is 72% before 300 ml more of O_2 is added (Table 8, p. 67).

In this ideal case, in which the tidal volume is constant and the lungs behave as a single, perfect mixing chamber, a graph of alveolar (end-inspiratory) N_2 concentration against the number of breaths results in the type of curve shown in Figure 19. This is called an exponential curve; such a curve, replotted on semi-log paper, yields a straight line.

Such an exponential curve may be very steep (Fig. 20, *above left*) if the lungs are washed out evenly and rapidly, or less steep (Fig. 20, *above right*) if the lungs are washed out evenly but at a slower rate. In either case, a straight line results from plotting these values on semi-log paper (Fig. 20, *below left*).

When there is uneven ventilation, there may be hundreds of different washout rates in different parts of the lungs, but as a rule the lung behaves as though there were *a poorly ventilated* portion and a *well-ventilated* portion, the first behaving like the lung in Figure 20, *above right,* and the other like the lung in Figure 20, *above left.* The curve obtained from the whole lung of this type is also shown (*below right,* dotted line). The extent of uneven ventilation is indicated by the *deviation* from a straight line of the *actual* values obtained in the patient. This test is seldom used because it is time-consuming and requires very precise measurements.

MULTIPLE-BREATH TECHNIQUE: CLOSED CIRCUIT.—If a precisely measured quantity of a relatively insoluble foreign gas such as helium is added to a closed circuit (see Fig. 4, p. 6), the *curve* of its dilution by alveolar gas, during rebreathing, gives an index of distribution (Fig. 21). The rate may be an exponential one, indicating uniform distribution, or it may be *rapid initially* because of contributions from the *well-ventilated* areas and then *slower* because of less rapid exchange with *poorly ventilated* areas.

The closed-circuit apparatus is of considerable value because of its versatility. During rebreathing with a gas such as helium to an *equilibrium point* (equal concentrations of helium in lungs and bellows), the functional residual capacity can be measured. When the *time* to attain equilibrium is measured, an index of the volume of alveolar ventilation is obtained. When the *curve* of attaining equilibrium is analyzed, an index of distribution of inspired gas is obtained (Fig. 21, p. 71).

BRONCHOSPIROMETRY.—This is a method for obtaining quantitative measurements of the function of the two lungs separately. It involves catheterization of the left main bronchus by a tube fitted with a distal distensible cuff, so that all the gas ventilating the lung is conducted through this airway. When a double-lumen tube is used, the air to and from the right lung passes through a second channel, the opening of which lies in the trachea above the bifurcation. When a single-lumen tube is

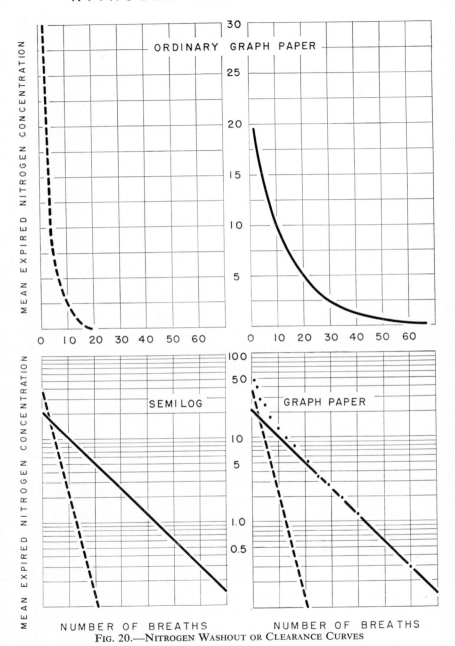

FIG. 20.—NITROGEN WASHOUT OR CLEARANCE CURVES

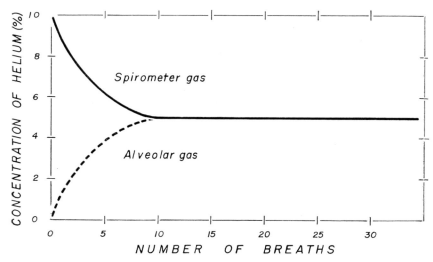

FIG. 21.—HELIUM CLOSED-CIRCUIT TECHNIQUE FOR MEASURING
DISTRIBUTION OF INSPIRED GAS

The method used is illustrated in Figure 4, (p. 16). Initially the bellows contains
10% helium and the lungs contain 0% helium. At equilibrium, concentrations of
helium are the same in both bellows and lungs; the rapidity with which equilibrium
is reached is influenced by the tidal volume. When this is allowed for, the curve
affords an index of the uniformity of distribution. The solid line shows rate of
decrease in concentration of helium, measured in the *bellows;* dotted line illustrates
probable rate of *increase* in concentration of helium in the *alveolar gas.*

_____

◄━━ FIG. 20.—In each case, O_2 is breathed and the mean concentration of N_2 in
the expired gas measured breath by breath. The graphs show mean expired (not alveolar) N_2 concentration plotted against the number of breaths (technique of Fowler,
Cornish, and Kety). *Above,* data are presented on ordinary linear graph paper:
left, rapid N_2 clearance, i.e., a well ventilated lung; *right,* slow N_2 clearance, i.e., a
poorly ventilated lung. *Below,* data are presented on semi-log paper, using the same
N_2 clearance data as in the graphs above. *Left,* each line is a straight line, indicating
that N_2 clearance proceeded in a regular fashion (exponential) from the well ventilated and the poorly ventilated lung. *Right,* dotted line shows N_2 clearance curve
that results from a patient with the *two systems* pictured above. The dotted line is
not a straight line but can be analyzed in terms of two straight lines. Initially the
curve is determined predominantly by the well ventilated lung; after the 20th
breath, this lung is cleared of its N_2 and the curve determined entirely by the N_2
clearance from the poorly ventilated lung. In this case, the uneven distribution must
be on a regional basis.

used, the gas to and from the right lung flows around the tube. In either case, the two lungs are separated as far as their gas flow is concerned, and it is possible to make measurements of the tidal volume of breathing, vital capacity and O_2 consumption of each lung by means of two recording systems. Studies on normal subjects have shown that the right lung is responsible for about 55% of the ventilation and 55% of the O_2 consumption, and the left lung for 45% of each. Marked deviation from these ratios indicates predominantly unilateral pulmonary disease. For example, if the right lung is responsible for 55% of the ventilation but 0% of the O_2 consumption, it would be reasonable to suppose that there was a marked impairment of diffusion or little or no pulmonary blood flow to the right lung.

B. CAUSES OF UNEVEN VENTILATION

The causes of uneven ventilation are shown schematically in Figure 22§; the disturbances shown are not necessarily localized geographically to one lung but may be scattered throughout both lungs. *A* represents regional reduction of the number or quality of elastic fibers in the lung such as occurs in advanced pulmonary emphysema. *B* represents regional obstruction (partial) such as occurs in asthma, pulmonary cysts, peribronchiolar or intrabronchial lesions. *C* represents combinations of *1* and *2* and is often seen in "obstructive emphysema"; the obstruction need not be bronchiolar constriction but may be of the check-valve type that occurs particularly on expiration (see p. 198). *D* represents regional changes in expansion of the type caused by fluid or exudate in the alveoli or interstitial spaces of the lung, pulmonary congestion, atelectasis, tumors or restrictive disease. These changes may also be caused by non-uniform pulmonary expansion, such as occurs in every thoracic operation, or by non-uniform thoracic expansion. Paradoxical breathing may result from the last-mentioned disorder; for example, if the left phrenic nerve is cut so that the left hemidiaphragm cannot descend on inspiration, expansion of the right hemithorax on inspiration may actually pull up the left hemidiaphragm and draw air from the left lung into the right. Movement of gas from one region of the lung to another may also occur when the "time-constants" of different regions vary markedly.

---

§ Figure 22 actually is a deliberate simplification of the changes in the alveoli and airways that result in uneven ventilation. Study of Chapter 7 will give the reader a better understanding of the factors causing non-uniform distribution of inspired gas.

CAUSES OF UNEVEN VENTILATION

A

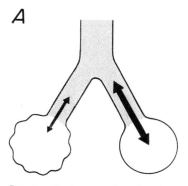

Regional changes in elasticity

B

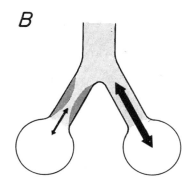

Regional obstruction

C

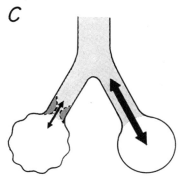

Regional check valves

D

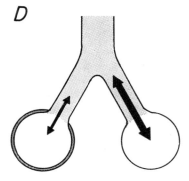

Regional disturbances in expansion

FIG. 22.—MECHANISMS RESPONSIBLE FOR NON-UNIFORM
DISTRIBUTION OF INSPIRED AIR

Circular areas represent the alveoli. Wavy lines in *A* and *C* represent alveoli that have lost their normal elastic recoil. Thick line in *D* signifies alveoli that expand less than normally, although their elastic tissue is normal and there is no airway obstruction. Size of arrows indicates the volume of gas ventilating each region.

73

Uneven ventilation is present to a slight degree in healthy young individuals and to a greater extent in older people, even though free from cardiopulmonary disease. Further, uneven ventilation may be accentuated in a normal person by a change from the supine to the lateral recumbent position. For these reasons, the tests must be done under standard conditions in order to evaluate data properly.

The degree of uneven distribution in different diseases, as detected by the single-breath test, is shown in Table 7 (p. 66). This indicates that uneven distribution, though most pronounced in patients with emphysema, is a fairly frequent finding in patients with cardiopulmonary disease. Though not pathognomonic of any one disease, the presence of uneven ventilation, like the finding of râles, or radiologic shadows serves to call attention to an abnormality which may be identified more specifically by other physiologic tests or by radiologic, bacteriologic or histologic studies. These tests of uneven distribution, then, do not replace other diagnostic procedures but provide a new technique for the detection of pulmonary disease. They are particularly valuable in conditions such as emphysema in which radiologic techniques may often reveal no abnormality or yield equivocal information regarding distribution.

One limitation of these tests is that they give no information regarding the distribution of pulmonary capillary blood flow to the various alveoli (see Chap. 4). Patients with serious pulmonary vascular disorders may have no airway or alveolar disease; in these, data from tests of distribution of gas are normal.

C. EFFECTS OF UNEVEN VENTILATION

Hypoventilation of the *whole* lung invariably leads to anoxemia, CO_2 retention and respiratory acidosis. *Uneven* ventilation causes anoxemia (unless considerable hyperventilation occurs or unless pulmonary capillary blood flow is reduced regionally in proportion to the decrease in ventilation: see Fig. 32, p. 102) but does not necessarily lead to CO_2 retention. The reasons for this are given schematically in Figure 23 and in greater detail in Chapter 4. In any case, uneven ventilation is an inefficient process because minute volume must increase to compensate for a certain amount of ineffective ventilation. The existence of uneven ventilation also prolongs the induction period of inhalation anesthesia because of the longer time required to establish a high concentration of the anesthetic gas in poorly ventilated areas.

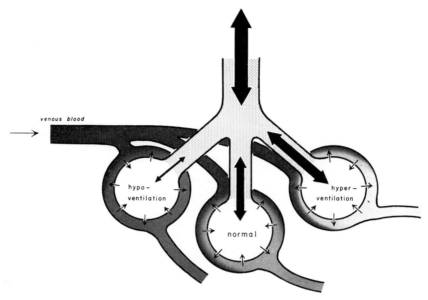

FIG. 23.—SCHEMA SHOWING HYPO-, NORMAL AND HYPERVENTILATION IN
DIFFERENT AREAS OF THE LUNGS

*Hyper*ventilation in relation to blood flow (*right*) can "blow off" CO_2 so that blood passing through hyperventilated parts may have a much lower Pco_2 than blood from normally ventilated regions; however, hyperventilation with air cannot raise the O_2 saturation of blood much above normal values since blood from "normal" regions (*center*) already has a high O_2 saturation (97.4%). Extreme *hypo*ventilation of other regions (*left*) may permit blood to pass that differs little from mixed venous blood in its O_2 saturation and Pco_2. When blood from these three areas mixes in the pulmonary veins and left heart, its O_2 saturation will be low but its Pco_2 may be normal or even less than normal.

Several cases of uneven distribution of inspired gas are presented on pages 224 and 232.

SUMMARY

1. Inspired air must pass through a conducting airway ("anatomic dead space") to reach the alveoli where rapid gas exchange occurs; only air reaching *alveoli* raises alveolar Po_2 and lowers Pco_2 (the requirements for proper gas exchange), and therefore only alveolar ventilation is useful for ventilation.

2. If the volume of inspired air reaching each alveolus is not uniform

(with proper respect for the size of each alveolus), not all of this ventilation is equally useful in arterializing venous blood; some is wasted or ineffective.

3. In the diagnosis of alveolar hypoventilation or hyperventilation, alveolar ventilation per minute may be calculated from rate, tidal volume and predicted anatomic dead space (if gas distribution is uniform). This value should then be compared to values in normal persons with a similar level of activity or metabolic rate; if low, hypoventilation exists. Alveolar ventilation must also be low if arterial blood (or end-expired alveolar gas) P_{CO_2} rises above normal levels. A decreased level of arterial O_2 is not necessarily diagnostic of hypoventilation because impairment of diffusion may cause this even in the face of *hyper*ventilation. Considerable error may result from attempting to estimate alveolar ventilation from rate alone, tidal volume alone, minute volume alone or from observation of the patient's respiratory *effort*.

4. Uneven pulmonary ventilation occurs in many pulmonary diseases. When it is present, useful alveolar ventilation cannot be calculated from measurements of rate, tidal volume and anatomic dead space, and special methods based on CO_2 elimination are used. Physicians must remember that *hyper*ventilation measured at the nose and mouth may be associated with *hypo*ventilation of many alveoli if gas is distributed unevenly throughout the lungs.

CHAPTER 4

The Pulmonary Circulation and Ventilation/Blood Flow Ratios

VESALIUS in 1543 was "driven to wonder at the handiwork of the Almighty by means of which the blood sweats from the right into the left ventricle through passages which escape human vision." Only 10 years later, Michael Servetus provided the first proof that the normal pathway (post-natally) for blood between the right and the left ventricle is through the pulmonary circulation. We know now the major function of that circulation—i.e., to provide the means for effective gas exchange between air and blood—and we also have methods for studying many aspects of that circulation. Studies of pulmonary function are often incomplete and unsatisfactory without study of the pulmonary circulation.

The pulmonary circulation has a pump (the right ventricle), a distributing system (arteries and arterioles), a gas exchange mechanism (the capillary bed) and a collecting system (venules and veins). The functional part of the pulmonary circulation is the capillary bed. It is a remarkable structure. Normally, at any single moment, it contains only 75–100 ml of blood, but this is spread out in a multitude of thin-walled vessels (0.1 micron thick) which have a surface area estimated at 50 square meters, or 30 times the body surface area. It is a readily expansible bed: as much as 30 liters of blood can be pumped through it each minute without the pressure rising high enough to exceed colloidal osmotic pressure and cause pulmonary edema.

In an evaluation of pulmonary function, these measurements of the pulmonary circulation are important:

I. Pressures, Resistance, Flow and Volume

A. PRESSURES

Three types of pressure may be measured: (1) *Intravascular pressure,* the actual blood pressure in the lumen of a vessel at any point, relative to atmospheric. (2) *Transmural pressure,* the difference between the pressure in the lumen of a vessel and that of the tissue around it; it is the pressure which tends to distend the vessel (according to its compliance, see p. 163). The pressure around the pulmonary arteries and veins is the intrathoracic pressure. The pressure around the smaller vessels (arterioles, capillaries, venules) is difficult to measure because it is neither intra-alveolar nor intrapleural pressure but something in between. (3) *Driving pressure,* the difference in pressure between one point in a vessel and another point downstream; it is the pressure which overcomes frictional resistance and is responsible for flow between these points.

It is important to think clearly about these three types of pressure. For example, the driving pressure for the total pulmonary circulation is the difference between the pressure at the beginning of the pulmonary circulation (the pulmonary artery) and that at the end of the pulmonary circulation (the left atrium); serious error may be introduced if the left atrial pressure is not measured but assumed to be normal. If mean pulmonary arterial pressure is 15 mm Hg and mean left atrial pressure is 5 mm Hg, the driving pressure is 15 — 5, or 10 mm Hg. If, as a result of mitral stenosis or left ventricular failure, the mean left atrial pressure rises to 20 mm Hg and the mean pulmonary arterial pressure rises to 30 mm Hg, calculations of pulmonary driving pressure are in serious error if one *measures* pulmonary arterial pressure and *assumes* that left atrial pressure is 5 mm Hg; actually, the driving pressure is 30 — 20, or again 10 mm Hg. In this example, although the driving pressure is the same in both cases, the circulation is not the same: in the second case the pulmonary arterial pressure, and hence right ventricular work, is increased twofold; in addition, the transmural pressure at each point in the pulmonary circulation is increased (assuming that no change occurred in extravascular pressures).

Why is this distinction important? There are two important effects of increased pulmonary vascular pressure. The first is the formation of pulmonary edema. When transudation of fluid occurs, it occurs across the pulmonary *capillary* walls—not across the arterial or venous walls. Fluid leaves the capillaries to enter the alveoli or interstitial tissues when *transmural* capillary pressure exceeds the transmural colloidal osmotic pressure. Capillary (intravascular) pressure (measured as left atrial pressure) may be greater than transmural colloidal osmotic pressure without evidence of gross pulmonary edema in some patients with mitral stenosis; presumably in these cases an elevated pericapillary *tissue* pressure reduces transmural pressure to safe levels.

The second important effect of increased pulmonary vascular pressure is right ventricular strain, hypertrophy and possibly failure. An increase in right ventricular pressure does not mean that the right ventricle *must* fail, any more than left ventricular failure necessarily follows systemic arterial hypertension, but failure is more likely to occur than if pressure remained normal. Right ventricular failure occurs more frequently when the pulmonary hypertension is associated with anoxemia, since this reduces the O_2 concentration in coronary blood.

The pressure may be extremely high in the pulmonary artery and *normal in the pulmonary capillaries;* in such a case, there must be unusual resistance to flow through the artery or arterioles. It is obvious that knowledge of the pulmonary *arterial* pressure alone provides no information about the pulmonary *capillary* pressure; there may be severe right ventricular strain and failure without any tendency to transudation across the capillary bed. On the other hand, an increase in pressure in the capillaries of only 20–25 mm Hg may cause fulminating pulmonary edema and death, even though this same increment of pressure usually would not impose severe strain on the right ventricle if it occurred only in the *precapillary* part of the circulation (between the right ventricle and the pulmonary capillaries).

The intravascular pressures in the pulmonary circulation are pictured in Figure 24. It is possible to place catheters in the main pulmonary artery, the right and left pulmonary artery branches, the pulmonary veins and the left atrium and to make pressure measurements at these specific

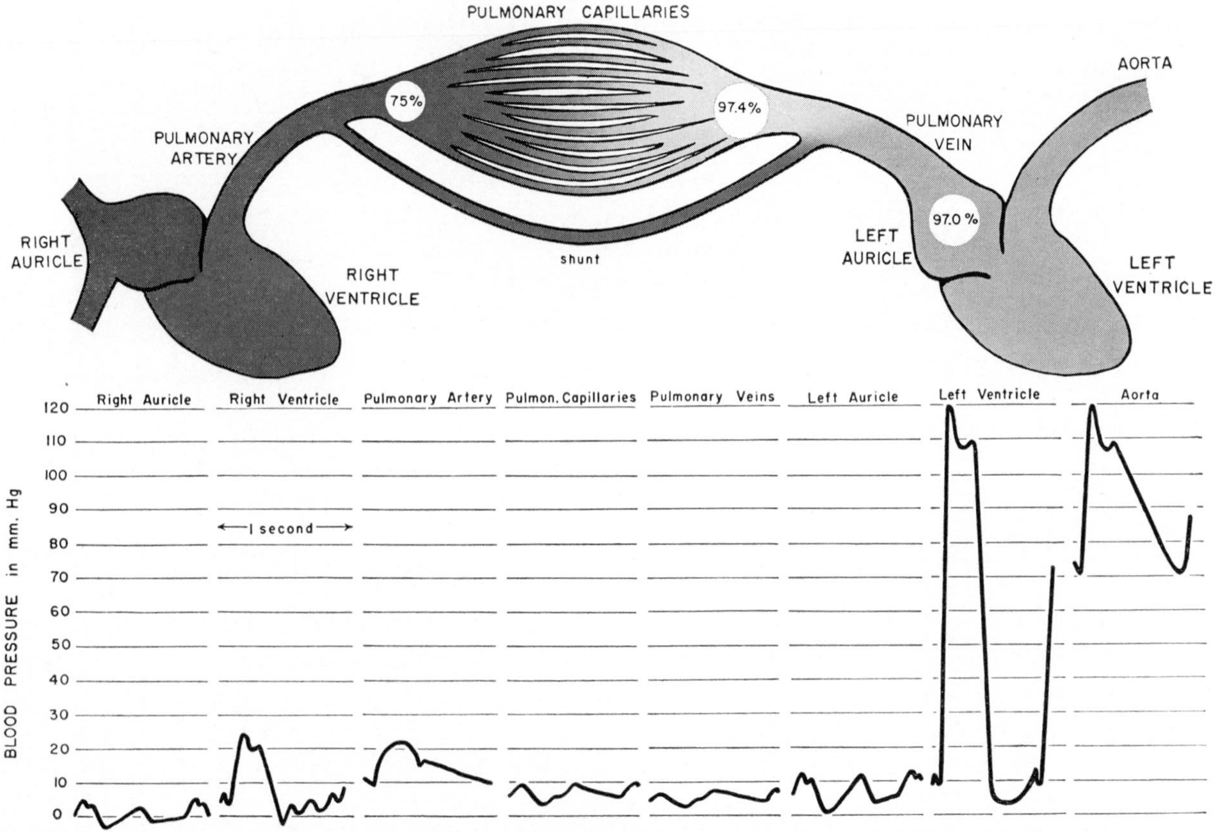

FIG. 24.—PRESSURES IN THE PULMONARY AND SYSTEMIC CIRCULATIONS

80

points. It is *not* possible to measure intracapillary pressure directly, and so there are no precise values for this pressure. Obviously, since blood flows from the pulmonary arterioles through the capillaries to the pulmonary venules, the capillary pressure must be less than the arteriolar and higher than the venular pressure. "Capillary" pressure is estimated by wedging a cardiac catheter as far as it can go into the finest branch of the arterial system and measuring the pressure there; this pressure is approximately equal to pulmonary venous pressure if there is no venular obstruction. "Capillary" pressure is sometimes estimated from measurements of left atrial pressure, using the transbronchial, transthoracic, or transeptal puncture technique.

Pulmonary arterial pressure may rise because of (1) elevation of the level of pressure beyond the pulmonary circulation (in the left atrium), (2) increase in resistance to flow somewhere in the pulmonary circulation (blood flow remaining constant), (3) increase in blood flow (left atrial pressure and pulmonary vascular resistance remaining constant), or (4) combinations of these.

If the level of pressure is increased beyond the pulmonary circulation (mitral stenosis with elevated left atrial pressure; left ventricular failure with increased end-diastolic ventricular pressure and left atrial pressure), the driving pressure must be restored to normal if the right ventricle is to maintain normal blood flow. This requires an increase in pulmonary arterial pressure, and this in turn requires an increase in right ventricular work. The pulmonary arterial pressure does not rise "because" the left atrial pressure increased; it rises because something influences the right ventricle to work harder. The mechanism involved is probably that described by Starling in his "Law of the Heart": initially, because the ventricle must beat against a higher pressure, it does not empty normally in diastole; the diastolic size of the right ventricle is thus increased, and this leads to increased energy of muscular contraction on the next beat.

In this type of pulmonary hypertension, intracapillary and transmural capillary pressure must also rise, if there is no increase in extracapillary pressure.

← ◀ Fig. 24.—Pressure pulse curves obtained by catheterization techniques in man, shown for each part of the intrathoracic cardiovascular system. Venous blood which flows past well ventilated alveoli becomes arterialized. Some venous blood does not come in contact with ventilated alveoli and some flows past poorly ventilated alveoli; this blood is not arterialized or is incompletely arterialized ("physiological shunt"). The numbers 75%, 97.4%, and 97.0% (in white circles) refer to the % saturation of hemoglobin with O_2 in each region.

The other causes of pulmonary hypertension will be discussed below under "Resistance" and "Flow."

B. RESISTANCE TO FLOW IN PULMONARY CIRCULATION

Vascular resistance is usually calculated from an equation similar to Ohm's Law governing resistance, current flow and electromotive force (emf) in electrical circuits.

In an electrical circuit, Resistance $= \dfrac{\text{emf}}{\text{current flow}}$

In the vascular system, Resistance $= \dfrac{\text{driving pressure}}{\text{blood flow}}$

In classic physical terms, pressure is measured in units of dynes/cm² (force per unit area). Blood flow is measured as cm³/sec. Pressure/flow becomes $\dfrac{\text{dynes/cm}^2}{\text{cm}^3/\text{sec}} = \dfrac{\text{dynes} \cdot \text{sec}}{\text{cm}^5} = $ dynes $\cdot$ sec $\cdot$ cm⁻⁵. Since this is a cumbersome term, some physiologists prefer to use simpler "resistance units," using pressure as mm Hg instead of dynes/cm²

$$\dfrac{\text{Resistance}}{\text{(in resistance units)}} = \dfrac{\text{mm Hg (driving pressure)}}{\text{ml/sec}}$$

To calculate resistance, one must know values for driving pressure (not merely pulmonary arterial pressure) *and* flow. If the driving pressure remains the same while flow doubles, the resistance has been reduced to one-half; if the driving pressure doubles but flow also doubles, the resistance has remained the same.

A normal value for resistance in the pulmonary circulation is:

$$\text{Resistance} = \dfrac{\text{mean pul. arterial pr.} - \text{mean left atrial pr.}}{\text{pul. blood flow}}$$

$$= \dfrac{14 - 5 \text{ mm Hg}}{90 \text{ ml/sec}} = \dfrac{9}{90} = 0.1 \text{ resistance unit}$$

The resistance in the pulmonary circulation is about 1/10 that in the systemic circulation of a healthy adult. Since it is so small, small errors in the measurement of the pulmonary arterial and left atrial pressures can produce large errors in calculated resistance; a 2 mm Hg error in each could give

$$\dfrac{12 - 7}{90} = \dfrac{5}{90} = 0.055 \text{ resistance unit}$$

We assume that the major resistance vessels in the pulmonary circulation are the arterioles, but this has not been proved because of our inability to measure the capillary pressure directly. If the mean pulmonary arterial pressure were 14 mm Hg, the mean capillary pressure 6 mm Hg and the mean pulmonary venous pressure 5 mm Hg, the resistance across the arterioles would be $\frac{14-6}{90}$, or 0.09 unit, and that across the capillaries only $\frac{6-5}{90} = 0.01$ unit. However, if the three values actually proved to be 14, 10 and 5, the arteriolar resistance would be $\frac{14-10}{90} = 0.044$ and the capillary resistance $\frac{10-5}{90} = 0.056$ unit.

Until recently it was believed that there was little physiologic regulation of the pulmonary resistance vessels and that the caliber of the resistance vessels changed passively with changing transmural pressure. Certainly no striking changes in resistance are noted following stimulation of efferent pulmonary nerves, sympathetic or parasympathetic. Further, many drugs with definite vasodilator or vasoconstrictor actions on systemic vessels produce little change in the normal pulmonary circulation. However, it now seems certain that there is some control over the pulmonary resistance vessels. Some of the evidence is: (1) Oxygen lack appears to cause vasoconstriction. (2) The raised left atrial pressure present in mitral stenosis is followed by increased pulmonary arteriolar resistance which is, at least in part, reversible. (3) In some patients with pulmonary hypertension, acetylcholine injected into the pulmonary artery causes a decrease in pulmonary arterial pressure by a direct vasodilator effect (the acetylcholine is destroyed by blood cholinesterase before the acetylcholine reaches the systemic circulation, where it would otherwise cause bradycardia, vasodilation and hypotension).

Total pulmonary resistance may increase in many pathologic conditions, and in these the increased resistance may be in the artery, arterioles, capillaries, venules or veins. Among the causes of increased resistance are: (1) intraluminal obstructions, such as thrombi and emboli (blood clots, parasites, fat cells, air, tumor cells, white blood cells, platelets); (2) disease of the vascular wall, such as sclerosis, endarteritis, polyarteritis and scleroderma; (3) obliterative or destructive diseases, such as emphysema and interstitial pulmonary restrictive disease; (4) arteriolar or venospasm (postulated but not yet proved satisfactorily); (5) critical closure of small vessels during and after a period of severe hypotension, and (6) compression of vessels by masses or infiltrative lesions.

The effects of increased resistance depend in part on its location. If it is in the venules or veins, intravascular and transmural pulmonary capillary pressures rise and pulmonary edema may result; if it is in the arteries or arterioles, pulmonary capillary pressure does not rise. In any location, increase in vascular resistance is followed by increased right ventricular pressure and right ventricular strain, if pulmonary blood flow does not decrease.

C. FLOW

Blood flow may be measured by many methods, including (*a*) the direct Fick method, which requires measurements of O_2 uptake/min and the O_2 concentration of arterial and mixed venous blood, and uses the equation:

$$\text{Blood flow (L/min)} = \frac{O_2 \text{ uptake (ml/min)}}{\text{A–V difference for } O_2 \text{ (ml/L)}}$$

(*b*) dye dilution methods, and (*c*) the body plethysmograph method. The last is of interest because it measures instantaneous flow through the pulmonary capillaries, whereas the first two yield values for average blood flow over minutes or seconds. The principle of the body plethysmograph method is shown in Figure 25. The patient sits in an air-tight chamber about the size of a telephone booth; pressure around the subject is measured continuously by a sensitive electrical manometer (Fig. 25, *1*). On request, the patient inhales 80% N_2O–20% O_2 from a bag into his alveoli (Fig. 25, *2*); as N_2O leaves the gas phase to dissolve in blood flowing through the pulmonary capillaries, the total gas pressure in the chamber decreases, and this change is registered continuously by the manometer (Fig. 25, *3*). Knowing alveolar N_2O pressure, solubility of N_2O in blood and alveolar volume (also measured plethysmographically), the pulmonary capillary blood flow can be calculated instant by instant throughout the cardiac cycle and the nature of the capillary volume pulse can be recorded. This method involves no catheterization, no injections and no collections of blood samples. However, when a patient is exercising, the plethysmograph is difficult to use because of the increased heat and water vapor produced within it; a "rigid thorax" method, which requires no plethysmograph, may be useful in a wider variety of conditions. At present, the direct Fick and dye methods are usually used to measure cardiac output during exercise.

Pulmonary blood flow may increase in many conditions, such as exercise, hyperthyroidism, fever, anemia, anoxemia and arterial-to-

PULMONARY CAPILLARY BLOOD FLOW

NITROUS OXIDE UPTAKE

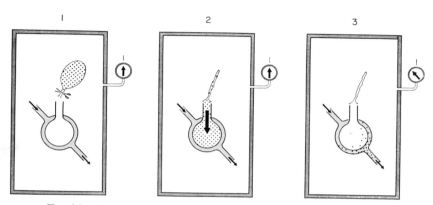

FIG. 25.—MEASUREMENT OF PULMONARY CAPILLARY BLOOD FLOW: BODY PLETHYSMOGRAPH TECHNIQUE

The rectangle is the same air-tight body plethysmograph pictured in Figure 5 (p. 20). Here, the "patient" is a little more complete: in addition to alveoli and conducting airway, he also has pulmonary capillary blood flow (stippled channel surrounding alveoli). The circle with pointer is a sensitive gauge which continuously records pressure within the plethysmograph (around the patient). The bag with black dots (N_2O molecules) represents an anesthesia bag filled with 80% N_2O–20% O_2. When N_2O molecules leave the alveolar gas and dissolve in the pulmonary capillary blood, these no longer occupy space; because the total number of molecules of gas in the alveoli, airway and body plethysmograph is less, pressure falls. Control measurements must be made while the patient breath-holds after inhalation of air; this is followed by inhalation of the N_2O–O_2 mixture and breath-holding for 10–15 sec. (See text.)

venous shunts (including left-to-right shunts associated with septal defects and patent ductus arteriosus). Since *flow = driving pressure/resistance,* one would expect that to increase flow through the pulmonary circulation there must be a corresponding increase in driving pressure. However, measurements in normal individuals have shown that pulmonary vascular pressures do not necessarily rise and certainly do not double when pulmonary blood flow is doubled by exercise. This means that pulmonary vascular resistance must decrease, either by dilatation of existing channels or by opening of new channels, or both. These measurements suggest that all available vascular channels are not in use during rest and that the total pulmonary tissue may be reduced by lobectomy or pneumonectomy without any significant increase in pulmonary vascular pressures. Pneumonectomy performed in a young patient for strictly unilateral disease usually does not lead to any increase in pulmonary vascular pressures even though the remaining vascular bed now conducts twice its former flow. It is more likely to rise in older patients because the aging process alone appears to reduce the size and distensibility of the pulmonary vascular bed. The pressure is apt to rise more if disease of the remaining lung has already destroyed, compressed or restricted part of its vascular bed. It is possible before operation to catheterize the pulmonary artery of the lung to be removed and to occlude it by inflation of a cuff around the catheter. This forces the whole right ventricular output to flow through the lung to be spared. If the pressure in the main pulmonary artery rises only transiently, the vascular bed in that lung is expansible; if it rises sharply and remains elevated, the surgeon may anticipate that the patient will have high pulmonary arterial and right ventricular pressures after pneumonectomy.

Increased flow (such as occurs during muscular exercise) will tend to produce right ventricular strain in patients who have abnormally high pulmonary vascular resistance. It may cause pulmonary edema if the increased resistance is postcapillary (venous thrombosis, mitral stenosis). Mitral stenosis represents a special case, since the original postcapillary resistance at the mitral valve and the consequent increase in pulmonary vascular pressures seem to trigger an increase in *pre*capillary resistance; the result is that pulmonary arterial and right ventricular pressures may rise far beyond the increase in pulmonary venous and capillary pressures.

D. VOLUME

Pulmonary blood volume is the volume of blood between the beginning of the pulmonary artery and the end of the pulmonary veins; in a healthy adult, it is about 900 ml.

Pulmonary *capillary* blood volume is the volume of blood in the *capillary* bed at any given moment. It is calculated from measurements of the diffusing capacity for CO when the patient breathes gas of a high and then a low O_2 concentration (see p. 116). These measurements are indirect and have not yet been correlated with actual anatomic volumes of the capillary bed. However, the values obtained are reasonable ones (75–100 ml in the resting adult), they increase as anticipated during exercise, hypervolemia and pulmonary congestion, and decrease in patients with destructive lesions of the pulmonary parenchyma. This measurement may provide useful information regarding the absolute volume of the capillary bed and its ability to enlarge its capacity. Again, just as pulmonary *arterial* pressure may change without change in pulmonary capillary pressure, so total pulmonary vascular blood volume may change without proportionate changes in capillary blood volume.

II. Distribution of Pulmonary Capillary Blood Flow: Ventilation/Blood Flow Ratios

In Chapter 3, we defined uniform and non-uniform distribution of inspired air to the alveoli, listed some causes of non-uniform distribution of gas and discussed several tests which identify non-uniform distribution of gas. We shall now define non-uniform distribution of pulmonary capillary blood flow and mention some of its causes and effects and several ways of identifying it.

Capillary blood flow may be considered uniform (*a*) when blood flow is the same to every unit of alveolar volume (anatomic uniformity) or (b) when blood flow is distributed to each alveolus in proportion to its ventilation (physiologic uniformity). The anatomist, pathologist or radiologist (the last by the use of pulmonary angiography) measures anatomic uniformity or non-uniformity; the physiologist usually measures blood flow in relation to alveolar ventilation (see p. 101).

A. CAUSES OF UNEVEN PULMONARY CAPILLARY BLOOD FLOW

PHYSIOLOGIC CAUSES.—Just as there is some non-uniformity of *gas* distribution in healthy persons, so there also seems to be some unevenness of *capillary blood flow* in healthy individuals. The latter occurs in large part because of the effect of gravity and therefore is minimal when man is supine or prone, greater when he is in a lateral position, and maximal when he is erect. When man is erect, gravitational force, acting on blood in the longitudinal vessels, increases the transmural vascular pressures in the lung bases relative to the apices; this causes vasodilatation and increased blood flow at the base of the lungs. One would suspect that compensatory vasoconstriction would occur at the bases in order to maintain uniform distribution of blood flow throughout the lung; pathologists have described thickening of the arteriolar smooth muscle at the base of the

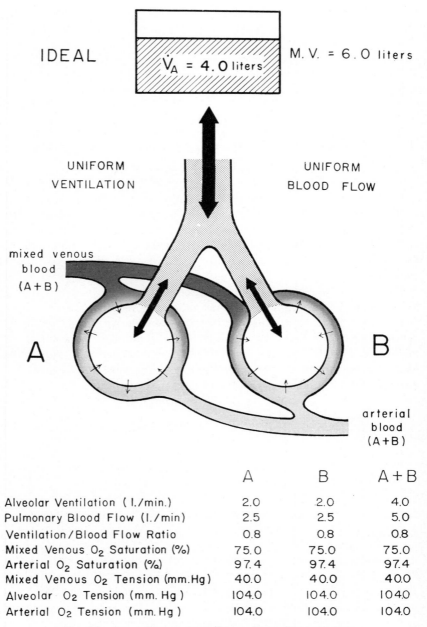

	A	B	A + B
Alveolar Ventilation (l./min.)	2.0	2.0	4.0
Pulmonary Blood Flow (l./min)	2.5	2.5	5.0
Ventilation/Blood Flow Ratio	0.8	0.8	0.8
Mixed Venous O_2 Saturation (%)	75.0	75.0	75.0
Arterial O_2 Saturation (%)	97.4	97.4	97.4
Mixed Venous O_2 Tension (mm.Hg)	40.0	40.0	40.0
Alveolar O_2 Tension (mm. Hg)	104.0	104.0	104.0
Arterial O_2 Tension (mm. Hg)	104.0	104.0	104.0

FIG. 26.—IDEAL VENTILATION/BLOOD FLOW RELATIONSHIP

lung in patients with mitral stenosis, but physiologists have not yet uncovered any evidence of rapidly acting vasomotion that might compensate for the effect of gravity during a change in posture.

PATHOLOGIC CAUSES.—Uneven capillary blood flow occurs in many pathologic conditions affecting the lungs and circulation. Some of these are:

(1) Embolization or thrombosis of parts of the pulmonary circulation by blood clots, fat, gas, parasites or tumor emboli.

(2) Partial or complete occlusion of one pulmonary artery or some of the arterioles by arteriosclerotic lesions, endarteritis, collagen disease or congenital anomalies.

(3) Compression or kinking of large or small pulmonary vessels by masses, pulmonary exudates or pneumo- or hydrothorax.

(4) Reduction of part of the pulmonary vascular bed by destruction of lung tissue or by fibrotic obliteration of pulmonary vessels.

(5) Regional congestion of vessels such as occurs in some types of heart failure.

(6) Closure of some pulmonary vessels, such as appears to occur when circulating blood volume is greatly reduced during severe hypotension and circulatory shock.

(7) Anatomic venous-to-arterial shunts such as pulmonary hemangiomas; in such shunts, however, the distribution of blood that is flowing to *capillaries* may be uniform, the abnormality being that some mixed venous blood by-passes capillaries completely to empty directly into pulmonary venules or veins.

B. EFFECTS OF UNEVEN DISTRIBUTION OF INSPIRED GAS AND PULMONARY CAPILLARY BLOOD FLOW

In discussing non-uniform distribution of *inspired gas* in Chapter 3, we postponed discussion of the effects of uneven distribution of inspired gas on arterial O_2 and CO_2. This is because, other factors being normal,

---

◄——◄ FIG. 26.—Ideal case with uniform ventilation and uniform blood flow to all parts of the lungs. Total area of the rectangle signifies minute volume of ventilation, and shaded area, alveolar ventilation/min. Mixed alveolar gas $(A + B)$ has the same Po_2 as gas in alveoli A and B. Mixed capillary blood $(A + B)$ has the same Po_2 as blood in capillaries A and B. There is no alveolar-arterial Po_2 difference. (For the sake of simplicity, mixed blood from pulmonary capillaries A and B is called arterial blood; this is true only when there is no anatomical shunt from right to left. This applies also to Figures 28, 29, 30 and 32.)

the O_2 and CO_2 in blood leaving the lungs is determined not by ventilation and not by blood flow as individual factors, but by the relationship or ratio between the ventilation of alveoli and their capillary blood flow.

EFFECTS OF UNEVEN RATIOS ON ARTERIAL BLOOD O_2.—Figure 26 shows the ideal relationship: Inspired air (all of the same composition) is distributed uniformly to all the alveoli so that the end-inspiratory Po_2 and Pco_2 is equal in all alveoli. Mixed venous blood (all of the same composition) is distributed uniformly to all of the pulmonary capillaries in relation to the ventilation of each group of alveoli. Alveoli A receive 2 L/min of ventilation and 2.5 L/min of capillary blood flow; alveoli B (which have a gas volume equal to that of alveoli A) also receive 2 L/min of ventilation and 2.5 L/min of capillary blood flow. This results in an alveolar and arterial O_2 tension of 104 mm Hg (it is assumed here that there is no barrier to diffusion of O_2) and arterial O_2 saturation of 97.4%.*

Does it make any difference if the ratios of ventilation to blood flow are not uniform throughout the lung if the *total* alveolar ventilation remains normal (let us say 4 L/min) and *total* capillary blood flow remains normal (5 L/min)? It does; because such a condition must produce arterial anoxemia and CO_2 retention. Indeed, uneven ventilation in relation to blood flow is the commonest cause of anoxemia in clinical medicine. A number of cases (see Table 9) will be presented to illustrate this.

An extreme case is illustrated in Figure 27; although it is an impossible situation in a living person, it serves to prove the point. In Figure 27, alveolar ventilation is normal in *volume* (4 L/min) and capillary blood flow is normal in *volume* (5 L/min). However, all of the ventilation goes to the left lung, which has *no* blood flow, and all of the blood

---

* An equation has been developed for the calculation of ventilation/blood flow ratios (see Appendix, p. 342). To make this calculation, one must know the concentration of O_2 in inspired and alveolar gas and the concentration of O_2 in mixed venous and pulmonary venous blood. Using values obtained in normal men under basal conditions, the ventilation/blood flow ratio is found to be 0.8 for the whole lung. It is sometimes convenient to think of the 0.8 ratio as a 4:5 ratio because alveolar ventilation in resting adult man is about 4 L/min and pulmonary blood flow is about 5 L/min. In this "ideal" situation, the ratio is 0.8 for alveoli A (2:2.5), 0.8 for alveoli B (2:2.5), and 0.8 for the whole lung, alveoli A and B (4:5).

This ratio is often called the $\dot{V}A/\dot{Q}c$ ratio ($\dot{V}A$ = alveolar ventilation in L/min; $\dot{Q}c$ = pulmonary capillary blood flow in L/min) or the ventilation/perfusion ratio. Because the term "perfusion" often brings to mind an isolated organ and a pump, we prefer the term "blood flow." The correct term "alveolar ventilation/pulmonary capillary blood flow ratio" is cumbersome, and we shall therefore use "ventilation/blood flow ratio."

TABLE 9.—ILLUSTRATIONS SHOWING RELATIONSHIPS BETWEEN ALVEOLAR
VENTILATION AND PULMONARY CAPILLARY BLOOD FLOW

ALVEOLAR VENTILATION	PUL. CAP. BLOOD FLOW	ILLUSTRATED IN FIGURE	REMARKS
Uniform	Uniform	26 (p. 88)	"Ideal"
		54 (p. 216)	"Ideal," but with alveolar hypoventilation
		57 (p. 242)	"Ideal," but with alveolo-capillary block
Non-uniform	Uniform	29 (p. 96)	"Normal"*
		28 (p. 94)	Uncompensated
		55 (p. 225)	Uncompensated
Uniform	Non-uniform	30 (p. 98)	Uncompensated
		59 (p. 249)	Uncompensated
		32 (p. 102)	"Compensated"
Non-uniform	Non-uniform	27 (p. 92)	Uncompensated
		56 (p. 229)	Uncompensated
		31 (p. 100)	"Compensated"

* Pulmonary capillary blood flow is not uniform when normal man is upright.

flows to the left lung, which has *no* ventilation. Minute *volumes* of alveolar ventilation and capillary blood flow are normal, but the patient is dead of asphyxia caused by uneven distribution of alveolar gas and capillary blood flow.

The left side of Figure 27 represents pure "alveolar" dead space ventilation such as might occur with left pulmonary arterial occlusion: the ratio $\frac{\text{alveolar ventilation}}{\text{capillary blood flow}} = \frac{4}{0} = \text{infinity}$. The right side represents a complete venous-to-arterial shunt such as might occur with complete bronchial obstruction: the ratio, $\frac{\text{alveolar ventilation}}{\text{capillary blood flow}} = \frac{0}{5} = 0$. These two extreme cases are discussed in greater detail on pages 103, 104 and 244. There may also be a continuous spectrum of alveoli *between* these extreme situations—alveoli which have ratios between zero and infinity. These alveoli have both ventilation and blood flow, but some will have too much ventilation in relation to blood flow and some too little.

Figure 28 illustrates a very common type of uneven distribution of gas in relation to blood flow. Here, as in Figures 26 and 27, *total* alveolar

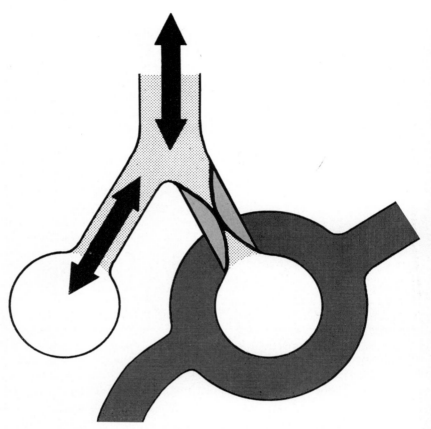

FIG. 27.—EXTREME CASE OF UNEVEN VENTILATION AND
UNEVEN BLOOD FLOW

Here and in Figures 26–33, circles represent groups of alveoli with their pulmonary capillary blood flow. Stippled areas represent the conducting airway (anatomical dead space). Size of arrows represents volume and distribution of alveolar ventilation; thickness of blood channels signifies volume of pulmonary capillary blood flow/min. Dark gray indicates poorly oxygenated blood; very light gray denotes well oxygenated blood. This represents the extreme (and impossible) situation in which total ventilation and total blood flow are normal but all the blood flow goes to non-aerated alveoli and all the ventilation to alveoli with no blood flow.

ventilation is normal ($A + B = 4$ L/min) and *total* blood flow is normal ($A + B = 5$ L/min). The only abnormality is uneven distribution of inspired gas; blood flow is evenly distributed to the alveoli. However, this results in uneven ratios: 3.2/2.5 in alveoli A (hyperventilation in relation to blood flow) and 0.8/2.5 in alveoli B (hypoventilation in relation to blood flow). Oxygen tension and saturation must decrease in blood leaving hypoventilated alveoli B; and O_2 saturation must rise in blood leaving the hyperventilated alveoli A, but because of the nature of the HbO_2 dissociation curve (see p. 142), this is not enough to compensate for the decrease effected in alveoli B. The mixed arterial blood has an O_2 saturation of 95% instead of 97.4%, as in the "ideal" case (Fig. 26, p. 88); therefore uneven ratios have resulted in anoxemia.†

In this connection it should be pointed out that the volume of the alveoli has nothing to do with the O_2 saturation of the blood leaving them, though there is sometimes confusion about this in learned articles. An alveolus may be very poorly ventilated compared to its volume, and this will be shown by a very slow washout of the N_2 in this alveolus when O_2 is breathed for a long time. This, however, tells us nothing about the effectiveness of this alveolus in oxygenating the blood. An alveolus with little ventilation and a large volume can be perfectly effective in oxygenating the blood if it has a very small blood flow. What matters for the blood is the ventilation/blood flow ratio, but what determines the rate of N_2 washout is the ratio of ventilation to alveolar volume.

Figure 29 shows the slight degree of uneven ventilation existing in "normal" man; this prevents him from having the maximal value for arterial O_2 saturation of the man with the "ideal" lung; because of uneven ventilation, he has only 97.1% instead of 97.4% saturation. Uneven blood flow may also exist in normal man (especially in the erect position); only uneven ventilation is pictured in Figure 29 for purposes of clarity.

In the case pictured in Figure 30, once more *total* alveolar ventilation and blood flow are normal (4 and 5 L/min, respectively), but here pulmonary capillary *blood flow is uneven,* being 1 L/min to alveoli A and

---

† The arterial O_2 saturation would rise to normal if a patient with this abnormality could hyperventilate enough to provide 2.0 L of ventilation to alveoli B per minute. However, the abnormality could still be detected by the existence of a considerable alveolar-arterial blood Po_2 difference which is not present in the "ideal" case; for a discussion of the alveolar-arterial Po_2 difference, see page 358. In the examples presented, we have held alveolar ventilation at the normal level in order to illustrate clearly the effect of uneven ratios, uncompensated by increased total ventilation or vasomotor or bronchomotor changes.

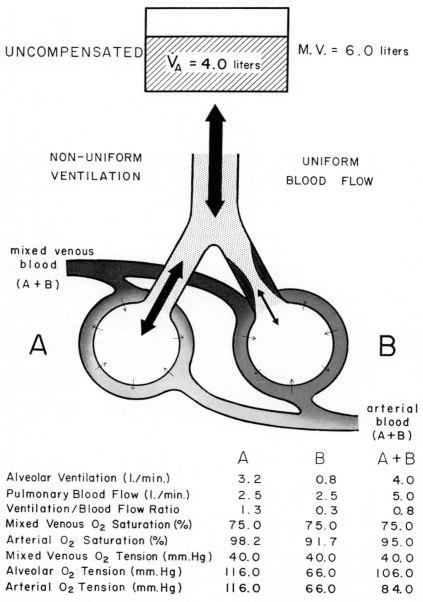

UNCOMPENSATED $\dot{V}_A = 4.0$ liters   M. V. = 6.0 liters

NON-UNIFORM
VENTILATION

UNIFORM
BLOOD FLOW

mixed venous
blood
(A + B)

A

B

arterial
blood
(A+B)

	A	B	A+B
Alveolar Ventilation (l./min.)	3.2	0.8	4.0
Pulmonary Blood Flow (l./min.)	2.5	2.5	5.0
Ventilation/Blood Flow Ratio	1.3	0.3	0.8
Mixed Venous O_2 Saturation (%)	75.0	75.0	75.0
Arterial O_2 Saturation (%)	98.2	91.7	95.0
Mixed Venous O_2 Tension (mm.Hg)	40.0	40.0	40.0
Alveolar O_2 Tension (mm.Hg)	116.0	66.0	106.0
Arterial O_2 Tension (mm.Hg)	116.0	66.0	84.0

FIG. 28.—NON-UNIFORM VENTILATION; UNIFORM BLOOD FLOW

4 L/min to alveoli *B*. *Even though alveolar ventilation is uniform* (2 L to *A* and 2 L to *B*), *the ratios are uneven* because of non-uniform blood flow. In *B*, the ratio is 2:1 (hyperventilation in relation to blood flow), and in *A* it is 2:4 (hypoventilation in relation to blood flow). The result again is anoxemia (arterial O_2 saturation of 96.2% instead of 97.4%).‡

We stated previously that the commonest cause of clinical anoxemia is uneven ventilation/blood flow ratios. In some patients, uneven ratios are caused only by uneven ventilation (see p. 72); in others, they are caused solely or predominantly by uneven blood flow (see p. 87). In the majority, *both* uneven ventilation and uneven blood flow exist (Case 5 and Fig. 56, p. 229) and cause even more severe anoxemia.

Figure 31 shows schematically a variety of ventilation/blood flow ratios that may exist in parts of the lungs and examples of clinical conditions in which these may be found. It emphasizes that a normal ratio of 0.8 can exist everywhere in the lungs if both ventilation and blood flow are reduced proportionately in some parts and increased proportionately in other parts. For example, if the ventilation of a collapsed lung is decreased and its blood flow is reduced proportionately (1:1.25), the ratio remains normal, 0.8. If the alveolar ventilation of a normal lung increases to 3 L/min and its blood flow increases to 3.75, its ratio remains 0.8. Figure 31 also indicates that alveoli, lobules, lobes or lungs with a normal, increased or decreased ratio may exist side by side in a large number of disorders affecting the cardiopulmonary system.

It is possible theoretically to have both uneven ventilation and uneven blood flow and *no anoxemia* (even without compensatory hyperventilation) because either chance or perfectly functioning compensatory mechanisms maintain *the same ratios* in all parts of the lungs. Figure 32 repre-

---

‡ Again, the anoxemia can be corrected if the patient increases his alveolar ventilation so that alveoli *A* receive 3.2 L/min. However, again there will be a considerable alveolar-arterial Po_2 difference, instead of none as in the "ideal" lungs.

◄——◀ Fig. 28.—Effect of non-uniform distribution of air in a patient with uniform blood flow, such as might occur in asthma. It differs from the "normal" (Fig. 29) in extent of uneven ventilation. Here the uneven ventilation results in an alveolar-arterial Po_2 difference of 22 mm Hg and a reduction of arterial O_2 saturation from the "ideal" value of 97.4% to 95.0%. Hyperventilation of alveoli *A* raises saturation of blood *A* to only 98.2%; this cannot compensate completely for the low O_2 saturation (91.7%) of blood coming from hypoventilated alveoli *B*. Values given for arterial blood (really mixed pulmonary capillary blood) represent the *immediate* effect of mixing equal volumes of blood from *A* and *B;* final "steady state" values will differ from these, depending upon cardiovascular and respiratory adjustments. Again it is assumed that no anatomical shunts exist.

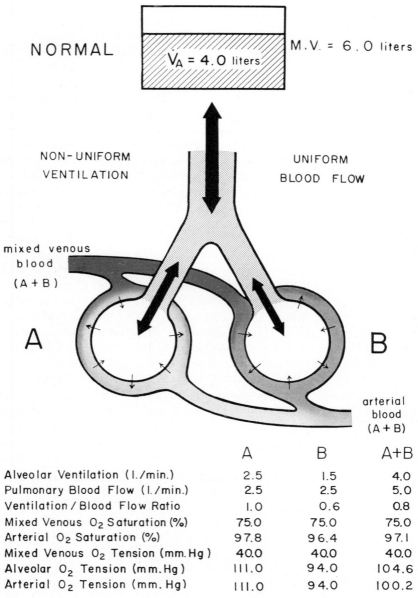

NORMAL $\dot{V}_A$ = 4.0 liters   M.V. = 6.0 liters

NON-UNIFORM
VENTILATION

UNIFORM
BLOOD FLOW

mixed venous
blood
(A + B)

A

B

arterial
blood
(A + B)

	A	B	A+B
Alveolar Ventilation (l./min.)	2.5	1.5	4.0
Pulmonary Blood Flow (l./min.)	2.5	2.5	5.0
Ventilation / Blood Flow Ratio	1.0	0.6	0.8
Mixed Venous O_2 Saturation (%)	75.0	75.0	75.0
Arterial O_2 Saturation (%)	97.8	96.4	97.1
Mixed Venous O_2 Tension (mm. Hg)	40.0	40.0	40.0
Alveolar O_2 Tension (mm. Hg)	111.0	94.0	104.6
Arterial O_2 Tension (mm. Hg)	111.0	94.0	100.2

FIG. 29.—VENTILATION/BLOOD FLOW RELATIONSHIP IN NORMAL MAN

sents such a hypothetical case: ventilation is 3 L/min and blood flow 3.75 L/min in alveoli A; ventilation is 1.0 L/min and blood flow 1.25 L/min in alveoli B. The ratio is 0.8 for alveoli A, 0.8 for alveoli B and 0.8 for the whole lung, and the blood is maximally oxygenated (saturation $= 97.4\%$). Such a situation apparently can exist in some cases of bronchopneumonia, in which arterial O_2 saturation remains normal.

It has been suggested that mechanisms exist within the lung which increase vascular resistance and decrease blood flow in poorly ventilated areas, and so shunt more blood to hyperventilated areas. It is known that a decrease in alveolar O_2 tension and a rise in alveolar CO_2 tension each can raise pulmonary arterial pressure, presumably by increasing pulmonary vascular resistance; there is no agreement on whether these mechanisms can operate regionally on a local level. Severinghaus, Swenson and associates have shown that a decrease in pulmonary blood flow through one lung results in a decrease in ventilation to that lung; this is effected by unilateral bronchial or bronchiolar constriction which occurs when alveolar CO_2 tension is reduced sharply because CO_2 is no longer excreted into these alveoli when pulmonary arterial blood flow ceases (see p. 105).

So far in this monograph we have discussed two causes of anoxemia: (1) alveolar hypoventilation (Chap. 3), and (2) uneven ventilation/blood flow ratios (Chap. 4). The two may co-exist. The ideal lung (Fig. 26, p. 88) has ratios of 0.8 in alveoli A and B and the blood is maximally arterialized for this amount of ventilation. If the "ideal" lung were hypoventilated (Fig. 54, p. 216) but still had uniform ventilation/blood flow ratios (let us say, 0.6), there would be anoxemia but the blood would be maximally arterialized for that amount of ventilation (2.4 L of ventilation for 4 L of blood flow). However, *when the ventilation/blood flow ratios vary* throughout the lungs, *the blood cannot be maximally arterialized* (for whatever volume of ventilation and blood flow exist). In other words, even if *total* alveolar ventilation and *total* pulmonary blood flow are normal and diffusion is unimpaired, arterial anoxemia will occur if

___

←◀ FIG. 29.—This differs from the "ideal" in that there is some uneven ventilation. Blood flow may also be uneven in normal individuals, but this has not yet been measured in man. The degree of uneven ventilation present is responsible for an alveolar-arterial P_{O_2} difference of about 4.0 mm Hg; the remainder of the normal P_{O_2} difference (Table 12, p. 132) is due to anatomical shunts, which are ignored in this illustration (arterial blood assumed to be identical to mixed blood from the pulmonary capillaries).

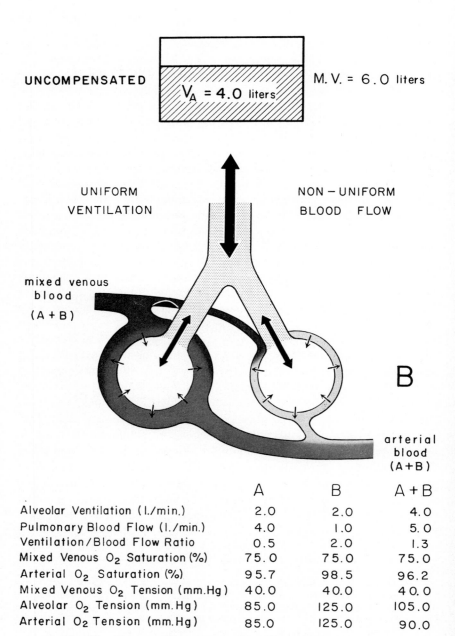

UNIFORM
VENTILATION

NON – UNIFORM
BLOOD FLOW

mixed venous
blood

(A + B)

B

arterial
blood
(A + B)

	A	B	A + B
Alveolar Ventilation (l./min.)	2.0	2.0	4.0
Pulmonary Blood Flow (l./min.)	4.0	1.0	5.0
Ventilation/Blood Flow Ratio	0.5	2.0	1.3
Mixed Venous O_2 Saturation (%)	75.0	75.0	75.0
Arterial O_2 Saturation (%)	95.7	98.5	96.2
Mixed Venous O_2 Tension (mm.Hg)	40.0	40.0	40.0
Alveolar O_2 Tension (mm.Hg)	85.0	125.0	105.0
Arterial O_2 Tension (mm.Hg)	85.0	125.0	90.0

Fig. 30.—Uniform Ventilation; Non-Uniform Blood Flow

the ratio of ventilation/blood flow is not the same everywhere in the lungs. If total alveolar ventilation is less than normal, so that there is arterial anoxemia on that account, *the addition of uneven ratios to over-all hypoventilation will further aggravate the anoxemia.*

EFFECTS OF UNEVEN RATIOS ON ARTERIAL BLOOD CO_2.—When the ventilation/blood flow ratios are the same throughout the lung, the P_{CO_2} must also be equal in blood and gas in *A, B* and *A + B*. However, when the ratios differ in *A* and *B*, the alveolar P_{CO_2} will also be different in *A* and *B*.

It is generally agreed that, because of the rapid rate of diffusion of CO_2 across body membranes, there is no detectable difference between the P_{CO_2} in the gas of any alveolus and its capillary blood (see Chap. 5). The fact that there is equality of gas tensions for the gas and blood *of any single alveolus* has led some to a misconception, namely, that a difference in CO_2 tension cannot exist between *mixed* end-capillary blood and mixed alveolar gas. Actually such a difference does exist in several conditions (see p. 359); one of these is when there are uneven ventilation/blood flow ratios. Calculations show that a difference must exist under conditions such as those in Figure 28 (p. 94). For example, the P_{CO_2} in alveoli *A* might be 39 mm Hg and that in alveoli *B* might be 47 mm Hg. Assuming that the P_{CO_2} of end-pulmonary capillary blood is equal to that of alveolar gas (for each alveolus), the P_{CO_2} of mixed blood from *A* and *B* would be $\dfrac{39 + 47}{2} = 43$ mm Hg, since regions *A* and *B* contribute an equal volume of blood to the "arterial" blood. However, alveoli *A* contribute 3.2 liters to the expired alveolar gas and alveoli *B* contribute only 0.8 liters; the true mean P_{CO_2} of expired alveolar gas is

---

◄━━ FIG. 30.—Effect of non-uniform distribution of blood in a patient with uniform distribution of air, as might occur following partial obstruction of a right or left pulmonary artery. Alveoli *A* receive a "normal" amount of ventilation, but this is insufficient to arterialize 4.0 L of mixed venous blood per minute; alveoli *B* also receive a "normal" amount of ventilation, but they are in fact *hyper*ventilated because alveoli *B* receive only 1.0 L of mixed venous blood per minute. The result of uneven ventilation/blood flow ratios (*total* ventilation and blood flow held constant) is again anoxemia.

Severinghaus, Swenson and associates have shown that occlusion of one pulmonary artery results in low P_{CO_2} in alveoli previously supplied by it and that this causes local bronchiolar constriction and a considerable shift of ventilation to the alveoli with unoccluded vessels; operation of such a mechanism would change this *un*compensated illustration to or toward a compensated picture (Fig. 32, p. 102).

VENTILATION/BLOOD FLOW RATIOS

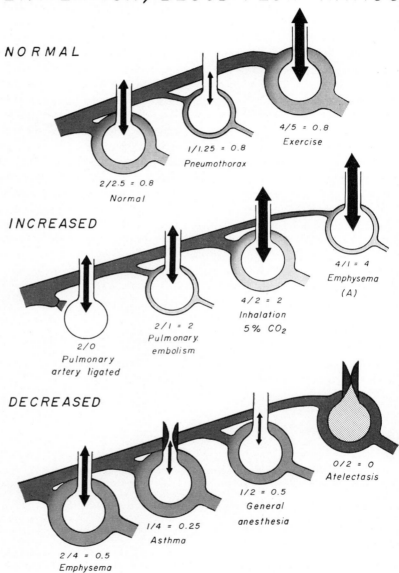

NORMAL

$2/2.5 = 0.8$
Normal

$1/1.25 = 0.8$
Pneumothorax

$4/5 = 0.8$
Exercise

INCREASED

$2/0$
Pulmonary
artery ligated

$2/1 = 2$
Pulmonary
embolism

$4/2 = 2$
Inhalation
5% CO_2

$4/1 = 4$
Emphysema
(A)

DECREASED

$2/4 = 0.5$
Emphysema
(B)

$1/4 = 0.25$
Asthma

$1/2 = 0.5$
General
anesthesia

$0/2 = 0$
Atelectasis

FIG. 31.—CLINICAL ABNORMALITIES IN VENTILATION/BLOOD FLOW RATIOS

100

therefore $\dfrac{(3.2 \times 39) + (0.8 \times 47)}{4} = 40.8$ mm Hg. Thus a P_{CO_2} difference of $43 - 40.8$, or 2.2 mm Hg, exists in this particular condition. The P_{CO_2} difference is much less than the P_{O_2} difference in the same circumstances, in part because the difference between venous and arterial tensions is less for CO_2 and partly because the dissociation curve for CO_2 is almost linear over the physiologic range, whereas that for O_2 is not (Fig. 41, p. 142). Therefore, for CO_2, regions with a high ventilation/blood flow ratio tend to compensate for those with a low ventilation/blood flow ratio.

We know that *hypoventilation* of the whole lung must lead to increase in alveolar and arterial P_{CO_2}. It is now clear, for reasons just given, that even though there is a *normal volume* of alveolar ventilation, there must be a difference in CO_2 tension between alveolar gas and arterial blood if ventilation/blood flow ratios are uneven throughout the lungs. However, this does not necessarily mean that arterial P_{CO_2} must be greater than normal. Many patients with pulmonary disease hyperventilate, and their arterial P_{CO_2} may be normal, increased or decreased depending on whether their hyperventilation has compensated, not compensated or overcompensated for the wasted ventilation that results from uneven distribution.

C. TESTS OF UNEVEN VENTILATION IN RELATION TO BLOOD FLOW

We have described several tests of uneven distribution of *inspired air* to the alveoli (p. 65). These tests per se do not provide the information needed to determine uneven *ratios* of ventilation to blood flow because (1) *blood flow* may be uneven to various alveoli even though their ventilation is uniform and (2) uneven ventilation may be compensated in part by correspondingly uneven blood flow. For these reasons, it is im-

---

◄━━━◄◼ FIG. 31.—Each circle represents *one* lung with its pulmonary capillary blood flow. Since normal volume of alveolar ventilation for one lung is about 2.0 L/min and normal volume of pulmonary capillary blood flow is about 2.5 L/min, the ventilation/blood flow ratio for one lung is 2.0/2.5, or 0.8. The diagrams illustrate conditions in which normal, increased or decreased ratios may occur. The specific physiologic or clinical states mentioned are merely examples of many conditions in which normal or abnormal ratios may be found; emphysema *A* (center row) and *B* (bottom row) show that different areas in the lungs may have widely different ratios. Note differences in O_2 saturation of blood leaving alveoli.

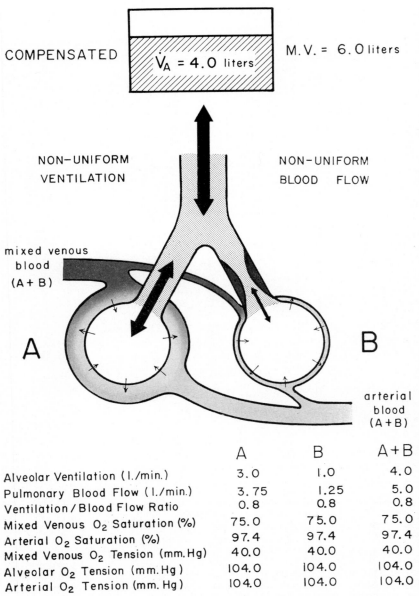

COMPENSATED   M.V. = 6.0 liters

$\dot{V}_A$ = 4.0 liters

NON-UNIFORM
VENTILATION

NON-UNIFORM
BLOOD FLOW

mixed venous
blood
(A + B)

A

B

arterial
blood
(A + B)

	A	B	A + B
Alveolar Ventilation (l./min.)	3.0	1.0	4.0
Pulmonary Blood Flow (l./min.)	3.75	1.25	5.0
Ventilation / Blood Flow Ratio	0.8	0.8	0.8
Mixed Venous O_2 Saturation (%)	75.0	75.0	75.0
Arterial O_2 Saturation (%)	97.4	97.4	97.4
Mixed Venous O_2 Tension (mm. Hg)	40.0	40.0	40.0
Alveolar O_2 Tension (mm. Hg)	104.0	104.0	104.0
Arterial O_2 Tension (mm. Hg)	104.0	104.0	104.0

FIG. 32.—COMPENSATED CASE OF UNEVEN VENTILATION AND
UNEVEN BLOOD FLOW

portant to detect and to measure non-uniformity of pulmonary blood flow, and uneven ventilation/blood flow ratios.

Test for Anatomic Venous-to-Arterial Shunt

Shunting of mixed venous pulmonary arterial blood around alveolar capillaries and directly into the pulmonary veins can be detected by an O_2 test. If an individual with such a shunt breathed pure O_2, there would be no opportunity for the shunted blood to be exposed to the O_2 in the alveoli and the venous blood would pass into the pulmonary veins without any increase in its O_2 content. However, mixed venous blood flowing to ventilated alveoli would become oxygenated maximally (100% saturation of Hb plus an additional 2 ml of dissolved O_2 in each 100 ml of blood; see p. 141). This is true even for poorly ventilated alveoli, because if the patient breathes O_2 long enough (10–20 min), N_2 will be eliminated even from these and the O_2 concentration will rise maximally. This is also true if there is impairment of diffusion for O_2 across alveolar-capillary membranes, because the partial pressure of O_2 rises to maximal values in arterial blood when patients with severe but uncomplicated alveolo-capillary block breathe pure O_2. Therefore, whenever a patient with an anatomic shunt breathes pure O_2, his systemic arterial blood cannot be oxygenated maximally because a stream of mixed venous (poorly oxygenated) shunted blood merges in the pulmonary veins with a stream of fully oxygenated blood from the alveolar capillaries.

When the shunt is so large that arterial hemoglobin does not become saturated fully with O_2 when the patient breathes O_2, the usual techniques for measuring blood O_2 content are adequate. When the shunt is smaller, O_2 inhalation may raise blood Po_2 sufficiently to saturate hemoglobin but not to increase dissolved O_2 to its maximal value; in this case, measurement of O_2 tension by an O_2 electrode provides more accurate data (equations which permit calculation of the amount of shunted blood are on p. 343).§

§ Healthy individuals have a small amount of "physiologic shunt" because some venous blood normally drains into the pulmonary veins, left atrium or left ventricle (some bronchial and coronary blood flow); because of this there is a small alveolar-arterial blood Po_2 difference which is normal.

◄———◄ Fig. 32.—Both ventilation and blood flow are non-uniform, but ventilation and blood flow are increased in proportion to each other in alveoli *A* and decreased in proportion to each other in alveoli *B*. Despite the non-uniformity, there is no alveolar-arterial Po_2 difference because ventilation/blood flow ratios are equal through the lungs.

The O_2 test proves that anoxemia is not due to hypoventilation, uneven distribution of gas or impaired diffusion, but is caused by a shunt. The O_2 test does not determine the location of a shunt, which may be intra-cardiac or intrapulmonary; intrapulmonary shunts include any condition in which pulmonary blood continues to flow through regions with no alveoli or non-aerated alveoli, such as pulmonary hemangiomas (see p. 244) and atelectasis.

TEST FOR PULMONARY VASCULAR OCCLUSION

The most frequent clinical cause of this occlusion is pulmonary embo-lism. To simplify the discussion, let us assume (a) that mixed venous blood of precisely the same O_2 and CO_2 concentration is pumped to each alveolar capillary, (b) that inspired air of the same composition is drawn into the alveoli, (c) that alveolar ventilation is uniform throughout the lung,‖ and (d) that the only abnormality in this patient is uneven distri-bution of blood to the alveolar capillaries. If we could insert needles into pulmonary venules and sample and analyze the O_2 and CO_2 in blood from each capillary, we would now find marked inequality of blood gas composition. For example, blood flowing past alveoli with almost com-pletely occluded capillaries would have a high O_2 and a low CO_2 tension because the ventilation/blood flow ratio is high. Again, if cardiac output remains the same, more blood must flow through non-occluded regions, and this blood must have a lower O_2 and higher CO_2 tension because the ventilation/blood flow ratio is lower. Even if we could measure the blood O_2 in each of thousands of alveolar capillaries, we could not rely on difference in *oxygen* values for a specific diagnosis of uneven pulmonary blood flow, because regional differences in diffusion across alveolar-capillary membranes might cause varying end-capillary O_2 values (see Chap. 5, p. 111). We could, however, rely on differences in blood *carbon dioxide,* because even severe alveolo-capillary block does not interfere appreciably with the diffusion of CO_2 molecules. There is, of course, no practical way of sampling end-capillary blood and measuring its CO_2, but we can assume that the CO_2 tension of the gas in each alveolus is equal to the CO_2 tension in the end-capillary blood around each alveolus.

‖ These assumptions are not necessarily true. Ventilation may *become* non-uniform as a result of pulmonary embolism, even though distribution was perfectly uniform before the embolism. Further, whenever there is uneven ventilation, there is the possibility that dead space gas may enter preferentially the regions with greater initial flow.

When there is uneven circulation (with uniform ventilation), the P_{CO_2} of alveolar gas must vary in different alveoli. In addition, the P_{CO_2} of *mixed expired alveolar gas* must be lower than the P_{CO_2} of *mixed end-capillary blood*. The second statement is true because gas expired from alveoli with no capillary blood flow will contain very little CO_2 and this will lower the CO_2 tension of *mixed* expired alveolar gas below that of the mixed capillary blood.

This is illustrated in Figure 33, which presents the conditions in a hypothetical patient with complete occlusion of the pulmonary blood flow to one lung (alveoli *A*) but with uniform ventilation. Because the lung still receives bronchial blood flow, it does not die and it continues to ventilate. However, all of the pulmonary blood must flow past alveoli *B*. Initially, the alveolar ventilation of *B* (2 L/min) would be inadequate to arterialize 5 liters of mixed venous blood each minute. However, let us assume that compensatory mechanisms have caused hyperventilation and alveoli *B* now receive 4 liters of air per min, which is sufficient to maintain normal alveolar CO_2 tension (40 mm Hg). Since there is no barrier across the alveolar-capillary membrane for CO_2, the CO_2 tension of end-capillary blood is also 40 mm Hg. However, the CO_2 tension of gas in alveoli *A* is very low—let us say, 8 mm Hg. (At first thought, we might expect that the CO_2 tension in alveoli *A* would be zero, but the bronchial artery blood contributes some CO_2 to *A* and, in addition, on inspiration some of the tracheal dead space gas enters alveoli *A* and this contains CO_2 contributed by alveoli *B* on the previous expiration.)

Assuming that ventilation is equal in *A* and *B*, then the *mixed* expired gas from alveoli *A* and *B* will have a CO_2 tension of $\frac{8 + 40}{2} = 24$ mm Hg. Since the CO_2 of arterial blood, all of which comes from alveoli *B* in this patient, is 40 mm Hg, there is a difference for CO_2 of 16 mm Hg between arterial blood and mixed expired alveolar gas.

Severinghaus has used the arterial-alveolar CO_2 difference as an index of the magnitude of uneven alveolar blood flow. When ventilation is uniform, this test should theoretically provide a good estimate of the fraction of pulmonary vascular bed that is occluded. However, two factors may decrease its diagnostic usefulness: (1) *When ventilation is non-uniform,* it is difficult to be sure that a sample of alveolar gas is truly representative of all alveolar gas, and the test gives diagnostic information only when a large portion of the pulmonary vascular bed is occluded. (2) The sensitivity of the test is decreased if compensatory mechanisms (p. 97) are active; for example, *acute* occlusion of one pulmonary artery to *A*

PULMONARY ARTERY LIGATION

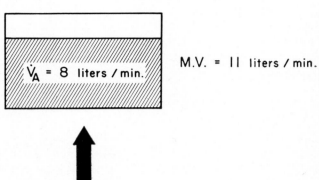

$\dot{V}_A$ = 8 liters / min.   M.V. = II liters / min.

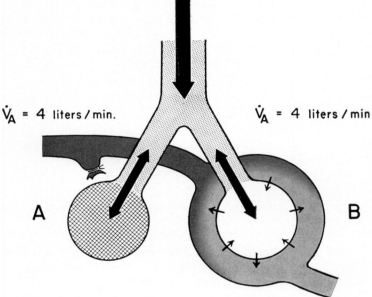

$\dot{V}_A$ = 4 liters / min. $\dot{V}_A$ = 4 liters / min.

A   B

$\dot{Q}_C$ = 0 liters / min. $\dot{Q}_C$ = 5 liters / min.

$$\dot{V}_A / \dot{Q}_C = 0.8$$

FIG. 33.—THEORETICAL EFFECTS OF PULMONARY ARTERY OCCLUSION

(by inflation of a balloon) may increase airway resistance ipsilaterally so that much of the tidal volume to alveoli A (Fig. 33) is redistributed to alveoli B. Thus the ventilatory contribution of alveoli A to mixed alveolar gas is much less than that shown schematically, and the alveolar gas to arterial blood Pco_2 difference will be reduced correspondingly.

TESTS OF UNEVEN VENTILATION/BLOOD FLOW RATIOS

1. SINGLE-BREATH CO_2 TEST.—Abnormal results of the single-breath O_2 test (N_2 meter test; Figs. 12, p. 40, and 18, p. 62) signify only that the distribution of inspired gas is non-uniform and expiration is asynchronous. The single-breath CO_2 test, in which expired gas is sampled and analyzed continuously by a CO_2 analyzer, provides information about ventilation/blood flow ratios. If expired alveolar CO_2 concentration rises significantly throughout expiration, different areas of the lung must have had different CO_2 concentrations at end-inspiration (which is indicative of uneven ventilation/blood flow ratios in various parts of the lung) *and* the lung must be emptying asynchronously during expiration. If the CO_2 concentration remains constant throughout expiration, ventilation/blood flow ratios may be equal throughout the lungs or there may be non-uniform blood flow coupled with uniform ventilation (as in Fig. 33, p. 106). Regardless of how different the CO_2 concentrations may be in different alveoli at end-inspiration, if expiration proceeds synchronously from all areas, streams of high and low CO_2 concentration will merge in constant proportions during expiration and result in constant expired alveolar CO_2 concentration. However, in the case pictured in Figure 33, arterial blood Pco_2 would be greater than mixed alveolar gas Pco_2.

The single-breath CO_2 test will be abnormal only when the N_2 meter test is abnormal; the latter, however, indicates only that uneven ventilation is present, while the former indicates that there must be uneven blood flow in relation to ventilation (i.e., perfect compensation has not occurred, as in Fig. 32, p. 102).

2. ESTIMATION OF "PHYSIOLOGIC DEAD SPACE" AND "VENOUS ADMIXTURE" (RILEY TECHNIQUE).—Riley and his associates calculate

---

FIG. 33.—Ventilation of alveoli A contributes nothing to arterialization of the venous blood and is therefore "dead space ventilation." Normal arterial O_2 saturation is maintained by hyperventilation so that the $\dot{V}A/\dot{Q}c$ ratio of alveoli B is 0.8. In fact, some increase in airway resistance occurs in A, and more than half of the total alveolar ventilation goes to B.

"physiologic dead space" using measured arterial P_{CO_2} to replace alveolar P_{CO_2} in Bohr's equation.¶

"Physiologic" dead space (p. 39) includes anatomic dead space and "alveolar dead space ventilation"; the latter includes part or all of the ventilation to (1) alveoli with *no* blood flow, (2) alveoli with decreased blood flow and increased, normal or only slightly decreased ventilation, and (3) alveoli with normal blood flow and marked overventilation. Since the physiologist cannot separate the different types of increased ventilation/blood flow ratios, he "makes believe" that a *portion* of the alveolar ventilation in (2) and (3) goes to the lung with *no* blood flow and measures this as a "make believe" alveolar dead space ventilation, even though actually there is some blood flow through these regions.*

If the "physiologic dead space" is large in relation to tidal volume, then some alveolar ventilation is being wasted. Since the physiologist really wants to measure "alveolar" and "anatomic" dead space separately, it is better, as Severinghaus suggests, to measure both "physiologic" and "anatomic" and, by subtraction, know "alveolar" dead space as well.

Riley also measures the "venous admixture" or "physiologic shunt" by an ingenious technique (see p. 131); if it exceeds the normal fraction of the cardiac output, a certain amount of "shunt" is present. However, the term "shunt" here includes (1) alveoli with blood flow but *no* ventilation (this can be detected by the O_2 test, p. 103), (2) alveoli with markedly decreased ventilation and normal, increased or only slightly decreased blood flow, and (3) alveoli with normal ventilation but markedly increased blood flow; in all three of these, the ventilation/blood flow ratio is reduced. Again, the physiologist "makes believe" that *some* of the blood flow in (2) and (3)—that which is in excess of the ventilation— behaves as a *complete* shunt and measures a "make believe physiologic

---

¶ The arterial P_{CO_2} may be 2–3 mm Hg above true mean alveolar P_{CO_2} if there is a large venous-to-arterial shunt or shuntlike effect; however, Severinghaus has calculated that a 50% anatomic shunt would yield calculated alveolar dead space of only about one-fourth as much as would a 50% vascular occlusion (true alveolar dead space).

* This relatively increased ventilation in (2) and (3) may be "wasted" as far as further oxygenation of the blood is concerned, because there is an upper limit to the amount of O_2 carried by hemoglobin and very little O_2 is added by raising alveolar P_{O_2} from 100 to 140 mm Hg. This excess ventilation is *not* "wasted" so far as elimination of CO_2 is concerned, because hyperventilation can reduce CO_2 in blood. However, when there are regions with excess ventilation in relation to alveolar blood flow, there may be other regions with too little ventilation in relation to blood flow; CO_2 tension rises in these. The ventilation is "wasted" as far as CO_2 is concerned, because it does not go where it might do more good.

shunt" (or "venous admixture"). The equations, derivations and calculations for making these estimates are given on pages 353–357.

Again, it is unfortunate that the terms "physiologic" dead space and "physiologic" shunt have their present meaning: only the normal anatomic shunts and anatomic dead space are truly physiologic; atelectasis, hemangiomas, and well-defined uneven alveolar ventilation/blood flow ratios occur only in disease.

3. REGIONAL DIFFERENCES IN VENTILATION/BLOOD FLOW RATIOS.— Several new techniques have been devised to compare these ratios in the upper versus the lower lobes and the right versus the left lung. In one, radioactive CO_2 is inhaled and the rate of disappearance from the various lung segments measured continuously by detectors placed on the chest wall. In the second, radioactive xenon or krypton is dissolved in saline or blood and injected intravenously and the rate of its appearance is noted, again by external counters (see p. 272 and Table 18, pp. 205–206).

TEST OF O_2 UPTAKE BY INDIVIDUAL LUNGS

Using the technique of bronchospirometry, the physiologist can separate the gas to and from the right and left lungs and measure the volume and composition of each of the streams. If he finds that only 50 ml of O_2 is absorbed from the right lung each minute, while 200 ml is being absorbed from the left lung, he may surmise that only one fifth of the total pulmonary blood is flowing past alveoli in the right lung while four fifths of the total is blowing through the left lung. However, he may be wrong on two accounts: (1) the right lung may be receiving very little ventilation and its O_2 uptake is limited by the O_2 supply, and (2) there may be a severe impairment of diffusion on the right side which limits the O_2 uptake.

The second factor may be eliminated in part by giving O_2 to breathe or by measuring the expired CO_2 (which is not limited by diffusion). However, the O_2 uptake or CO_2 elimination must always be related to the ventilation to each lung.

DIAGNOSIS BY EXCLUSION

The diagnosis of variations in ventilation/blood flow ratios can also be made by exclusion. If the patient is anoxemic, this may be due to hypoventilation (which is readily measured), to impairment of diffusion (which can be measured by methods described in Chap. 5) or to variations in ventilation/blood flow ratios throughout the lung. If the last diagnosis is made by this process of exclusion, the presence of an anatomic shunt can be determined by giving the patient O_2 to breathe.

Differential diagnosis of this type has considerable value, because both hypoventilation and abnormal anatomic shunt can be treated by specific means, and if the variation in ventilation/blood flow ratios is due largely to uneven ventilation caused by reversible airway obstruction, this too can be corrected by proper therapy.

SUMMARY

The functional parts of the pulmonary circulation are the pulmonary capillaries. The right ventricle, pulmonary arteries and arterioles represent a distributing system and the venules and veins a collecting system for the pulmonary capillary blood. The pressure and resistance to flow in the pulmonary capillaries is normally low and must remain so to prevent transudation of fluid into the intermembrane spaces or into alveoli. The pressure and resistance to flow in the pulmonary artery and arterioles is normally low and must remain so to prevent right ventricular strain and hypertrophy and possibly failure. Normally, all mixed venous blood in the pulmonary arteries is distributed uniformly to the alveolar capillaries, in relation to the ventilation of alveoli; when it is not, anoxemia results unless there is hyperventilation.

Tests of pulmonary function can measure pressures, blood flow, vascular resistance and distribution of blood flow in the pulmonary circulation; they can indicate the presence of venous-to-arterial shunts, vascular occlusion, diminution in pulmonary capillary volume and, in some instances, locate the specific area involved.

CHAPTER 5

Diffusion

FOR SOME YEARS it has been possible by a combination of clinical and radiologic skills to make a tentative diagnosis of "alveolar-capillary block" or "impairment of diffusion" in certain patients with pulmonary disease. The classic picture of pure alveolar-capillary block includes dyspnea, rapid and deep breathing (overventilation), decreased vital and total lung capacity, relatively little decrease in maximal voluntary ventilation, cyanosis and decreased O_2 saturation aggravated by exercise, normal or decreased arterial blood P_{CO_2} and radiologic evidence of diffuse mottling throughout the lungs (see p. 232). However, only microscopic examination of the pulmonary tissues during life or after death really confirmed this diagnosis.

Recently, physiologists have devised methods for studying the diffusion of gases across the alveolar-capillary membranes and have developed them so that they are useful clinically. The advantages of these physiologic tests for measuring diffusing capacity are:

1. They permit the diagnosis during life, and sometimes even during early stages of the disease, of "alveolar-capillary block" such as occurs in patients with Boeck's sarcoid of the lung, beryllium granulomatosis, asbestosis, pulmonary scleroderma, alveolar cell (terminal bronchiolar) carcinoma, sulfur dioxide poisoning and certain diffuse metastatic lesions of the lungs.

2. They permit recognition of impairment of diffusion in other types of pulmonary diseases in which the primary defect may be uneven distribution, a shunt or hypoventilation.

3. Since the tests are relatively simple (as far as the patient is concerned) and easy to repeat, it is now possible to study the diffusing capacity of a patient frequently and to evaluate the effects of therapy or of spontaneous change in the course of the disease.

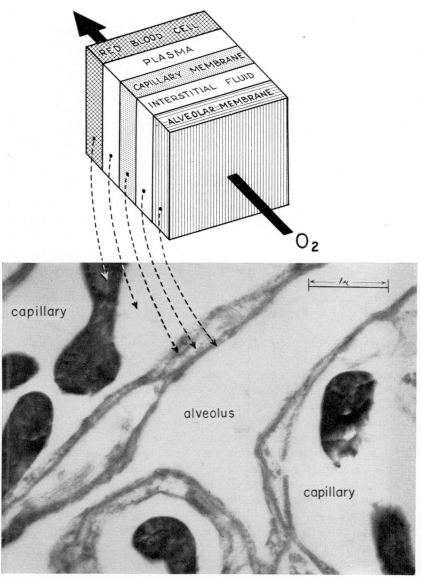

RED BLOOD CELL

PLASMA

CAPILLARY MEMBRANE

INTERSTITIAL FLUID

ALVEOLAR MEMBRANE

O_2

capillary

alveolus

capillary

1μ

FIG. 34.—ELECTRON MICROSCOPY OF RAT LUNG

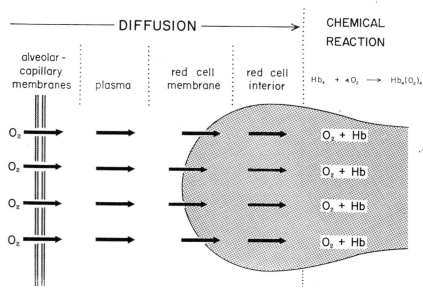

FIG. 35.—SCHEMATIC REPRESENTATION OF PASSAGE OF O_2 MOLECULES FROM ALVEOLAR GAS TO PULMONARY CAPILLARY BLOOD

From left to right are shown the *diffusion* of O_2 molecules (1) across the alveolar-capillary membranes (and normal or pathologic interstitial fluid or tissues), (2) through the plasma, (3) across the red blood cell membrane and (4) within the erythrocyte, and finally the *chemical reaction* within the erythrocyte whereby O_2 becomes associated with hemoglobin.

4. Since some of the tests are very rapid, it is possible to apply them to population studies in communities or industries to study the epidemiology of pulmonary disease.

These physiologic tests of diffusion require the use of gases that combine chemically with hemoglobin (see p. 117), i.e., O_2 and CO. They measure the quantity of O_2 or CO that is transferred in a minute from alveolar gas to blood in the pulmonary capillaries. Figures 34 and 35 indicate the various processes involved in the transfer. First, O_2 or CO

◀━━ FIG. 34.—The photograph ($\times 20,000$) illustrates clearly the tissues through which O_2 must pass from the gas phase in the alveolus until it combines with hemoglobin within the red blood cell. No attempt has been made in the schema to portray relative thickness of the different tissues. (Photograph from Low, F. N.: Anat. Rec. 117:241, 1953.)

must diffuse across the alveolar-capillary membranes; the rate of diffusion here depends on (a) the difference between the partial pressure of O_2 or CO in the alveolar gas and that in the plasma, (b) the thickness of the tissues, (c) the surface area available for diffusion of gas, and (d) the characteristics of the tissues. Second, the gas must diffuse in the plasma until it meets a red blood cell. Third, it must pass across the red blood cell membrane. Fourth, it must meet and combine chemically with Hb molecules; this is dependent on the chemical reactions of O_2 or CO with Hb.

The clinician who wishes to have an evaluation of his patient's pulmonary function is interested mainly in the first of these—the rate of diffusion of gases across the alveolar-capillary membranes. Recent work suggests that specific measurements of *membrane* diffusion are possible and meaningful. At the moment, however, the tests of diffusion used most widely measure all of these processes together. The measurement made is termed *"pulmonary diffusing capacity"; its units are ml of O_2 or CO transferred per minute for each mm Hg pressure difference for O_2 or CO across the lung.*

A. FACTORS INFLUENCING DIFFUSING CAPACITY

Because some clinicians think that "impairment of diffusion" occurs only with pulmonary "fibrosis" or thickening of the alveolar membrane, we believe it important to present in more detail each of the factors which may alter the diffusing capacity.

DISTANCE FOR DIFFUSION.—Before entering the blood, molecules of O_2 or CO must first traverse a surface film covering the alveolar lining, the alveolar membrane, the interstitial fluid and a capillary endothelium which is shown clearly in Figure 34 (p. 112) as a second membrane, distinct from the alveolar membrane. Normally, the path for diffusion is very short, 0.1 micron, but in disease it may be very much longer: (1) the alveolar wall may be thickened, (2) the capillary membrane may be thickened, (3) the two membranes may be separated by interstitial edema fluid and exudate, which may be replaced by fibrous tissue, (4) there may be intra-alveolar edema fluid or exudate,* and (5) the intra-capillary path may be increased if capillaries are dilated and contain sev-

---

* When pulmonary edema fluid is interstitial (between the capillary and alveolar membranes), it decreases the diffusing capacity by causing "alveolar-capillary block"; when it enters alveoli and wells up into bronchioles and bronchi, it again causes a diffusion defect, but the main problem is really airway obstruction and a decrease in area of ventilated alveoli in contact with functioning pulmonary capillaries.

eral red blood cells abreast. Anything which lengthens the path for O_2 or CO must, on this account, decrease the rate of diffusion and the "diffusing capacity." The term "alveolar-capillary *block*," if employed in its proper sense, should be used only when there is indeed a block between the alveolus and its capillary bed, namely, a longer pathway across the alveolar-capillary membranes. It should not be used in referring to conditions described below in which there is a decrease in pulmonary diffusing capacity for other reasons.

SURFACE AREA FOR DIFFUSION.—A decrease in the number of patent capillaries or in the number of ventilated alveoli can lead to a decrease in diffusing capacity even though the length of the diffusion path is not increased at any point. It must be emphasized that the critical area for diffusion is neither of the *alveoli* nor of the pulmonary *capillaries* but of the *functioning alveoli in contact with functioning capillaries.*

The surface area can be *decreased* by diseases which disrupt normal alveolar architecture (pulmonary emphysema, cysts), by diseases which decrease the functioning pulmonary capillary bed (pulmonary embolism, some types of restrictive disease, emphysema) or by diseases which cause significant block of airways and so decrease the number of alveoli available for gas exchange. In all of these conditions, the diffusing capacity is reduced, but pathologically the dominant lesion is not alveolar-capillary "*block,*" but a decrease in effective surface area.

It is important to point out here that the "diffusing capacity" can increase as well as decrease. The *distance* for diffusion probably cannot become much shorter (0.1 micron), but the surface area can become greater by (1) increase in the number of pulmonary capillaries with active circulation, (2) dilatation of capillaries already functioning and (3) increase in surface area of functioning alveoli.

The diffusing capacity of a healthy man increases during exercise, probably because his pulmonary capillary bed enlarges as the cardiac output and pulmonary blood flow increase. When one is evaluating pulmonary function, therefore, it is useful to know whether the diffusing capacity is normal at rest and increases during exercise, whether it is normal at rest but incapable of increasing during exercise, or whether it is decreased at rest and fixed.

CHARACTERISTICS OF THE ALVEOLAR-CAPILLARY MEMBRANES.—Gases move from alveoli to capillaries by going from a gaseous state to a state of solution on the surface of tissues and then move through the tissue because of concentration gradients (see p. 349). Therefore the solubility of the test gases in pulmonary tissues could be a factor influencing diffusing capacity.

Little is known regarding this factor, although it is possible that fibrotic tissue might impede gas diffusion more than normal tissue of similar thickness and area.

RED BLOOD CELLS IN PULMONARY CAPILLARIES.—One of the factors influencing the diffusing capacity for O_2 or CO might be the rate at which these gases pass through the membrane of the red blood cells and combine chemically with Hb. If this rate were infinitely rapid, it could not influence the measurement of diffusing capacity since the alveolar-capillary barrier would then be the only rate-limiting factor. Recent studies, however, have shown that the rate at which normal red blood cells take up O_2 or CO from the surrounding plasma is about the same as the rate of transfer across the normal alveolar-capillary membranes. The pulmonary diffusing capacity thus depends to a certain extent on (a) the number of red blood cells in the pulmonary capillaries and their Hb content, (b) the rate of transfer of O_2 and CO from the outside of an erythrocyte to the immediate vicinity of a Hb molecule in the interior, and (c) the chemical rate of association of O_2 or CO with Hb.

Some investigators (Roughton and Forster; Kruhøffer) believe that it is possible, from knowledge of the reaction rates of Hb and O_2 or Hb and CO and other data, to separate the pulmonary diffusing capacity in man into its two component parts: (1) the *membrane* diffusing capacity, and (2) the red blood cell and Hb component. The method proposed for accomplishing this measures diffusing capacity for CO at two different alveolar O_2 tensions. The theory is as follows:

If the concentration of O_2 molecules in the alveoli is increased (by breathing 40–100% O_2), there is increased competition between O_2 and CO molecules for the available Hb, and CO uptake by the red blood cell is decreased, though the transfer of CO across the alveolar-capillary *membranes* is presumably unaffected. If the concentration of O_2 molecules in the alveoli is decreased (by breathing 10–12% O_2), the rate of uptake of CO by the red blood cell is increased, presumably because the Hb + CO reaction rate is more rapid and not because of changes in the alveolar-capillary membrane. By making measurements of the diffusing capacity of a patient while he is breathing CO in high and again in low concentrations of O_2, it has been possible to estimate the *membrane* diffusing capacity. Measurements to date suggest that, in a healthy individual whose *pulmonary* diffusing capacity is about 35 ml O_2/min/mm Hg, the *membrane* diffusing capacity is about 70 ml O_2/min/mm Hg.

The methods for achieving this separate estimation of the *membrane* diffusing capacity require further examination. If they do gain general acceptance, their chief usefulness will be in patients in whom the diffusing capacity for CO is low but the membrane diffusing capacity is normal. Such a reduction in over-all diffusing capacity would then be wholly or in part because of changes in the character of the erythrocytes (decreased permeability of the red blood cell membrane), in the Hb molecule itself (decrease in the chemical reaction rate of Hb with CO) or in the total quantity of Hb in the pulmonary capillary bed (very marked reduction in the amount of available Hb could limit CO uptake; see p. 138).

COMBINATION OF FACTORS.—It is uncommon to find a single defect in the lungs of patients with pulmonary disease. The diffusing capacity may be decreased by several factors (longer diffusion path, decreased contact surface) operating in the same direction or, conceivably, may remain normal if two defects operate in opposite directions; for example, in pulmonary congestion associated with mitral stenosis, the capillary surface area may be increased but the diffusion distance may be increased by interstitial edema or by a very long intracapillary path when a single capillary may be so dilated that 4–8 erythrocytes are abreast.

B. MEASUREMENT OF PULMONARY DIFFUSING CAPACITY

GENERAL PRINCIPLES

The test requires the use of a gas which is considerably more "soluble" in blood than in the alveolar-capillary membranes. As stated previously, only two such gases are known, O_2 and CO. Both of them owe this unusual pattern of "solubility" to the chemical association that occurs with hemoglobin. Both presumably measure the same process, and the diffusing capacity measured by CO can be converted to the diffusing factor for O_2 by multiplying by a factor of 1.23. Figure 36 presents schematically the basis for the measurement of diffusing capacity, employing CO or O_2.

1. CO UPTAKE.—A low concentration of CO is maintained in the alveolus† by adding about 0.2% CO to inspired air. The concentration of CO in mixed venous blood entering the pulmonary capillaries is zero for all practical purposes. Therefore, molecules of CO diffuse across the membrane and dissolve in the watery parts of blood. Carbon monoxide is a remarkable gas because of the great affinity between it and Hb; it has

---

†There is no danger in using CO in these tests since the concentrations used are very low and the gas is breathed for only short intervals.

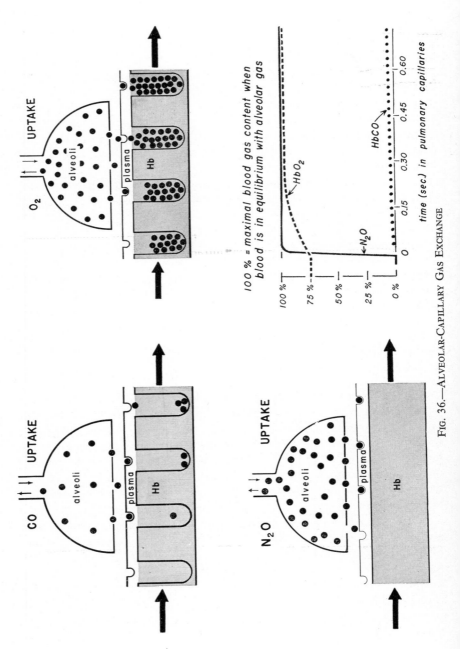

FIG. 36.—Alveolar-Capillary Gas Exchange

118

210 times the affinity for Hb that O_2 does. Thus a partial pressure of CO of only 0.46 mm Hg (equivalent to 0.065% CO) produces the same per cent saturation of Hb, at equilibrium, as does a partial pressure of 100 mm Hg O_2 (equivalent to 14% O_2) (Fig. 37, p. 120). For this reason, any CO in the vicinity of a Hb molecule becomes bound to it, so that the partial pressure of dissolved CO stays at a very low level in the red blood cell. The Hb "compartments" for CO are so large (except when the patient has severe anemia) that they cannot possibly be filled by the number of molecules of CO that diffuse from the alveolar gas to the capillary blood at these low alveolar CO tensions. Even if pulmonary blood flow stopped, transfer of CO would continue until the "pockets" became full. Therefore, the transfer of CO is not limited by the rate of pulmonary blood flow; it is limited largely by the rate of diffusion across the alveolar-capillary membrane and to a smaller extent by the rate of diffusion across the erythrocytic membrane and the intraerythrocytic chemical reaction rate of Hb and CO.

On the other hand, gases such as N_2O (Fig. 36), ethyl iodide and acetylene are soluble to an equal extent in the alveolar-capillary membranes and in blood, since they do not combine chemically with any of the components of blood. These gases diffuse across the alveolar-capillary

---

← ◄ FIG. 36.—In each *schema*, the black dots signify gas molecules. The bottom of each alveolus represents the alveolo-capillary membrane with numerous pores to permit diffusion of gas molecules. Blood moves from left to right through the pulmonary capillary beneath the pulmonary membrane. The blood stream, solely for purposes of illustration, is divided into two portions: upper portion represents plasma (and all other watery parts of the blood), with a certain number of pockets to indicate its capacity for dissolving each gas; lower portion represents hemoglobin; there are no compartments in the hemoglobin layer for N_2O because it does not combine chemically with hemoglobin, but large pockets are available for CO and O_2. Mixed venous blood enters the capillary with no CO or N_2O in the plasma and hemoglobin compartments (since these are foreign gases) but with the O_2 compartments partly full.

The *graph* presents blood gas content (ordinate) plotted against the time that the blood spends in the pulmonary capillary. The horizontal line at the top indicates maximal gas content of the blood when it is *saturated* at the gas pressure maintained in the alveoli. In the case of CO, there is only a very slight increase in HbCO concentration along the capillary; it never approaches the maximal value because of the low partial pressure of CO in the alveoli. It must be remembered that 100 ml of blood, when saturated with CO, will contain about 20 ml of CO, yet the alveolar gas at any instant contains only about 1.3 ml CO (assuming that functional residual capacity is 2000 ml and contains 0.065% CO). In the case of N_2O, the blood attains maximal concentration before it has gone 1/20 the distance along the capillary. In the case of O_2, saturation increases from 75 to 97% along the capillary.

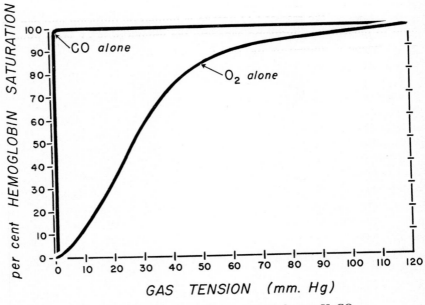

FIG. 37.—DISSOCIATION CURVES FOR HBO₂ AND HBCO

Dissociation curves are plotted on the same scale. Maximal saturation of hemoglobin with O₂ is not reached until the Po₂ is greater than 120 mm Hg; with CO,
however, maximal saturation is attained with a Pco of less than 1 mm Hg.

membranes and quickly fill up all of the plasma "compartments"; since
the plasma is now saturated, further diffusion is prevented until the blood
is replaced by fresh blood, with empty "compartments," entering the pulmonary capillaries. The rate of uptake of these gases is limited, therefore,
by the rate at which blood enters the pulmonary capillaries rather than by
the rate of diffusion of gases across the alveolar-capillary and red blood
cell membranes. Actually, the first measurements of pulmonary capillary
blood flow were made by Krogh and Lindhard, using N₂O as the test gas;
their original method is no longer used because, when there is uneven
distribution of the inspired gas, it is difficult to achieve a uniform concentration of N₂O in the alveoli before recirculation of the blood occurs. If
there were no red blood cells and Hb, and only plasma flowed through
the pulmonary capillaries, CO uptake would then also be "flow-limited"
and would measure capillary blood flow; in patients with very severe ane-

mia and Hb deficiency, CO uptake may be partly "flow-limited" and partly "diffusion-limited."

In summary, the rate of CO uptake is limited by diffusion and can be used to measure the diffusing capacity; the uptake of N_2O, ethyl iodide, or acetylene is limited by the rate of pulmonary blood flow and can be used to estimate pulmonary capillary blood flow.

2. O_2 UPTAKE.—Figure 36 (p. 118) shows O_2 diffusing across the pulmonary membranes into the plasma and then associating chemically with hemoglobin. An obvious difference between the CO and O_2 schemas is that both the plasma and the hemoglobin "compartments" are partly filled with O_2 when mixed venous blood enters the pulmonary capillaries. The rate of diffusion of O_2 into the blood depends upon the difference in pressure of O_2 in the alveolar gas and that in the blood at every point along the capillary. As O_2 is transferred across the alveolar-capillary membranes, the capillary Po_2 rises and the increase in capillary Po_2 narrows the difference between alveolar and capillary Po_2 and slows the rate of diffusion. This means that the blood Po_2 must be known at every moment along the capillary. Fortunately, this information can be obtained by certain measurements and a series of mathematical computations (pp. 356–357).

CARBON MONOXIDE METHODS FOR MEASURING PULMONARY DIFFUSING CAPACITY

Pulmonary diffusing capacity for CO =

$$\frac{\text{ml CO transferred from alveolar gas to blood/min}}{\text{mean alveolar CO pressure — mean capillary CO pressure}}$$

Therefore, to measure the pulmonary diffusing capacity for CO, three measurements must be made:

1. ml of CO transferred from alveolar gas to blood/min
2. the mean alveolar CO pressure
3. the mean pulmonary capillary CO pressure

There are four methods which measure CO uptake: (1) the steady-state technique, (2) the single-breath technique, (3) the rebreathing technique, and (4) the fractional CO uptake. The first three methods provide all the data required for quantitative measurement of the diffusing capacity of the lungs; the fourth gives only an index of the rate of diffusion.

STEADY-STATE TECHNIQUE.—In this method, the patient breathes a mixture containing a low concentration of CO (about 0.1–0.2%). After about 12 breaths, the alveolar Pco reaches a plateau and the measurements are made.

The amount of CO transferred from alveolar gas to capillary blood per minute is calculated by measuring CO in the inspired and expired gas and subtracting that expired from the amount inspired. The mean capillary Pco is so small that it can be neglected. The *mean alveolar* Pco can be calculated if one measures the Pco in *expired* gas and knows the volume of the "physiologic dead space" (p. 352). Thus all the data necessary for the computation of the diffusing capacity for CO can be obtained.

This method has the advantages that it requires little co-operation on the patient's part, is carried out under normal breathing conditions and can be used during severe exercise. The analysis of CO in inspired and expired gas is usually done with an infra-red analyzer.

The test has the disadvantages of using CO, which is not a physiologic gas, and of requiring arterial puncture and analysis of the arterial Pco_2 in order to compute mean alveolar Pco. Another problem is that in certain circumstances, particularly in patients with uneven distribution of inspired gas with respect to pulmonary capillary blood flow (see p. 87), slight errors in the analyses of CO_2 and CO can lead to large errors (as much as 40%) in the calculation of the diffusing capacity for CO. It is also affected by changes in the pattern of breathing.

There are other possible ways of estimating alveolar Pco, such as (*a*) collecting an expired alveolar sample or (*b*) assuming a respiratory dead space and calculating alveolar Pco from the inspired and expired CO concentrations. Although these methods avoid the necessity of sampling of arterial blood, they are at least theoretically susceptible to considerable errors in the presence of uneven distribution of gas in the lung; (*a*) is subject to all the errors attendant on calling a single sample of gas representative of alveolar gas, and (*b*) is quite unreliable at rest because the value of dead space chosen is exquisitely critical.

Single-breath test using CO.—In this test, the patient inspires a gas mixture containing a low concentration of CO, then holds his breath for approximately 10 sec, during which time some CO leaves the alveolar gas and enters the blood; the larger the diffusing capacity, the greater is the amount of CO that enters the blood during the 10 sec period.

Again, three values are required: (1) *the ml of CO transferred* can be calculated from measurements of the per cent CO in the alveolar gas at the beginning and at the end of the breath-holding period if the *volume* of alveolar gas (functional residual capacity) is also known (see p. 13);

(2) *the mean capillary* Pco, which is so small that it can be neglected, and (3) *the mean alveolar* Pco.

In the single-breath test, alveolar Pco is not maintained at a nearly constant concentration as in the steady-state method because here the breath is held after the CO is inspired, and CO is absorbed during the period of breath-holding. Further, the mean alveolar Pco is not the average of the Pco at the beginning and end of the breath-holding period. However, by a special equation (p. 351), the mean alveolar Pco can be calculated and the diffusing capacity measured.

The single-breath test has the advantage of being quick and of requiring little co-operation from the patient, who has only to inhale and hold his breath for 10 sec. The analyses are performed with an infra-red analyzer. No blood samples are needed. The test can be repeated a number of times in rapid succession if desired. However, a measurement of the patient's functional residual capacity is needed, because a value for the total alveolar volume during the period of breath-holding is required in order to measure CO uptake. Further, one must inhale a gas such as helium along with CO in order to correct for uneven distribution of the inspired CO. The method also has the disadvantages that CO is a non-physiologic gas and breath-holding is not a normal breathing state. Finally, dyspneic patients or exercising patients may find it difficult to hold their breath for 10 sec.

REBREATHING TECHNIQUE USING CO.—In this test, the patient rebreathes for about 1½ min from a bag containing approximately 6 liters of a mixture of air and a low concentration of CO. He breathes quite rapidly (about 25/min) so that the gases in the bag may be well mixed with those in the lung. The pulmonary diffusing capacity can be calculated in a manner similar to that for the single-breath technique. The change of CO concentration in the gas within the bag is measured over a portion of the rebreathing period. The total volume of the system, residual volume plus bag volume, multiplied by the change of CO concentration gives the *volume of CO transferred*. The mean capillary Pco can again be neglected. *Mean alveolar* Pco is calculated from the concentration in the bag at the start and end of the period of measurement, using the same equation as that for the single-breath test (p. 351).

The relative advantages of the test are that it does not require arterial samples or breath-holding, and the rebreathing tends to compensate for uneven distribution of gas and blood throughout the lung. On the other hand, breathing at such a rapid rate requires considerable co-operation from the patient and is not natural. In addition, a measure of the functional residual capacity is needed; if a low concentration of helium is included in the original gas mixture, the lung volume can be calculated from the final helium concentration in the same manner as for the closed-circuit helium measurement of functional residual capacity (p. 17).

FRACTIONAL CO UPTAKE.—The percentage of the inspired CO that is taken up by the blood over a period of several minutes yields an *index* of the diffusing capacity because, in general, the greater the diffusing capacity, the greater the amount of CO that will be absorbed per minute; it does not provide a measure of *diffusing capacity* in any quantitative sense.

$$\text{Fractional CO uptake (in \%)} = \frac{\text{CO absorbed/min}}{\text{CO inspired/min}} \times 100$$

This index is approximately 50% in normal subjects. Values of less than 30% generally indicate an impairment of diffusion.

This test has the advantage of relative simplicity, because the only measurements are of the CO concentration in the inspired and expired gas. If the mean alveolar P_{CO} is not estimated, a calculation of diffusing capacity cannot be made.

Fractional CO uptake is influenced by the minute volume and the frequency of breathing; the higher the minute volume, the lower the fractional CO uptake, even though the diffusing capacity is the same. Thus it is difficult to tell whether a low fractional CO uptake is the result of impairment of diffusion or of a high alveolar ventilation. It is possible to make corrections if the alveolar ventilation per minute is known.

OXYGEN METHOD FOR MEASURING PULMONARY DIFFUSING CAPACITY

The more difficult and time-consuming O_2 method has been largely displaced in clinical laboratories by the CO methods for measuring diffusing capacity. An account of the concepts underlying the O_2 method is presented here because the basic principles and reasoning involved in the test are fundamental to an understanding of pulmonary gas exchange.

Pulmonary diffusing capacity for $O_2 =$
$$\frac{\text{ml } O_2 \text{ transferred from alveolar gas to blood/min}}{\text{mean alveolar } O_2 \text{ pressure} - \text{mean capillary } O_2 \text{ pressure}}$$

To measure the diffusing capacity for O_2, three measurements must be made:

1. ml of O_2 transferred from alveolar gas to blood/min
2. the mean alveolar O_2 pressure
3. the mean pulmonary capillary O_2 pressure

MILLILITERS OF O_2 TRANSFERRED.—This is measured easily, since it is the O_2 consumption of the patient per minute.

MEAN ALVEOLAR PO_2.—In Chapter 3, it was emphasized that uneven distribution of inspired gas occurs frequently in pulmonary disease, and this makes it difficult to call any "spot" sample of expired alveolar gas truly representative of *all* alveolar gas. However, it is possible to calculate a value for mean alveolar PO_2 by use of the alveolar air equation.

This equation (see Appendix, p. 339) has been used extensively to solve complex problems in gas exchange. Though the equation itself is quite formidable, the principle underlying it is simple. The equation merely states that, at sea level, the total pressure of gases (O_2, CO_2, N_2 and H_2O) in the alveoli equals 760 mm Hg and that if the partial pressures of any three of these four are known, that of the fourth can be obtained by subtraction. Suppose, for example, it is desired to calculate the partial pressure of O_2 in alveolar gas:

$$
\begin{array}{ll}
760 \text{ mm Hg} = PO_2 + PCO_2 + PN_2 + PH_2O \\
- \quad 47 \text{ mm Hg } PH_2O \\
\hline
713 \text{ mm Hg} = PO_2 + PCO_2 + PN_2 \\
- \ 563 \text{ mm Hg } PN_2 \text{ (assumed)} \\
\hline
150 \text{ mm Hg} = PO_2 + PCO_2 \\
- \quad 40 \text{ mm Hg } PCO_2 \text{ (measured as arterial } PCO_2) \\
\hline
110 \text{ mm Hg} = PO_2
\end{array}
$$

In the process of determining PO_2 by subtracting the PH_2O, PCO_2 and PN_2, there are certain measurements and assumptions. It is generally agreed that the water vapor pressure at $37°C$ is approximately 47 mm Hg, and this presents no problem. However, it is no more logical to use a "spot" sample of expired alveolar gas for determination of alveolar PCO_2 than it is to use this sample for measurement of alveolar PO_2. Therefore another method of measuring alveolar PCO_2 must be found. Recently, values for arterial PCO_2, which can be measured with reasonable accuracy (±2–3 mm Hg), have been used as representative of mean alveolar PCO_2. This is done because the arterial blood coming from all the alveoli approaches an integrated value of alveolar PCO_2 with respect to the different regions of the lung and to different times during the respiratory cycle; further CO_2 diffuses through body membranes so readily that its partial pressure in blood leaving any alveolus will always be equal to its partial pressure in the gas of that alveolus. While it is true that non-uniformity of alveolar ventilation with respect to alveolar capillary blood flow throughout the lung can produce a difference between the PCO_2 of mixed capillary blood and mixed alveolar gas in spite of diffusion equilibrium across any single individual alveolus (see p. 99), this difference is relatively small except in the presence of extreme non-uniformity of alveolar ventilation/ alveolar blood flow or large venous-to-arterial shunts.

It is also assumed in the foregoing calculation that $PN_2 = 563$ mm Hg. This would be true if the respiratory quotient were 1.0, i.e., if the amount of CO_2 added to the alveoli were exactly equal to the amount of O_2 removed from the alveoli each minute; in this case the inspired N_2 would be neither diluted

ALVEOLAR-CAPILLARY DIFFUSION

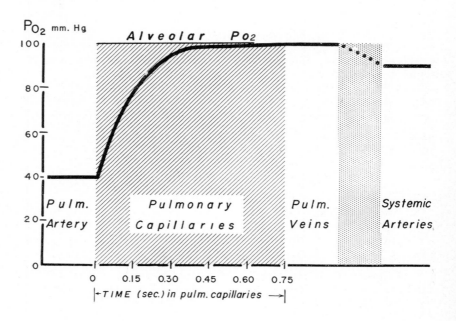

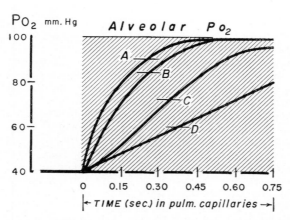

Fig. 38.—Changes in Po₂ of Blood during Passage through Pulmonary Capillaries

nor concentrated as it entered the alveoli, and alveolar P_{N_2} would equal moist inspired P_{N_2} (79.03% × 713 = 563 mm Hg). Actually, in most cases, more O_2 is removed per minute than CO_2 is added. The usual respiratory exchange ratio (R) $= \dfrac{200 \text{ ml } CO_2/\min}{250 \text{ ml } O_2/\min} = 0.8$. This results in the N_2 molecules being slightly more concentrated, since the same number of N_2 molecules is now present in a smaller gas volume. If the alveolar N_2 rises to 81%, the alveolar P_{N_2} would rise to 577 and the alveolar P_{O_2} would fall to 96 mm Hg. It is therefore essential to calculate alveolar P_{N_2} accurately by determining the respiratory exchange ratio.

MEAN PULMONARY CAPILLARY O_2 PRESSURE.*—Its measurement presents a real challenge. With CO, the capillary pressure was so low that it could be neglected. With O_2, the P_{O_2} at the beginning of the pulmonary capillary is that of mixed venous blood, about 40 mm Hg; the P_{O_2} at the end of the capillary is normally very nearly the same as alveolar P_{O_2}, about 100 mm Hg (Fig. 38).

Fortunately, one can compute (by Bohr's integration procedure, p. 353) the mean capillary P_{O_2} if one knows four things:

1. The pressure of O_2 in the blood just at the beginning of the pulmonary capillaries (mixed venous blood).

2. The pressure of O_2 in the alveoli, which establishes the pressure gradient across the alveolar capillary membranes.

3. The pressure of O_2 in the blood just at the end of the pulmonary capillaries.

4. The physiologic oxygen-hemoglobin dissociation curve.

---

* In the interest of clarity of presentation, we are ignoring the pressure gradient between the plasma and the interior of the red blood cell. "Capillary P_{O_2}" really should read "P_{O_2} within the erythrocyte in the pulmonary capillary."

◄━━◀ FIG. 38.—*Above*, mixed venous blood enters pulmonary capillaries with P_{O_2} of 40 mm Hg. Blood normally requires about 0.75 sec to pass through the capillaries. At the end of this time, its P_{O_2} has risen to almost 100 mm. Hg. The P_{O_2} of arterial blood is lower because of venous to arterial shunts.

Below, illustrations of different rates at which venous blood may be oxygenated in pulmonary capillaries depending upon diffusing capacity of the lung (see Table 10, p. 129). In each, alveolar P_{O_2} is 100 mm Hg; end-pulmonary capillary P_{O_2} is 99.99, 99.9, 96 and 81.4 mm Hg for *A*, *B*, *C* and *D*, respectively. Although the gradients between alveolar gas and end-pulmonary capillary blood are not measurably different (by present techniques) for *A* and *B*, mean pulmonary capillary O_2 pressures calculated by Bohr's integration procedure are quite different. End-pulmonary capillary blood in *A*, *B* and *C* would all have normal O_2 saturation though diffusing capacity is different in each case (only in *D* would blood O_2 saturation at the end of the capillary be reduced). If the *time* in the capillary were shortened, as by exercise, from 0.75 to 0.30 sec, O_2 saturation at this time would then be low in *B*, *C* and *D*.

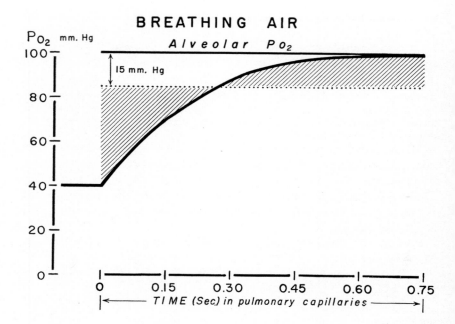

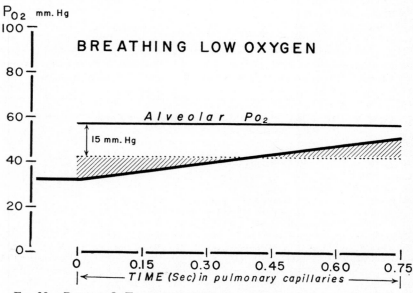

FIG. 39.—RATE OF O₂ TRANSFER AT DIFFERENT ALVEOLAR OXYGEN TENSIONS

TABLE 10.—ALVEOLAR AND END-CAPILLARY Po_2 IN PATIENTS WITH
NORMAL AND DECREASED DIFFUSING CAPACITIES
(data of Fig. 38, *below*, p. 126; Po_2 in mm Hg)

EXAMPLE	Do_2	ALVEOLAR Po_2	END-CAP. Po_2	END-CAP. GRADIENT (Po_2)	MEAN CAP. Po_2	MEAN CAP. GRADIENT (Po_2)
A	> 27.7	100	> 99.99	< 0.01	91	9
B	> 16.6	100	> 99.9	< 0.1	85	15
C	9.1	100	96.0	4.0	72.5	27.5
D	6.4	100	81.4	18.6	61	39

It is possible to measure (1), estimate (2) and consult tables or graphs for (4). The measurement of the end-capillary Po_2 is more difficult, but can be accomplished.

END-CAPILLARY Po_2.—Assume for the moment that it is possible to obtain blood for analysis from the end of the pulmonary capillaries or from the pulmonary veins. However, even then, there is no method available for measuring the Po_2 in this blood with the accuracy required. Figure 38 and Table 10 show that the *mean* capillary Po_2 (calculated by Bohr's integration procedure) will be 91 if end-capillary pressure is more than 99.99 mm Hg (example *A*), 85 if end-capillary Po_2 is approximately 99.9 (example *B*) and 72.5 mm Hg if end-capillary pressure is 96 mm Hg (example *C*). Methods for measuring blood Po_2 have an error of $\pm$ 2 mm Hg, and one is not justified in measuring a 0.1 mm Hg difference with a method that has a 2 mm Hg error!

However, if the end-capillary Po_2 were considerably lower than the alveolar Po_2, the difference could be measured with reasonable accuracy. Fortunately, Lilienthal and Riley found that this end-capillary O_2 gradient can be increased, presumably without any change in the diffusing capacity of the lungs, by giving the patient a low O_2 mixture to breathe (Fig. 39). When air (20.93% O_2) is breathed, the O_2 pressure gradient at the beginning of the capillary is *large* (about 60 mm Hg), the initial transfer of O_2 across the

◄━━◀ FIG. 39.—When the patient breathes air (20.93% O_2), the high initial alveolo-capillary Po_2 gradient results in rapid transfer of O_2 so that the Po_2 of end-pulmonary capillary blood and of alveolar gas are almost identical. When the patient breathes a low O_2 mixture (12–14% O_2), the initial gradient is low, O_2 is transferred at a slower rate and a measurable end-capillary gradient is present. The curves are plotted from data obtained by the procedure outlined on page 353. Once the curve of increase in Po_2 vs. time is plotted, the *mean* capillary pressure is determined graphically by drawing a horizontal line (dotted) so that the shaded area above the line (right) equals the shaded area below the line (left). The mean gradient (mean alveolar Po_2 — mean pulmonary capillary Po_2) must be the same breathing the low O_2 mixture as breathing air if the diffusing capacity and amount of O_2 transferred are the same in the two cases.

EFFECT OF VENOUS TO ARTERIAL SHUNT

ON ARTERIAL OXYGEN PRESSURE

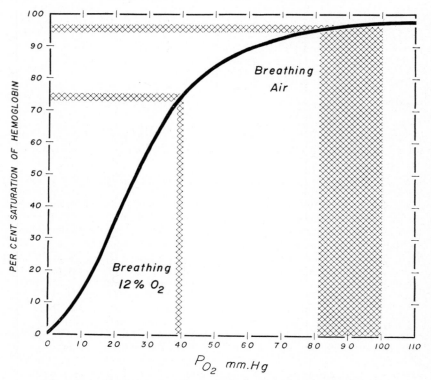

FIG. 40.—EFFECT OF VENOUS TO ARTERIAL SHUNT ON ARTERIAL P_{O_2}

If 10% of the mixed venous blood by-passes the lungs, arterial P_{O_2} is reduced by 19 mm Hg when the patient breathes room air, but only by 1.2 mm Hg when the patient breathes 12% O_2. This is a graphic representation of the calculations in Table 11. In each case, the A-V O_2 saturation difference is 22% and a 10% shunt results in a 2.2% reduction in arterial O_2 saturation.

membranes is rapid, and near equilibrium with alveolar gas is reached quickly. A healthy subject has practically no alveolar to end-capillary Po_2 difference when he breathes air. When 14% O_2 is breathed, the O_2 pressure gradient at the beginning of the capillary is small (about 25 mm Hg), the initial transfer is less rapid, and a measurable pressure gradient still exists at the end of the capillary. *Therefore, decreasing the alveolar Po_2 increases the alveolar to end-capillary Po_2 difference; increasing alveolar Po_2 decreases alveolar to end-capillary Po_2 difference.* A sample calculation illustrating this point is included in the Appendix (p. 357). The clinical measurement of the diffusing capacity of the lung for O_2 includes measurements made during the inhalation of 12–14% O_2 in order to provide a measurable end-capillary diffusion gradient.

It was assumed earlier that a representative sample of end-capillary blood could be obtained. Unfortunately, this cannot be done. Samples of pulmonary "capillary" blood have been obtained by the catheterization technique, but these are not representative of all capillary blood; indeed, this is really blood

---

TABLE 11.—EFFECT OF VENOUS-TO-ARTERIAL SHUNT UPON ARTERIAL O_2 SATURATION AND TENSION IN SUBJECT BREATHING (A) 20.93% AND (B) 12% O_2

	A. BREATHING AIR	B. BREATHING 12% O_2
Assume:		
Cardiac output =	5.0 liters	5.0 liters
Shunted blood =	0.5 liters	0.5 liters
Non-shunted blood =	4.5 liters	4.5 liters
Blood O_2 capacity =	20 vol% or 200 ml O_2/liter of blood	20 vol% or 200 ml O_2/liter of blood
O_2 tension of mixed venous blood =	40 mm Hg	27.5 mm Hg
HbO_2 saturation of mixed venous blood =	75%	53%
Alveolar oxygen tension =	101 mm Hg	44 mm Hg
O_2 tension of end-pul. capillary blood =	100+ mm Hg	40 mm Hg
HbO_2 saturation of end-pul. capillary blood =	97%	75%
Then:		
4.5 l non-shunted blood contains	4.5(0.97 × 200 ml) = 873 ml O_2	4.5(0.75 × 200 ml) = 675 ml O_2
0.5 l shunted blood contains	0.5(0.75 × 200 ml) = 75 ml O_2	0.5(0.53 × 200 ml) = 53 ml O_2
5.0 l arterial blood contains	948 ml O_2	728 ml O_2
100 ml arterial blood contains	948/50 = 18.96 ml O_2	728/50 = 14.56 ml O_2
HbO_2 saturation of arterial blood =	$\dfrac{18.96}{20}$ = 94.8%	$\dfrac{14.56}{20}$ = 72.8%
O_2 tension of arterial blood =	81 mm Hg	38.8 mm Hg
Difference between end-pul. capillary and arterial O_2 tension =	100 − 81 = 19 mm Hg	40 − 38.8 = 1.2 mm Hg

⟨with a high ventilation/blood flow ratio since it has twice passed ventilated alveoli.

On the other hand, *arterial* blood *can* be obtained and its Po_2 measured reasonably accurately. Can *arterial* blood be used as representative of end-pulmonary capillary blood? Figure 38 shows that it cannot because its Po_2 is lower than that of end-pulmonary capillary blood, owing to the existence of a "physiologic shunt" even in normal individuals (pp. 87 and 103 and Fig. 24, p. 80); this "physiologic shunt" includes blood from areas with a decreased ventilation/blood flow ratio.

The Po_2 difference between alveolar gas and *arterial* blood thus includes two components: (1) an *alveolar* to *end-capillary* difference owing to incomplete equilibrium between the Po_2 of alveolar gas and that of end-capillary blood ("membrane component"), and (2) an *end-capillary* to *arterial* difference due to the "physiologic shunt" ("venous admixture"). Fortunately, the second of these can be eliminated almost entirely by giving the patient 12–14% O_2 to inhale.

The explanation for this depends entirely on the unique shape of the O_2 dissociation curve, which has a flat portion and a very steeply sloping portion. When the patient breathes air (20.93% O_2), his arterial Po_2 and O_2 saturation lie on the flat part, and a small decrease in arterial O_2 saturation, caused by shunted blood, is associated with a large decrease in arterial Po_2. On the other hand, when the patient breathes 12–14% O_2, his arterial Po_2 and saturation are lowered and fall on the steep slope; now the same decrease in arterial O_2 saturation, caused by the same amount of shunted blood, is associated with a very small decrease in arterial Po_2. This effect is shown graphically in Figure 40 and by the calculations in Table 11.

If the breathing of 12–14% O_2 *completely* abolished the Po_2 difference owing to the "physiologic shunt," the whole alveolar to arterial Po_2 difference under these conditions would be the end-capillary gradient, and all the information required for calculation of the diffusing capacity would be available. However, it does not, and a "trial and error" method (described in the Appendix, p. 356 is necessary to determine the end-capillary Po_2 gradient. This permits calculation of the diffusing capacity.

It is fortunate indeed that this one maneuver, the inhalation of 12–14% O_2 solves two problems. It increases the "membrane component," so that it becomes a measurable value and at the same time practically eliminates the "physiologic shunt" component, so that the "membrane component" is prac-

TABLE 12

	WHEN PATIENT IS BREATHING		
	12–14% O_2	AIR	50–100% O_2
Total difference between Po_2 in alveolar gas and arterial blood is............	10 mm Hg	9 mm Hg	35–50 mm Hg
"Venous admixture component" is......	1	8	35–50
"Membrane component" is...........	9	1	0

tically equal to the alveolar-arterial Po_2 difference. A summary of these effects is given in Table 12.

The advantages of the O_2 method are that it uses a physiologically important gas and the measurement is made during steady-state conditions. The analyses can be made with equipment available or easily procurable for a routine chemistry laboratory. The disadvantages are that (a) the "bubble" technique of estimating blood Po_2 and Pco_2 is difficult to learn and requires considerable practice (newer techniques employing O_2 and CO_2 electrodes may overcome this problem); (b) arterial blood and gas samples must be taken from the patient once while he is breathing air and again while he is breathing a low O_2 mixture, (c) inhalation of low O_2 may be contraindicated in some patients, (d) the experimental error is great when the diffusing capacity is normal, and (e) the method involves the assumptions that the diffusing capacity, cardiac output and venous admixture are all the same during the breathing of 21% and 12–14% O_2.

C. NORMAL VALUES FOR PULMONARY DIFFUSING CAPACITY

Normal values are given in Table 13. These are only approximate because not enough studies have been performed with standardized procedures to warrant more precise "normal" data. Some of the factors which probably affect "normal" values are:

TABLE 13.—NORMAL VALUES FOR PULMONARY DIFFUSING CAPACITY*

	Do_2, ML/MIN/MM HG	Dco, ML/MIN/MM HG	REFERENCE
Carbon Monoxide Methods			
1. Steady-state technique (mean alveolar CO tension calculated) ..	(21)†	17	J. Clin. Invest. 33:530, 1954 *Tilley et al.*
2. Steady-state technique (expired alveolar CO tension measured) ..	(22)	18	J. Physiol. 129:237, 1955
3. Single-breath test (10 sec breath-holding)..	(31)	25	J. Clin. Invest. 36:1, 1957
4. Rebreathing technique	(31)	25	Acta Physiol. scandinav. 32:106, *Krulffer* 1954
Oxygen method			
1. Steady state	21	(17)†	Am. J. Physiol. 147:199, 1946 *Lilienthal et al.*

* Data are average values for resting subjects.
† Numbers in parentheses were computed from the equation $Do_2 = 1.23\ Dco$.

1. *Body size.*—The Dco has been found to vary with body surface area according to the equation:

$$\text{Dco} = [(\text{surface area in M}^2)\ (18.84)] - 6.8$$

2. *Age.*—*Maximal* diffusing capacity for O_2 (Do_2 during maximal exercise) has been found to decrease with advancing age, according to the equation:

$$\text{Max. } Do_2 = [0.67\ (\text{ht. in cm})] - [0.55\ (\text{age in yr})] - 40.9$$

3. *Lung volume.*—If Dco (single breath) is measured at two different lung volumes, Dco is increased 10–25% when lung volume is increased approximately 50%; the single-breath test is performed at a large lung volume, and this may be a partial explanation of higher "normal" values obtained when it is used.

4. *Exercise.*—The effect of exercise on increasing Dco or Do_2 has been mentioned on page 115. Presumably it is caused not by increase in pulmonary capillary blood *flow* but by increase in the surface contact area of functioning alveoli and pulmonary capillaries; exercise may cause a doubling of pulmonary diffusing capacity.

5. *Body position.*—The Dco is 15–20% greater in the supine than in the sitting position and about 10–15% greater sitting than standing, possibly because of changes of pulmonary capillary blood volume associated with changes in posture.

6. *Alveolar O_2 tension.*—Because of its influence on the rate of chemical association of CO with Hb, changes in alveolar oxygen tension or partial pressure influence Dco. For example, the diffusing capacities measured at alveolar O_2 tensions of 40 and of 600 mm Hg were 45 and 18 ml/min/mm Hg respectively. The changes in Dco that are caused by variations in alveolar Po_2 in the physiologic range are much smaller. In patients with severe hypoxia, increase in pulmonary blood flow and dilatation of the pulmonary capillary bed may occur; Dco may change on this account as well as because of change in the Hb and CO reaction rate.

7. *Alveolar CO_2 tension.*—The addition of 6–7.5% CO_2 to the inspired gas for some minutes before measuring Dco increases it by 5–25%. When 6% CO_2 is added just for the 10 sec breath-holding period that is required by the single-breath test, only a 5% increase occurs.

It is obvious that clinicians and physiologists using Dco tests must standardize conditions and state them; only in this way can small deviations from "normal" become meaningful.

D. LABORATORY DIAGNOSIS OF IMPAIRMENT
OF DIFFUSION

At the beginning of this chapter we indicated that measurements of diffusing capacity have become helpful in the diagnosis of certain types of pulmonary disease, but we did not state why the estimation of diffusing capacity is of more diagnostic help than other laboratory methods, such as the measurement of arterial blood O_2 or CO_2 at rest, during exercise or during inhalation of O_2. Reasons for preferring to measure diffusing capacity follow:

1. DIFFUSING CAPACITY RATHER THAN ARTERIAL O_2 SATURATION:

(a) *Arterial O_2 saturation may be reduced for many reasons; an impairment of diffusion is only one of these.*

(b) *Arterial O_2 saturation may be normal even though there is definite impairment of the diffusion process.* The reason for this may be found in Figure 38 (p. 126) and Table 10 (p. 129). In *A,* the diffusing capacity is normal (27.7) and the end-capillary Po_2 is more than 99.9 mm Hg; in *B,* it is reduced (16.6), but the end-capillary Po_2 is still approximately 99.9; in *C,* it is further reduced (9.1), but the end-capillary Po_2 is reduced to only 96 mm Hg. The arterial O_2 saturation will be "normal" in all three cases; only in *D,* in which the end-capillary Po_2 is 81.4 mm Hg, will the arterial O_2 saturation be decreased sufficiently to be detected by ordinary laboratory methods.

(c) During exercise, the arterial O_2 saturation may decrease below normal in *B* and *C,* because after maximal dilatation of pulmonary capillaries has occurred, a further increase in pulmonary blood flow shortens the time that the blood spends in the pulmonary capillaries. Thus blood would leave the capillary in 0.3 or 0.4 sec instead of 0.75 sec, and at this time the diffusion process is still far from complete. *However, the decrease in arterial O_2 saturation during exercise is not diagnostic because such a decrease may occur during exercise in patients with many types of pulmonary disease* (venous-to-arterial shunt, uneven distribution, hypoventilation) and *impairment of diffusion is only one of these.*

2. DIFFUSING CAPACITY RATHER THAN ARTERIAL O_2 TENSION.—A measurement of arterial Po_2 means little as far as the process of diffusion is concerned unless related to the simultaneously measured alveolar Po_2. However, even then the difference between the Po_2 of alveolar gas and that of arterial blood may be due to many causes, of which impairment of diffusion is only one (see p. 358). The test of diffusing capacity specifically measures the diffusing properties of the alveolar-capillary bed.

When O_2 is breathed, arterial O_2 saturation and tension rise to maximal values even in patients suffering from impairment of diffusion. When the alveolar Po_2 rises from 100 to 673 mm Hg, the initial alveolar to blood O_2 gradient (at the beginning of the capillary) is increased tremendously and end-capillary blood is near equilibrium with alveolar gas despite severe impairment of diffusion. However, anoxemia caused by all types of pulmonary disease except a venous-to-arterial shunt is also corrected by O_2 therapy, so that the correction of anoxemia affords no sure diagnostic clue. On the other hand, if impairment of diffusion is associated with a venous-to-arterial shunt, inhalation of O_2 will correct the anoxemia only partially.

3. DIFFUSING CAPACITY RATHER THAN ARTERIAL CO_2 CONTENT AND TENSION.—Carbon dioxide retention rarely, if ever, results from an impairment of diffusion unless it be in a patient kept alive by O_2 therapy. This is because CO_2 diffuses 20 times as readily as O_2 through the pulmonary membranes. Therefore, arterial CO_2 may be (1) normal, (2) low, if there is hyperventilation, or (3) high, if the impairment of diffusion is associated with emphysema or other diseases in which there is hypoventilation or marked non-uniformity of ventilation and blood flow.

4. METHOD OF CHOICE FOR MEASURING DIFFUSING CAPACITY.—Because of the newness and multiplicity of tests, there has not been sufficient time to compare the various procedures in large numbers of patients with a wide variety of diseases. Further, to be meaningful to the clinician, measurements of diffusing capacity must eventually be correlated with patterns of disease familiar to the pathologist. Because it is difficult to correlate a physiologic measurement of diffusing capacity of the whole lung with pathologic diagnoses made on bits of lung removed for biopsy or on whole lungs at autopsy months or years after the physiologic tests were performed, there are no extensive and satisfactory comparisons of the same pulmonary disease as seen by physiologists and pathologists.

The present trend is to use the CO methods rather than the O_2 methods, because of the many advantages of the former for clinical studies. Among the CO methods, no specific recommendation can really be made until physiologic-pathologic correlations are more complete. All diffusing capacity tests demonstrate a defect in diffusion when "alveolo-capillary block" is known to be present by other criteria. The steady-state methods are more apt to yield lower values in diseases in which there is both impairment of diffusion and marked unevenness of gas distribution; for this reason they appear to be more sensitive tests than the single-breath (breath-holding) test in patients with emphysema. On the other hand, the single-breath test is more likely to represent a true measure of the characteristics of the membranes and pulmonary capillary bed of the ventilated parts of the patient's lungs. None of the methods can differentiate between impairment of diffusion due to a longer pathway for diffusion of CO and that due to a reduced surface area for diffusion; these can be distinguished only by histologic studies of tissues.

E. DIFFUSING CAPACITY IN PATIENTS WITH CARDIOPULMONARY DISEASE

Some of the diseases in which the diffusing capacity is reduced are discussed here (see also pp. 234, 236 and 240).

ALVEOLAR-CAPILLARY BLOCK.—This disorder refers specifically to conditions in which there is a longer path for O_2 to travel between alveolar gas and arterial blood; the tissues traversed may also be abnormal. It includes diseases associated with thickening and separation of the capillary and alveolar walls. The interstitial or alveolar pulmonary fibrosis seen in patients with sarcoidosis, berylliosis, asbestosis and scleroderma falls in this category; Dco may be reduced markedly in these. It is well to remember that the physiologist can diagnose "impairment of diffusion" and can infer that it is caused by fibrous tissue, but only the pathologist can legitimately diagnose "fibrosis."

The effective length of the diffusion path may also be increased when the alveolar and capillary walls are separated by edema fluid (interstitial edema); when the alveoli and airways actually fill with fluid, these alveoli can be considered as non-ventilated and their blood flow as venous-to-arterial shunts. In either case, one would expect a decrease in pulmonary diffusing capacity.

Not all patients with alveolar-capillary block have progression of the disease; some patients (those with "farmer's lung" in particular) may become completely well despite considerable impairment of diffusion.

CHRONIC OBSTRUCTIVE EMPHYSEMA.—The impairment of diffusion seen in some patients with emphysema is due not to alveolar-capillary block but rather to a decrease in surface area for gas exchange. Classically, destruction of the alveolar and capillary walls is seen in histologic sections. Pulmonary diffusing capacity may be reduced (demonstrated by all methods of measurement), although generally not to the extent found in alveolar-capillary block. The diffusing capacity is relatively normal in uncomplicated bronchial asthma. The test of diffusing capacity thus can serve on occasion to differentiate asthma from obstructive emphysema.

LOSS OF PULMONARY TISSUE.—The pulmonary diffusing capacity is decreased when the total surface area of the capillaries is decreased, as in pneumonectomy or a space-taking lesion of the lung; however, the decrease actually found is generally less than might be expected, because of the great reserve of the pulmonary capillary bed and possibly because of growth of new capillaries.

VASCULAR DISORDERS.—Any abnormality which occludes the arterial flow to part of the lung tends to decrease the diffusing capacity in that region. For example, congenital absence of, or embolic occlusion of, a pulmonary artery is accompanied by a decreased diffusing capacity in the region supplied. Pulmonary hypertension need not be accompanied by a reduction in diffusing capacity unless there is obliteration of part of the pulmonary *capillary* bed. Pulmonary congestion, such as that associated with mitral stenosis, may cause no reduction in diffusing capacity in early stages of the disease because the pulmonary capillary bed may be enlarged; however, when interstitial or intra-alveolar edema or deposition of fibrous tissue occurs, the diffusing capacity decreases. In conditions associated with increase in blood volume, the pulmonary capillary blood volume may also be increased, with a consequent increase in diffusing capacity.

ANEMIA AND POLYCYTHEMIA.—The diffusing capacity (at least for CO) is decreased in anemia. This could occur because of changes in the pulmonary membrane, because of early heart failure or because the red cells in the pulmonary capillary bed at any instant cannot absorb all the gas if allowed to equilibrate; however, in simple uncomplicated anemia, the decrease in D_{CO} appears to be caused simply by reduction of the number of red blood cells to the extent that the test gas cannot be taken up fast enough. The diffusing capacity for CO may be increased in patients who have marked polycythemia.

SUMMARY

The exchange of gases between alveolar air and pulmonary capillary blood occurs by the passive physical process of diffusion and not by active processes of gas secretion; the work is done by the respiratory muscles (ventilation of the alveoli) and by the right ventricle (pulmonary blood flow). The process of diffusion can be measured quantitatively in man by determining the pulmonary diffusing capacity (D) for oxygen (O_2)

or carbon monoxide (CO). The units of D_{O_2} or D_{CO} are ml of O_2 or CO/min/mm Hg pressure differences between the O_2 or CO in alveolar gas and pulmonary capillary blood. D_{O_2} or D_{CO} may be decreased when (*a*) the alveolar and/or capillary membrane is thickened or these membranes are separated by transudate, exudate or abnormal tissue, or (*b*) the surface area of contact between ventilated alveoli and functioning pulmonary capillaries is reduced. Since the rate of transfer of O_2 and CO may also be limited by the rate of diffusion across the membrane of the red blood cell, by the rate of chemical association of O_2 or CO with Hb and occasionally by the amount of Hb in the pulmonary capillary blood, a test measuring diffusion *across the pulmonary membranes* alone is preferable to the over-all test; *membrane* diffusing capacity alone has been determined by special techniques.

The pulmonary diffusing capacity is usually determined clinically by quantitative studies of CO uptake; several tests have been advocated, and each has its advantages and disadvantages. D_{CO} should be measured whenever pure alveolar-capillary block (longer pathway for O_2 or CO) is suspected; it is useful to detect early disease, to determine the severity of more advanced diseases and to follow the course of disease and the influence of treatment. D_{CO} measurements also provide better understanding of disease processes in which impairment of diffusion complicates other types of pulmonary disease.

CHAPTER 6

Arterial Blood Oxygen, Carbon Dioxide and pH

So far we have discussed the dynamic processes of ventilation, diffusion and blood flow. These have as their function the maintenance of normal pressures of O_2 and CO_2 in the alveolar gas and pulmonary capillary blood, i.e., the arterialization of the venous blood. For this reason, it is logical to examine the *arterial* blood for its O_2 and CO_2 pressure and content to determine how adequately the lung has accomplished its primary purpose. Analyses of peripheral *venous* blood serve no useful purpose in the analysis of *pulmonary* function because the O_2 and CO_2 in the venous blood from any part of the body (such as the arm, leg, kidney, brain or heart muscle) or even of *mixed* venous blood depend not only on the O_2 and CO_2 in the arterial blood but also on the metabolism and rate of blood flow through the tissues.

I. Arterial Blood Oxygen

A. THE OXYGEN-HEMOGLOBIN DISSOCIATION CURVES

Blood combines with O_2 in two ways: (1) in physical solution in the watery parts of the blood as dissolved O_2, and (2) in chemical combination with hemoglobin as HbO_2. In each case, the amount of O_2 taken up depends on the Po_2 to which the plasma or blood is exposed (see Table in Fig. 41). If plasma is exposed to 10, 20, 30, 40, 50, 60, 70, 80, 90 and 100 mm Hg Po_2 in 10 different flasks at body temperature and the amount of O_2 in the plasma is measured in each flask after the plasma has dissolved as much O_2 as it will at each Po_2, it is found that at 10 mm Hg Po_2, 0.03 ml of O_2 is dissolved in 100 ml of plasma, at 20 mm Hg Po_2, twice this amount, and at 100 mm Hg, 10 times this amount. Therefore the amount of dissolved O_2 is directly proportional to the partial pressure (i.e., 0.003 ml O_2/100 ml blood/mm Hg Po_2), and this is true no matter how high the O_2 pressure rises. For example, if the arterial Po_2 rose to 600 (because the patient breathed a high O_2 mixture), the dissolved O_2 would be 1.8 ml; if a subject breathed O_2 at 3 atmospheres and the arterial Po_2 were 2000 mm Hg, the dissolved O_2 would be 6 ml O_2/100 ml blood. Only in the latter case would the *dissolved* O_2 be sufficient to supply the O_2 needed by man, and even then only for a man at rest.

Fortunately, a special chemical compound, hemoglobin, is present in red blood cells. One gram of this remarkable substance is capable of combining chemically, or *associating,* with 1.34 ml of O_2; thus, if 100 ml of blood contains 15 gm of Hb, it can combine chemically with $15 \times 1.34 = 20.1$ ml O_2. However, the *actual* amount of O_2 combined depends on the partial pressure of O_2 in the blood.

In the case of Hb, the amount of O_2 associated is *not* linearly related to the Po_2, as it is in the case of dissolved O_2. If *whole blood* is exposed in 10 different flasks to 10 different O_2 pressures ranging from 10 to 100 mm Hg and the amount of O_2 combined with Hb (total O_2 minus dissolved O_2) is measured in each when equilibrium is reached, the values in Figure 41 will be found. A graph of O_2 content (or % saturation) against Po_2 is not a straight line but an S shaped curve which has a very steep slope (between 10 and 50 mm Hg Po_2) and a very flat portion (between 70 and 100 mm Hg Po_2).

The unusual shape of this HbO_2 dissociation curve is a distinct advantage to the patient for several reasons: (1) If arterial Po_2 decreases from 100 to 80 mm Hg as the result of cardiopulmonary disease, the Hb of arterial blood will still be almost maximally saturated (94.5%) and the tissues will not suffer from anoxia. (2) When the arterial blood passes into tissue capillaries and is exposed to the tissue tension of O_2 (about 40 mm Hg), Hb gives up large quantities of O_2 for utilization by the tissues. The shape of the dissociation curve is also of great advantage to the physiologist because, by deliberately varying the position of the patient's arterial blood on this curve (by giving the patient O_2, air or 12–14% O_2 to breathe), he can differentiate anoxemia caused by impairment of diffusion from that caused by "physiologic shunts" (see p. 132).

Unfortunately, from the diagnostic point of view, the shape of the

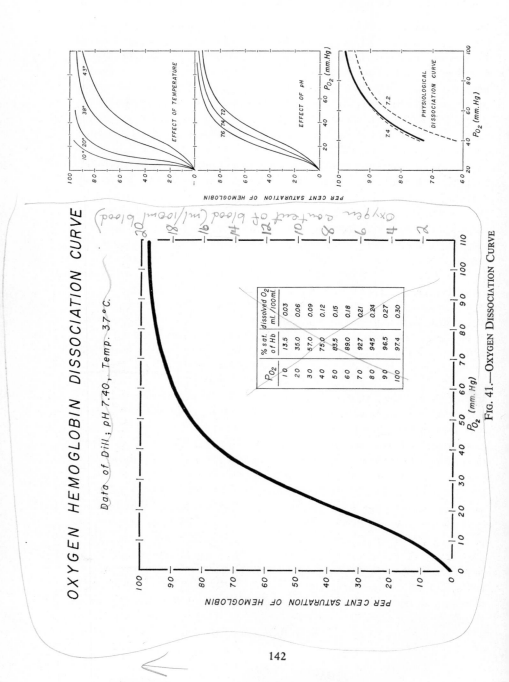

OXYGEN HEMOGLOBIN DISSOCIATION CURVE

Data of Dill; pH 7.40, Temp. 37°C.

Oxygen content of blood (ml/100ml blood)

PO₂	% sat. of Hb	dissolved O₂ ml./100ml.
10	13.5	0.03
20	35.0	0.06
30	57.0	0.09
40	75.0	0.12
50	83.5	0.15
60	89.0	0.18
70	92.7	0.21
80	94.5	0.24
90	96.5	0.27
100	97.4	0.30

P_{O_2} (mm.Hg)

PER CENT SATURATION OF HEMOGLOBIN

EFFECT OF TEMPERATURE

EFFECT OF pH

PHYSIOLOGICAL DISSOCIATION CURVE

FIG. 41.—OXYGEN DISSOCIATION CURVE

HbO_2 dissociation curve is such that the arterial O_2 tension does not fall measurably below normal values even when pulmonary disease is severe enough to cause a definite difference between the Po_2 of alveolar gas and of arterial blood. The physician living at high altitude has a diagnostic advantage (although his patient is at a disadvantage) because his patient breathes air at decreased total barometric pressure and therefore of lower Po_2; a further decrease in arterial blood Po_2 owing to pulmonary disease results in larger and more easily measurable changes in arterial O_2 saturation (see Fig. 41, p. 142).

The question is often asked, "Which is more important to normal body function—normal arterial blood Po_2 or O_2 content?" *Both* are important. The body tissues extract 4–5 ml O_2 from each 100 ml of capillary blood in man at rest and much larger amounts when man is exercising; this can be supplied only from stores of O_2 associated with Hb. On the other hand, an adequate Po_2 is necessary for the loading of O_2 on to Hb in the lungs and for diffusion of O_2 from the tissue capillaries to the cells. In vitro cellular respiration continues at very low O_2 tensions (6–8 mm Hg), but intact man has symptoms of cerebral anoxia when the inspired Po_2 is lowered abruptly to 60–70 mm Hg (see p. 151 for compensatory mechanisms in chronic anoxia).

B. METHODS OF ESTIMATING OR MEASURING BLOOD O_2

CYANOSIS.—The estimation of arterial O_2 saturation by the visual impression of blueness of the skin or mucous membranes is far from quantitative for many reasons. Some of these are: (1) local cyanosis may occur because of regional slowing of the circulation even though the arterial saturation is normal; (2) cyanosis is difficult to detect in

---

← ◀ FIG. 41.—The large graph shows a single dissociation curve, applicable when the pH of the blood is 7.4 and temperature 37°C. The blood O_2 tension and saturation of patients with CO_2 retention, acidosis, alkalosis, fever or hypothermia will not fit this curve because the curve "shifts" to the right or left when temperature, pH, or Pco_2 is changed.

Effects on the O_2-hemoglobin dissociation curve of change in temperature (*upper right*) and in pH (*middle right*) are shown in the smaller graphs. A small change in blood pH occurs regularly in the body; e.g., when mixed venous blood passes through the pulmonary capillaries, Pco_2 decreases from 46 to 40 mm Hg and pH rises from 7.37 to 7.40. During this time, blood changes from a pH 7.37 dissociation curve to a pH 7.40 curve; an approximate "physiological" dissociation curve (*solid line, bottom right*) has been drawn to describe this change.

patients with anemia (because the absolute amount of Hb pigment is too low) or in patients with deeply pigmented skin, and (3) the visual perception of "blueness" varies greatly in various physicians; the average physician does not perceive cyanosis with certainty until the arterial O_2 saturation is reduced to 85% and some not until 75% is reached. For this reason, it is usually desirable to make quantitative measurements of blood O_2 by chemical or physical means.

ARTERIAL BLOOD O_2 SATURATION.—The pulmonary physiologist always relates the actual amount of O_2 in arterial blood (O_2 content) to the capacity of the blood for holding O_2. This ratio, the % *saturation*

$$100 \times \frac{\text{ml } O_2 \text{ actually combined with Hb}}{\text{max. ml } O_2 \text{ capable of combining with Hb}}$$

expresses the ability of the lungs to raise alveolar and pulmonary capillary Po_2 and so oxygenate the mixed venous blood; O_2 content, on the other hand, varies with the amount of Hb/100 ml of blood (with anemia and polycythemia) as well as with the oxygenating function of the lung.

There are several important ways of measuring the saturation of arterial blood with O_2. In the manometric method of Van Slyke and Neil, O_2 content (O_2 combined with Hb + dissolved O_2) of arterial blood is measured; part of the blood is then exposed to atmospheric O_2 so that its Hb combines fully with O_2 and the *capacity* is measured. Saturation is calculated after corrections are made for dissolved O_2. The method is laborious but has the advantages that arterial blood CO_2 can be measured during the same procedure and that the amount of dissolved O_2 can be estimated when the O_2 test for diagnosing venous-to-arterial shunts is used (p. 103).

The spectrophotometric method measures the ratio of reduced or oxyhemoglobin to total hemoglobin. It is often the preferred method when knowledge of the CO_2 content is not essential and when large numbers of measurements of O_2 saturation are needed (e.g., comparison of O_2 saturation of blood sampled at multiple sites during cardiac catheterization).

An oximetric method uses a filter photometer which is applied to the ear so that arterial O_2 saturation can be estimated continuously and without withdrawing arterial blood. Although less accurate than other methods for measuring absolute values, it has considerable usefulness in measuring *changes* in saturation (e.g., rate of increase during inhalation of O_2, or change during exercise or hyperventilation) and in comparing the effectiveness of measures designed to increase arterial O_2 saturation to its maximal value. (e.g., different types of ventilators or different methods of increasing the inspired concentrations of O_2).

ARTERIAL O_2 TENSION.—In cardiopulmonary disease, whenever arterial Po_2 decreases, so does arterial O_2 saturation (see Table 15, p. 149). However, the measurement of O_2 tension has certain advantages: (a) It is a more sensitive test when the arterial blood saturation is near-normal. For example, when *saturation* has decreased from 97.4 to 96.5% (a barely detectable change in saturation), Po_2 has decreased from

TABLE 14.—MEAN VALUES FOR BLOOD O_2, CO_2 AND pH IN
HEALTHY YOUNG MEN

	ARTERIAL BLOOD	MIXED VENOUS BLOOD
1. O_2 pressure (mm Hg)	95	40
2. Dissolved O_2 (ml O_2/100 ml W.B.*)	0.29	0.12
3. O_2 content (ml O_2/100 ml W.B.)	20.3	15.5
4. O_2 combined with Hb (ml O_2/100 ml. W.B.)	20.0	15.4
5. O_2 capacity of Hb (ml O_2/100 ml W.B.)	20.6	20.6
6. % saturation of Hb with O_2	97.1	75.0
7. Total CO_2 (ml CO_2/100 ml W.B.)	49.0	53.1
(mM/L)	21.9	23.8
8. Plasma CO_2 (ml CO_2/100 ml plasma)	59.6	63.8
a) Dissolved CO_2 (ml CO_2/100 ml)	2.84	3.2
b) Combined CO_2 (ml CO_2/100 ml)	56.8	60.5
c) Combined CO_2/dissolved CO_2	20/1	18.9/1
d) CO_2 pressure (mm Hg)	41	46.5
9. Plasma pH	7.40	7.376

Modified from Albritton, E. C. (ed.): *Standard Values in Blood* (Philadelphia: W. B. Saunders Company, 1952).
* W.B. = whole blood.

100 to 90 mm Hg (an easily measurable change by modern polarigraphic techniques). (b) During the change from breathing air to inhalation of O_2, the saturation increases only 2.6%, whereas O_2 tension increases by 550 mm Hg.

Arterial O_2 tension may be measured directly and precisely by the membrane-covered oxygen electrode which permits O_2 but not red blood cells or plasma proteins to diffuse to the electrode tip. The electrode can be used for either continuous or discontinuous measurements.

Normal values are given in Table 14. The Po_2 and saturation of arterial blood may be normal even though there is definite pulmonary disease (uneven distribution or impaired diffusion). This is because hyperventilation can raise alveolar Po_2 well above usual values and bring arterial

Po$_2$ to normal, even though a large alveolar-arterial Po$_2$ difference exists. (The arterial blood saturation in Figs. 27–33 is low because total alveolar ventilation was kept normal, for purposes of illustration.) Hyperventilation can similarly maintain normal Po$_2$ of arterial blood in a patient with impaired alveolar-capillary diffusion.

C. CAUSES OF ANOXEMIA

Anoxia is a general term referring to a decrease in O$_2$ content or tension in any part of the body, including the blood. *Anoxemia* refers specifically to a decrease in the amount of O$_2$ in arterial blood. (some prefer the more accurate terms *hypoxia* and *hypoxemia* since, during life, complete absence of O$_2$ does not exist for long in any tissue.) There are many causes of anoxia (Table 15), and some of these occur even though pulmonary function is completely normal (p. 149).

The pulmonary physiologist is particularly interested in arterial anoxemia caused by respiratory or pulmonary disease. Any type of alveolar *hypoventilation,* whether due to central respiratory depression or nueromuscular disorder (Table 15, *1,b*) in a patient with normal lungs or due to airway obstruction or rigid lungs or pleura (Table 15, *2,a*), must of course result in lower alveolar Po$_2$ decrease in arterial Po$_2$ and decrease in arterial O$_2$ saturation.

When there is uneven distribution of alveolar gas and blood (Table 15, *2,b*), there must be a decrease in arterial blood Po$_2$ relative to mean alveolar Po$_2$. Unless total alveolar ventilation is increased, this must result in arterial anoxemia (p. 74). However, the patient may increase his total alveolar ventilation enough so that even previously poorly ventilated regions of his lungs receive enough O$_2$ to arterialize the blood flowing through alveolar capillaries there. It is not proper to say that such lungs are functioning normally simply because the patient's arterial O$_2$ saturation is normal; in order to maintain a normal Po$_2$ in some alveoli, he must be hyperventilating others and forcing his respiratory muscles to expend more than the usual amount of energy.

When there is impairment of diffusion (Table 15, *2,c*), arterial Po$_2$ must be low relative to alveolar Po$_2$; but, as emphasized earlier (p. 129), the difference may be insignificant in a resting patient. The great majority of patients who have a significant decrease in pulmonary diffusing capacity for CO still have normal arterial O$_2$ saturation; in many cases, this may be achieved by the hyperventilation characteristic of this disorder.

Intrapulmonary venous-to-arterial shunts (Table 15, *3*) represent a special type of uneven ventilation in relation to blood flow; because some mixed venous blood by-passes ventilated alveoli, both the Po_2 and the saturation of arterial blood must be reduced below normal.

D. DIFFERENTIAL DIAGNOSIS OF ANOXEMIA CAUSED BY RESPIRATORY OR CARDIOPULMONARY DISEASE

HYPOVENTILATION.—This is defined as a decrease in alveolar ventilation per minute in relation to the O_2 consumption of the patient (see Fig. 15 and p. 46). It must be associated with a decrease in calculated alveolar ventilation (Figs. 7, p. 29; 8, p. 30; and 14, p. 43) or an increase in O_2 consumption. Alveolar gas and arterial blood Po_2 must be decreased and arterial Pco_2 must be increased. All of the effects of hypoventilation are corrected by providing *normal* volume of ventilation with *air*. Inhalation of O_2, with continued hypoventilation, will correct the anoxemia but not the CO_2 retention. Many patients with hypoventilation (e.g., during ether, thiopental or cyclopropane anesthesia) have no anoxemia when the inspired gas is rich in O_2; here CO_2 retention (increased end-expired Pco_2; increased arterial blood Pco_2) is the important diagnostic sign.

UNEVEN VENTILATION IN RELATION TO BLOOD FLOW.—This always results in an arterial blood Po_2 that is less than mean alveolar Po_2. When total ventilation is normal, arterial blood Po_2 and saturation must be decreased and Pco_2 must rise. When total ventilation increases, arterial blood Po_2 and saturation may be maintained at normal levels; if the disease is severe, hyperventilation cannot prevent arterial Po_2 and saturation from falling and Pco_2 from rising. Inhalation of O_2 will wash out N_2 even from poorly ventilated alveoli and establish a high alveolar gas Po_2 which results in high arterial blood Po_2 and full saturation of Hb; it will also abolish the alveolar-arterial Po_2 difference due to uneven ventilation/blood flow ratios, thus differentiating it from an anatomic or pathologic venous-to-arterial shunt. Inhalation of O_2 and relief of anoxemia may, however, remove reflexes stimulant to respiration and cause hypoventilation, CO_2 retention and respiratory acidosis (see p. 313).

IMPAIRMENT OF DIFFUSION.—This does not necessarily result in arterial anoxemia (Fig. 38, p. 126), either because of the reserve in the oxygenating mechanism or because of hyperventilation. Anoxemia may be caused or worsened when the patient exercises, because the velocity of pulmonary capillary blood flow increases and shortens the time that the blood remains in contact with the diffusing surface. The alveolar-arterial Po_2 difference increases when the patient breathes 12–14% O_2 (Fig. 39,

p. 128). Anoxemia, if present, is corrected by inhalation of O_2, which also abolishes any alveolar-arterial PO_2 difference due to impairment of diffusion; the very high initial gradient for PO_2 diffusion (alveolar gas = >600 mm Hg; mixed venous blood = 40 mm Hg) rapidly saturates Hb and the capillary blood then comes into tension equilibrium rapidly with alveolar gas (O_2 behaves like an inert gas once Hb is fully saturated).

Since CO_2 diffuses 20 times as rapidly as O_2 through the alveolar capillary membranes, CO_2 retention does not occur, with the possible exception of a patient with very serious impairment of diffusion kept alive only by breathing 100% O_2. As a rule, blood CO_2 is *low*, because either the anoxemia or the disease process in the lungs causes reflex hyperventilation.

VENOUS-TO-ARTERIAL SHUNTS.—The arterial blood PO_2 and saturation must be low even if the patient is hyperventilating. Inhalation of O_2 cannot oxygenate the blood fully (p. 103). If the shunt is large, inhalation of O_2 may increase arterial O_2 saturation 8–10% (e.g., from 70 to 80%). If the shunt is small, inhalation of O_2 may result in 100% saturation of arterial blood (e.g., from 93 to 100%) but *will never bring the dissolved O_2 or arterial PO_2 to maximal values (>600 mm Hg). This is the only type of anoxemia in which inhalation of O_2 will not eventually increase arterial blood PO_2 to >600 mm Hg.*

Exercise usually results in a further decrease in arterial blood PO_2 and saturation because the shunted venous blood contains less O_2. Inhalation of 12–14% O_2 almost eliminates the alveolar-arterial PO_2 difference, because of the shape of the O_2 dissociation curve (Fig. 41, p. 142).

Carbon dioxide tension in the arterial blood may be elevated if the shunt is very large. However, if the lungs are normal and capable of increased ventilation, arterial PCO_2 may remain normal. If anoxemia is severe and results in hyperventilation, arterial PCO_2 may be below normal. Long-standing, severe anoxemia often causes *metabolic* acidosis, hyperventilation and decreased arterial PCO_2 on that account.

Combinations of these four types of anoxemia may occur in the same individual. A patient under anesthesia may have both hypoventilation and uneven ventilation in relation to blood flow. A patient with an open hemithorax may have hypoventilation, uneven ventilation in relation to blood flow and venous-to-arterial shunts. A patient with severe emphysema may have hypoventilation, variations in ventilation/blood flow ratios and impaired diffusion.

It must be emphasized that anoxemia is not always present, even in serious pulmonary disease. When diseased areas of the lungs receive *no* blood supply (as in some patients with carcinoma, cysts or tuberculous lesions), arterial O_2 saturation remains normal as long as there is sufficient normal pulmonary tissue; even after pneumonectomy, arterial O_2 saturation can be normal, at least in a resting patient, if the remaining lung is healthy.

E. NON-PULMONARY AND NON-RESPIRATORY CAUSES OF ANOXIA

Not all anoxemia or anoxia is caused by pulmonary or respiratory disorders. Table 15, *1,a,* shows that a decrease in the Po_2 of inspired gas

TABLE 15.—CAUSES OF ANOXIA

($\uparrow$ = increased; $\leftrightarrow$ = no change; $\downarrow$ = decreased)

CAUSE OF ANOXIA	EFFECT ON ARTERIAL BLOOD			
	O_2 Tension	O_2 Content	O_2 Saturation	CO_2 Tension
1. Normal lungs but inadequate oxygenation				
a) Deficiency of O_2 in atmosphere (decreased ambient pressure; addition of other gases to air)	$\downarrow$	$\downarrow$	$\downarrow$	$\downarrow$
b) Hypoventilation (neuromuscular disorders)	$\downarrow$	$\downarrow$	$\downarrow$	$\uparrow$
2. Pulmonary disease				
a) Hypoventilation due to airway or pulmonary disease	$\downarrow$	$\downarrow$	$\downarrow$	$\uparrow$
b) Uneven distribution of alveolar gas and/or pul. capillary blood flow	$\downarrow$*	$\downarrow$*	$\downarrow$*	$\downarrow$, $\leftrightarrow$ or $\uparrow$
c) Impairment of diffusion	$\downarrow$*	$\downarrow$*	$\downarrow$*	$\downarrow$
3. Venous-to-arterial shunts (intrapulmonary or intracardiac)	$\downarrow$	$\downarrow$	$\downarrow$	$\downarrow$, $\leftrightarrow$ or $\uparrow$
4. Inadequate transport and delivery of O_2				
a) Anemia; abnormal (inactive) Hb	$\leftrightarrow$	$\downarrow$	$\leftrightarrow$†	$\leftrightarrow$
b) General circulatory deficiency	$\leftrightarrow$	$\leftrightarrow$	$\leftrightarrow$	$\leftrightarrow$
c) Localized circulatory deficiency (peripheral, cerebral, coronary vessels)	$\leftrightarrow$	$\leftrightarrow$	$\leftrightarrow$	$\leftrightarrow$
5. Inadequate tissue oxygenation				
a) Tissue edema	$\leftrightarrow$	$\leftrightarrow$	$\leftrightarrow$	$\leftrightarrow$
b) Abnormal tissue demand	$\leftrightarrow$	$\leftrightarrow$	$\leftrightarrow$	$\leftrightarrow$
c) Poisoning of cellular enzymes	$\leftrightarrow$	$\leftrightarrow$	$\leftrightarrow$	$\leftrightarrow$

* Unless the patient is hyperventilating.
† Saturation of *active* hemoglobin is normal.

(such as occurs at high altitudes and in a mixture of 90% N_2O–10% O_2) must lead to a decrease in arterial Po_2 and saturation, even though the lungs and respiratory system are normal. Again, intracardiac venous-to-arterial shunts (septal defects) cause anoxemia (Table 15, *3*) even though the lungs are normal. A reduction in active Hb, due either to a decrease in total Hb (anemia) or to a decrease in active, O_2-carrying Hb (caused by CO poisoning or methemoglobinemia) causes anoxemia (Table 15, *4,a*) thought neither the arterial Po_2 nor the saturation of the active Hb is reduced. Hypotension and shock, or localized circulatory obstructions, cause tissue anoxia without anoxemia because of decreased blood flow to the tissues per minute (Table 15, *4,b* and *c*). Tissue edema (by causing capillary-tissue block), abnormally high O_2 requirements, or poisoning of cellular enzymes can also lead to tissue anoxia in the absence of anoxemia (Table 15, *5,a, b* and *c*).

The measurement of arterial blood Po_2 or of O_2 saturation does not provide information regarding the Po_2 of any particular *tissue*. Tissue Po_2 may be estimated by the use of special tissue O_2 electrodes or inferred from measurements of the Po_2 of venous blood coming from an organ; these measurements, however, do not indicate whether *all* cells of the tissue are exposed to this Po_2 or are utilizing O_2.

Anoxemia could also occur because of a shift in the dissociation curve of Hb, so that less O_2 combines with Hb at a given Po_2 ("shift of the curve to the right"). This occurs when the blood Pco_2 is high, the pH is low or the blood temperature is increased (see Fig. 41, p. 142). Similar "shifts to the right" have been reported in natives living at high altitudes and in children 2–10 years of age. A "shift to the left" (greater affinity of O_2 for Hb) occurs in the fetus because of the existence of the special compound, fetal hemoglobin. Electrolyte imbalance within the red blood cell may also change the curve, but this aspect has been little studied.

F. EFFECTS OF ANOXEMIA AND ANOXIA

Anoxemia does not necessarily produce disability or even symptoms. Healthy people live long and active lives at high altitudes with arterial blood O_2 saturations in the 85–95% range. Few patients with cardio-pulmonary disease have an O_2 saturation less than 85% (exceptions are patients with large right-to-left shunts and patients with very severe pulmonary disease). Therefore few patients with chronic pulmonary disease are disabled because of chronic anoxemia; disability usually arises from mechanical factors and is rarely relieved by correction of anoxemia by O_2 therapy.

Moderate anoxia can cause changes in cerebral function, generally manifested as mental confusion and restlessness. More severe anoxia may cause dimness of vision, reduced efficiency, impaired judgment, changes in disposition and dulling of mental power. Very severe anoxia causes delirium and unconsciousness.

Chronic anoxemia is usually associated with compensatory mechanisms: an increase in tidal volume and frequency of breathing (p. 53), tachycardia with only slight increase in systolic and diastolic blood pressure, polycythemia and an increase in the density of systemic capillary bed per unit of active tissue. All of these combine to increase the O_2 available to the cells of the body.

The lower limit of arterial O_2 saturation compatible with moderately active existence depends on the abruptness with which the anoxemia develops, the effectiveness of compensatory mechanisms and other limiting factors in the disease process. Certainly in patients with congenital heart disease or pulmonary hemangiomas, the saturation may be well below 80% without producing disability. On the other hand, an asthmatic patient may, by increased effort, succeed in maintaining adequate alveolar gas exchange and normal arterial O_2 saturation, but only by performing an inordinate amount of work which results in dyspnea and pulmonary disability (see p. 260). Patients with pulmonary emphysema may be disabled despite the fact that arterial O_2 saturation is between 90 and 95%; in this disease, the arterial O_2 saturation depends on the minute volume of breathing and the distribution of inspired gas and capillary blood to the alveoli, whereas disability is probably more closely related to the mechanical factors involved in ventilation.

II. Arterial Carbon Dioxide and pH

Inspired air contains insignificant amounts (0.04%) of CO_2. Unless CO_2 has been added to inspired gas, the CO_2 of venous blood, alveolar gas and arterial blood originates in tissue metabolism. Carbon dioxide diffuses from tissue cells into the capillary blood and is carried in chemical combination and in physical solution in the venous blood to the lungs, where a part of it diffuses into alveolar gas and is eliminated in the expired gas.

A. CO_2 TRANSPORT

The loading, transport and unloading of CO_2 are described in detail in Davenport's monograph *The ABC of Acid-Base Chemistry*. Stated briefly, the processes involved in loading and transport are:

1. *Diffusion of CO_2 from tissue cells into capillary blood.*—In actively metabolizing cells, tissue P_{CO_2} is greater than the P_{CO_2} of arterial blood flowing through systemic capillaries. Carbon dioxide therefore diffuses from the cells into the plasma.

2. *Chemical reactions in the plasma.*—(*a*) Some CO_2 dissolves in the plasma. A very small amount of this reacts slowly with water to form carbonic acid ($H_2O + CO_2 \rightleftharpoons H_2CO_3$). This H_2CO_3 dissociates into $H^+ + HCO_3^-$ and the H^+ is buffered by plasma buffering systems.

(*b*) Dissolved CO_2 in plasma reacts with the amino group of plasma proteins to form carbamino compounds.

3. *Chemical reactions within the erythrocyte.*—Most of the CO_2 that diffuses from tissue cells into the plasma passes into the erythrocytes. Intra-erythrocytic CO_2 reacts in three ways:

(*a*) Some remains within the red blood cell as dissolved CO_2.

(*b*) Some combines with the NH_2 groups of Hb to form carbamino compounds.

$$R - NH_2 + CO_2 \rightleftharpoons R - NHCOO^- + H^+$$

This is a very rapid chemical reaction which requires no special catalyst. The H^+ is buffered by portions of the Hb molecule (isohydric reaction). This process is facilitated by the simultaneous loss of O_2 from capillary blood to the tissues ($HbO_2 \rightleftharpoons Hb + O_2$) because the conversion of oxyhemoglobin to reduced Hb causes Hb to become a weaker acid and to take up additional H^+ with little change in pH.

(*c*) Some CO_2 combines with water to form H_2CO_3, which then dissociates to form H^+ and HCO_3^- ions. The conversion of CO_2 and H_2O into H_2CO_3 is a very rapid reaction only because of the presence of an enzyme, carbonic anhydrase. Carbonic anhydrase is concentrated within the erythrocyte, and this reaction (the hydration of CO_2) is an important and rapid one in blood only within red blood cells.

This reaction results in the formation of H^+ ions which are also buffered by chemical groups of the Hb molecule with minimal change in pH (isohydric reaction); like the reaction in 3(*b*), this is aided by simultaneous conversion of some HbO_2 to Hb as O_2 passes into the tissues.

This reaction also results in the accumulation of a high level of HCO_3^- ions within the red blood cell. Bicarbonate ions then diffuse into the plasma to re-establish equilibrium of HCO_3^- between cells and plasma. If this diffusion of anions were accompanied by diffusion of an equal number of cations, electrical neutrality of the erythrocyte would be maintained. However, the red cell membrane is not freely permeable to cations and so anions from the plasma (Cl^-) diffuse into the erythrocyte (chloride shift) to achieve electrical neutrality. (Some movement of water inward occurs simultaneously to maintain osmotic equilibrium; this results in a slight swelling of erythrocytes in venous blood, relative to those in arterial blood.)

The reverse of the foregoing reactions occurs in the pulmonary capillaries when O_2 is added and CO_2 is unloaded.

Several points are of especial interest:

(1) Although plasma contains much more CO_2 (in all forms) than do the red blood cells (in all forms), and although the plasma *transports* more than 60% of CO_2 added to capillary blood, the chemical reactions within the red blood cell provide practically all of the additional bicarbonate ions transported in the plasma. If the enzyme carbonic anhydrase is completely inhibited, the reaction $CO_2 + H_2O \rightleftharpoons H_2CO_3$ proceeds slowly and is not complete in the systemic capillary or even in the time that the blood flows through the veins en route to the heart. The reverse reaction, $H_2CO_3 \rightleftharpoons CO_2 + H_2O$, which normally occurs during the time that venous blood is in the pulmonary capillaries, is also slow in the absence of carbonic anhydrase and continues long after the blood has left the pulmonary capillaries and entered the systemic circulation. Therefore, after inhibition of carbonic anhydrase (as by administration of large doses of Diamox), the Pco_2 continues to decrease in venous blood until it reaches the pulmonary capillaries, where some CO_2 is excreted; however, Pco_2 rises as blood flows through the systemic arteries and the *un*loading reaction goes slowly to completion. The net result is a rise in tissue Pco_2. The precise dynamics are not known because blood Pco_2 methods are inaccurate when carbonic anhydrase has been inhibited; there is no instantaneous method for measuring Pco_2 in blood.

(2) Carbon dioxide loading and O_2 unloading in body tissue capillaries are mutually helpful; an increase in capillary blood Pco_2 (and decrease in pH) facilitates the unloading of O_2 (the Bohr effect), and the unloading of O_2 (change from HbO_2 to Hb) facilitates the loading of CO_2 (the Haldane effect). This is pictured in Figures 41 and 42.

(3) Just as the amount of O_2 carried by the blood is related to the Po_2 to which blood is exposed, so the amount of CO_2 in blood is related to the Pco_2 of the blood. The CO_2 dissociation curve is pictured in Fig-

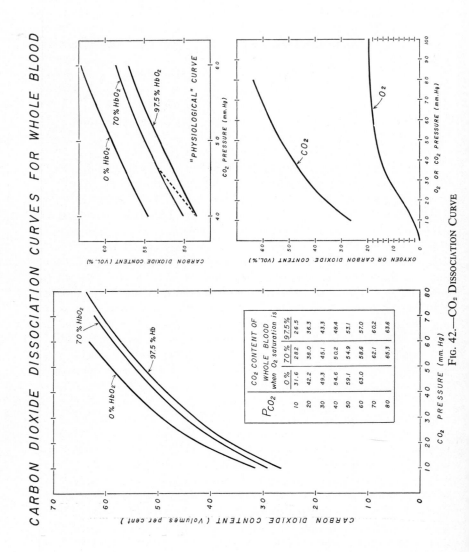

CARBON DIOXIDE DISSOCIATION CURVES FOR WHOLE BLOOD

P_{CO_2}	CO₂ CONTENT OF WHOLE BLOOD when O₂ saturation is		
	0%	70%	97.5%
10	31.6	28.2	26.5
20	42.2	38.0	36.3
30	49.3	45.1	43.3
40	54.6	50.2	48.4
50	59.1	54.9	53.1
60	63.0	58.6	57.0
70	—	62.1	60.2
80	65.3	65.3	63.6

Fig. 42.—CO₂ Dissociation Curve

154

ure 42. Note that in the physiologic range of CO_2 content and tension, the relationship between the two is almost linear, whereas the O_2 dissociation curve is S-shaped.

B. METHODS FOR MEASURING CO_2 AND pH

CARBON DIOXIDE IN BLOOD.—It is obvious from the previous section that CO_2 content or CO_2 tension may be measured; it is also evident that the CO_2 content of whole blood, of plasma, and of red blood cells will be different (Table 14, p. 145). As a rule, arterial CO_2 content is measured in whole blood (handled under anaerobic conditions), because this measurement can be made as part of the determination of arterial blood O_2 content. Knowing the proportion of cells to plasma (hematocrit), one can determine the plasma CO_2 content from a nomogram. Then, if the pH is known, the P_{CO_2} can be calculated by application of the Henderson-Hasselbalch equation.

$$pH = pK + \log \frac{[HCO_3^-]}{[CO_2]}$$

This equation requires knowledge of plasma $[HCO_3^-]$ and $[CO_2]$ separately, whereas the laboratory test provides a value only for *total* CO_2 (or $[HCO_3^-] + [CO_2]$). The problem is resolved by substituting in the numerator "total $CO_2 - [CO_2]$" (which $= [HCO_3^-]$). Then

$$pH = pK + \log \frac{\text{total } CO_2 - [CO_2]}{[CO_2]}$$

Since $[CO_2] =$ the partial pressure of $CO_2 \times$ the solubility coefficient α, the equation becomes

$$pH = pK + \log \frac{\text{total } CO_2 - \alpha\, P_{CO_2}}{\alpha\, P_{CO_2}}$$

◄──◄ FIG. 42.—The large graph shows relationship between P_{CO_2} and CO_2 content of whole blood; this varies with changes in saturation of hemoglobin with O_2. Thus, CO_2 tension of the blood influences oxygen saturation ("Bohr effect"), and oxygen saturation of the blood influences CO_2 content ("Haldane effect"). The O_2-CO_2 diagram (Fig. 61, p. 346), by combining much of Figures 41 and 42 into one, gives the correct figure for both CO_2 and O_2 at every P_{O_2} and P_{CO_2}.

Above right: Greatly magnified portion of the large graph to show the change that occurs as mixed venous blood (70% HbO_2, P_{CO_2} 46 mm Hg) passes through the pulmonary capillaries and becomes arterial blood (97.5% HbO_2, P_{CO_2} 40 mm Hg). Dashed line is a hypothetical transition between the two curves. *Below right:* O_2 and CO_2 dissociation curves plotted on same scale to show the important point that the O_2 curve has a very steep and a very flat portion and the CO_2 curve does not.

pK for the bicarbonate/CO_2 buffer system $= 6.1$, and $\alpha = 0.0301$. Knowing pH and total plasma CO_2, plasma P_{CO_2} can be calculated.

Arterial blood P_{CO_2} can be determined directly by the bubble equilibration technique of Riley or by the CO_2 electrode of Severinghaus. The latter will probably become the method of choice. The CO_2 electrode is a glass electrode covered by a membrane freely permeable to CO_2. Carbon dioxide diffuses through the membrane and forms H_2CO_3 in the watery film; the H_2CO_3 dissociates in H^+ and HCO_3^- ions, and the former are measured by the glass electrode.

CARBON DIOXIDE IN GAS.—Because gas and blood P_{CO_2} are assumed to be equal across the membranes of any single alveolus, alveolar gas P_{CO_2} is often measured (spot samples, or continuous infra-red analysis) and assumed to equal arterial blood P_{CO_2}. This estimate is probably accurate in individuals with normal lungs, but may be seriously in error when the patient has a large venous-to-arterial shunt, pulmonary vascular occlusion, serious maldistribution of blood and gas, rapid and shallow breathing or has received large doses of Diamox.

Mixed venous blood P_{CO_2} is usually about 6 mm Hg greater than arterial blood P_{CO_2}. If end-expired P_{CO_2} exceeds 50 mm Hg, it is certain that mixed venous blood P_{CO_2} is abnormally high (if the patient is at rest) and reasonably certain that arterial blood P_{CO_2} is greater than normal. It is easy to detect hypoventilation (e.g., during anesthesia, in patients in respirators) when end-expired P_{CO_2} is definitely in an abnormal range (if the patient is not rebreathing through an abnormally large dead space).

ARTERIAL BLOOD PH.—If one knows plasma CO_2 content and tension, one can calculate plasma pH by use of the Henderson-Hasselbalch equation. In general, it is well to measure pH of blood directly, using a glass electrode, anaerobic techniques and temperature control or temperature corrections.

C. SIGNIFICANCE OF CHANGES IN ARTERIAL BLOOD P_{CO_2}

INCREASE IN ARTERIAL BLOOD P_{CO_2}.—This must mean either that the whole lung or a major portion of it is hypoventilated (see Table 3, p. 45). Arterial P_{CO_2} is never increased by pure impairment of diffusion. It may be increased slightly by a venous-to-arterial shunt, though as a rule hyperventilation reduces the P_{CO_2} in the alveolar capillary blood sufficiently to compensate for the higher P_{CO_2} in shunted blood. When there is uneven distribution of gas in relation to blood, arterial P_{CO_2} will rise if alveolar ventilation is decreased or normal; it will also rise if total alveolar ventilation is increased if the major portion of the alveolar ventilation is going to regions with little pulmonary capillary blood flow.

Whenever there is pulmonary insufficiency for CO_2, there must be pulmonary insufficiency for O_2 as well, unless high concentrations of O_2 are breathed.

DECREASE IN ARTERIAL BLOOD P_{CO_2}.—This occurs whenever all or a major portion of the lungs is being hyperventilated (see p. 50).

Arterial blood P_{CO_2} may be normal or even low in patients with uneven distribution. The shapes of O_2 and CO_2 dissociation curves (Figs. 15, p. 46; 41, p. 142, and 42, p. 154) are such that a hyperventilated area can compensate or more than compensate for a poorly ventilated region with respect to CO_2 but not to O_2. For example, in patients with emphysema, a region with a low ventilation/blood flow ratio tends to cause anoxemia and CO_2 retention (Fig. 15, *left*), but an area with a high ventilation/blood flow ratio can contribute little additional O_2 to the blood though it can "blow off" enough CO_2 to keep arterial P_{CO_2} normal or low (Fig. 15, *right*).

NORMAL ARTERIAL BLOOD P_{CO_2}.—This does not exclude pulmonary disease. Patients with a major reduction in functioning pulmonary tissue (pneumonectomy, pulmonary embolism) or other types of disease (pulmonary vascular disease, impairment of diffusion) may have normal arterial blood P_{CO_2} if their alveolar ventilation matches the metabolic rate of the body. It is possible to have severe pulmonary disability, because of mechanical difficulties in breathing, without having an elevated P_{CO_2}; in fact the increased work of breathing which keeps arterial blood P_{CO_2} normal may be responsible for the dyspnea and disability.

D. EFFECTS OF MARKED DEVIATIONS IN ARTERIAL BLOOD P_{CO_2}

A marked decrease in arterial blood P_{CO_2} (caused by hyperventilation) is associated with light-headedness, confusion (associated with a decrease in cerebral blood flow), numbness and tingling in the face and extremities, tachycardia, cutaneous vasoconstriction and eventually actual tetany.

A pronounced increase in arterial blood P_{CO_2} causes cerebral vasodilatation and increased intracranial pressure and is associated with headache, dizziness, disorientation, mental clouding, analgesia, unconsciousness and anesthesia. Other symptoms include hypertension, tachycardia, palpitation and sweating.

The symptoms associated with increase or decrease in arterial P_{CO_2} are far less severe when hypoventilation or hyperventilation is chronic. For example, we have seen a healthy man become completely unresponsive after inhalation of 10% CO_2 in air for 3 min, but have observed a patient with arterial blood P_{CO_2} between 100 and 140 mm Hg for more than a year who was mentally alert throughout.

E. CARBON DIOXIDE, pH AND ACID-BASE BALANCE

The elimination of CO_2 is of great importance in the regulation of acid base balance because $CO_2 + H_2O \rightleftharpoons H_2CO_3$, or carbonic acid. Since several excellent monographs discuss the subject of acid-base balance in great detail, only a few important points will be discussed here.

1. The lungs are the most important organ in the body for acid excretion. In ordinary circumstances, the kidney excretes 40–80 mEq/day (of *fixed* acids), whereas the lungs excrete about 13,000 mEq (of carbonic acid). Although concentrations of carbonic acid and bicarbonate are measured clinically as volumes per cent of CO_2, it is important in an analysis of acid-base balance to convert volumes per cent CO_2 into mM or mEq/L, since sodium and chloride are always expressed as mEq/L. Dividing volumes per cent CO_2 by 2.23 converts the concentration to mM or mEq/L.* Thus

$$\frac{59.6 \text{ vol } \%}{2.23} = 26.6 \text{ mM/L}$$

2. Although in a chemical sense the HCO_3^-/CO_2 system is a poor buffer in blood, it is important physiologically in maintaining the normal pH of the blood, because HCO_3^- can be regulated by the kidneys and CO_2 by the lungs. The Henderson-Hasselbalch equation states that it is the *ratio* of HCO_3^-/CO_2 that determines blood pH, rather than the absolute amounts of each.

---

* The factor 2.23 is obtained as follows:
    1 mole (1 gram molecular weight) of CO_2 occupies 22.3 liters or 22,300 ml
    1 millimole (mM) (1/1000 of a gram molecular weight of CO_2 occupies
        22.3 ml
  1 mM Co_2/L blood = 22.3 ml gas/L blood
                 = 2.23 ml gas/100 ml blood
Therefore   1 mM/L = 2.23 volumes per cent

$$pH = pK + \log \frac{[HCO_3^-]}{[CO_2]^\dagger} \qquad (1)$$

The pK for this system is 6.1. Values for HCO_3^- and CO_2 are given in Table 14. Substituting in equation (1):

$$pH = 6.1 + \log \frac{56.8 \text{ vol\% } CO_2}{2.84 \text{ vol\% } CO_2} \text{ or } \frac{25.4 \text{ mM } CO_2/L}{1.27 \text{ mM } CO_2/L} \qquad (2)$$

In either case

$$pH = 6.1 + \log 20$$
$$= 6.1 + 1.30$$
$$= 7.40$$

The pH would still be 7.40 if both $[HCO_3^-]$ and $[CO_2]$ doubled $\left(\frac{113.6}{5.68}\right)$, or were halved $\left(\frac{28.4}{1.42}\right)$, since the ratio remains 20/1.

3. Normally, this ratio is maintained by pulmonary ventilation which keeps arterial P_{CO_2} at 41 mm Hg at sea level (equivalent to a dissolved CO_2 of 2.84 vol%).‡ Whenever arterial P_{CO_2} tends to rise, the medullary respiratory center is stimulated, alveolar ventilation is increased and the P_{CO_2} is restored to normal. This delicate mechanism operates only when the sensitivity of the respiratory center is normal, the nervous connections between the center and the respiratory muscles are intact, the respiratory muscles are normal and the lung is not seriously diseased. Whenever hypoventilation occurs (see Table 3, p. 45), either because of depression of the neuromuscular mechanisms or because of mechanical limitations, CO_2 must accumulate in the blood. The very first change is in the dissolved CO_2 or $[CO_2]$. If arterial P_{CO_2} rises to 51 mm Hg, the $[CO_2]$ increases to 1.6 mM/L and equation (1) becomes:

$$pH = 6.1 + \log \frac{25.4 \text{ mM } CO_2/L}{1.6 \text{ mM } CO_2/L} \qquad (3)$$
$$= 6.1 + \log 16$$
$$= 6.1 + 1.20 = 7.30$$

According to equation (3), the total increase in CO_2 is 0.3 mM/L, all of which is due to the increase in $[CO_2]$. However, Figure 42 (p. 154)

---

† The denominator $[CO_2]$ is sometimes written as $[H_2CO_3]$. Actually, both dissolved CO_2 and H_2CO_3 are present, since $CO_2 + H_2O \rightleftharpoons H_2CO_3$, but at equilibrium the concentration of dissolved CO_2 in the plasma is almost 1000 times that of H_2CO_3.

‡ "Normal" values for arterial P_{CO_2} have been reported as 39, 40 or 41 mm Hg; the value of 41 is used in Albritton's *Standard Values in Blood* (Philadelphia: W. B. Saunders Company, 1952).

shows that an increase of 10 mm Hg P_{CO_2} leads to a much greater increase in total blood CO_2 than 0.3 mM/L. The additional CO_2 represents an increment in $[HCO_3^-]$. What is the origin of this increase in $[HCO_3^-]$? When hypoventilation occurs and blood P_{CO_2} rises, the increase in $[CO_2]$ drives the reaction to the right:

$$CO_2 + H_2O \rightleftharpoons H_2CO_3 \rightleftharpoons H^+ + HCO_3^-$$

Some of the increment of H^+ ion is neutralized by blood buffers (especially by Hb protein) with an increase in $[HCO_3^-]$. The H^+ ions not neutralized cause a decrease in blood pH. In the case mentioned, the increase in the $[HCO_3^-]$ of the *numerator* occurs almost simultaneously with the increase in the *denominator* and results in a ratio of about 17:1 instead of 16:1 and a pH of 7.34 instead of 7.30.

When CO_2 is retained more gradually, renal compensation has time to occur. The renal tubular cells secrete a more acid urine by exchanging H^+ for Na^+; the H^+ is excreted as HCl or NH_4Cl (the tubular cells can form NH_4^+) and HCO_3^- is reabsorbed. (The bicarbonate ion eventually returned to the extracellular fluid and plasma in combination with sodium is not the filtered anion but rather the intracellular anion derived from $CO_2 + H_2O \rightleftharpoons H_2CO_3 \rightleftharpoons H^+ + HCO^-_3$, but the end-result is the same as if $NaHCO_3$ per se had been reabsorbed.)

If renal compensation were complete, equation (2) would become

$$pH = 6.1 + \log \frac{32 \text{ mM } CO_2/L}{1.6 \text{ mM } CO_2/L} \qquad (4)$$

$$= 6.1 + \log 20 = 6.1 + 1.30 = 7.40$$

However, it is important to note three points:

a) Renal compensation is rarely perfect, and the arterial pH is usually less than normal.

b) When arterial P_{CO_2} rises (respiratory acidosis), the concentrations of arterial CO_2 and HCO_3^- increase and total blood CO_2 must rise. When such blood is sent to the chemistry laboratory for determination of total plasma CO_2, the laboratory report is: "The plasma CO_2 is increased." Most physicians have learned by rote that an *increase* in CO_2 content represents *alkalosis*. As a result, it is difficult for them to accept the statement that increased plasma (or blood) CO_2 content may and very often does occur in *acidosis* (respiratory acidosis). The physician must remember that total blood CO_2 content can be either *high* or *low* in either *acidosis* or *alkalosis*. Thus:

Total blood CO_2 will be *high* in *respiratory acidosis* and *metabolic alkalosis*.

Total blood CO_2 will be *low* in *respiratory alkalosis* and *metabolic acidosis*.

Therefore, data on total blood CO_2 should always be accompanied by a measurement of pH and a calculation of plasma P_{CO_2}. If the arterial pH is low and the P_{CO_2} is high, respiratory acidosis is present. If the arterial pH is high and the P_{CO_2} is low, respiratory alkalosis is present.

If pH and P_{CO_2} measurements cannot be made, blood CO_2 data must be interpreted only after evaluation of the patient's pulmonary status.

c) Renal compensation for respiratory acidosis involves the excretion of NH_4Cl instead of $NaCl$. Sodium normally combined with Cl in the blood as neutral $NaCl$ is now combined as $NaHCO_3$. Therefore, although the plasma Na concentration does not decrease, plasma Cl concentration does. As a rule, in compensated or partly compensated respiratory acidosis, plasma Cl in mEq/L decreases by the same amount that plasma HCO_3 increases.

SUMMARY

Anoxemia may be due to pulmonary disease that causes inadequate alveolar ventilation, uneven alveolar ventilation in relation to pulmonary capillary blood flow, impaired diffusion or venous-to-arterial shunts. Measurement of O_2 content, capacity and tension of arterial blood sampled while the patient breathes air and again while he breathes O_2 often provides data for differential diagnosis. The CO_2 tension of arterial blood or alveolar gas rises when the patient has pulmonary insufficiency; if there is no renal compensation, this leads to respiratory acidosis. Measurement of both pH and CO_2 tension of arterial blood permits differential diagnosis between metabolic alkalosis and respiratory acidosis.

CHAPTER 7

Mechanics of Breathing

PULMONARY GAS exchange requires flow of gas and blood to the alveoli and alveolar capillaries. In Chapter 4, we discussed the pressures and resistances which determine the flow of mixed venous blood to the alveolar capillaries; here we shall discuss the forces and resistances which determine the flow of gas in and out of the lungs.

Patients with pulmonary disease usually consult a physician because of difficulty in breathing. Pulmonary function tests are valuable in such patients in determining the specific cause of the mechanical problem, its severity and the most effective form of therapy. However, interpretation of physiologic data requires an understanding of the general principles governing the flow of air through tubes and the fundamental factors involved in the mechanics of breathing.

Air flows from a region of higher pressure to one of lower pressure. At end-expiration, when there is no air flow, alveolar gas pressure is equal to atmospheric pressure. If air is to flow into the alveoli, the alveolar pressure must be less than atmospheric during inspiration. Active contraction of the inspiratory muscles enlarges the thorax and further lowers intrathoracic pressure (normally subatmospheric, because the elastic lung tends to recoil inward, away from the thoracic cage). The decrease in intrathoracic pressure enlarges the alveoli, expands the alveolar gas and lowers the total alveolar gas pressure to less than atmospheric so that air flows into the alveoli.

During inspiration, active muscular contraction provides (*a*) the force necessary to overcome elastic recoil of the lungs and thorax, (*b*) the force required to overcome frictional resistance during movement of the tissues of the lung and thorax and (*c*) the force necessary to overcome frictional resistance to air flow through the hundreds of thousands of fine tubes and ducts of the tracheobronchial tree.

At end-inspiration, potential energy created by contraction of the inspiratory muscles is stored in the elastic tissues of the lungs and thorax. When the muscles of inspiration relax and no longer exert a force which distends the lungs and thorax, the elastic tissues of the lungs and thorax now recoil. If non-elastic tissue resistance and airway resistance are negligible, the elastic recoil causes the lungs and thorax to return very rapidly to the resting expiratory level even though expiration is completely passive. When the expiratory resistances opposing elastic recoil are abnormally great, active contraction of expiratory muscles may be needed, unless the time for expiration is long (see p. 187).

A. COMPLIANCE OF LUNGS AND THORAX

Elasticity is a property of matter that causes it to return to its resting shape after having been distorted by some external force. A perfectly elastic body, such as the spring in the upper part of Figure 43, will obey Hooke's law; i.e., when it is acted upon by 1 unit of force it will stretch 1 unit of length, when acted upon by 2 units of force it will stretch 2 units, and so on, until the elastic limit is reached or exceeded.

Some tissues of the lungs and thorax possess the property of elasticity. Like springs, these tissues must be stretched during inspiration by an external force (muscular effort); when the external force is removed, the tissues recoil to their resting position. Since elastic tissues obey Hooke's law just as springs do, springs are used in Figure 43 to depict the elastic properties of the lungs. The greater the muscular force applied, the more the springs are stretched and the greater the volume change on inspiration. This relation between force and stretch or between pressure and volume is dependent only on the change in distance or volume, measured under static conditions, and not on the speed with which the new position or volume is attained. The slope of the line that results from plotting the external force (pressure) against the increase in volume serves as a measure of the stiffness of the "springs" or the distensibility of the lungs and thorax; if the slope is more nearly vertical, the tissues are more distensible, and if more nearly horizontal, they are "stiffer."

Physiologists call this the "mechanical compliance" or, more simply, the "compliance" of the tissues; it is defined as the volume change per unit pressure change, and its units are L/cm H_2O.

Compliance is sometimes referred to as "elastic resistance."[*] In the

---

[*] "Elastance," which is the reciprocal of compliance, is an older term and no longer in common use.

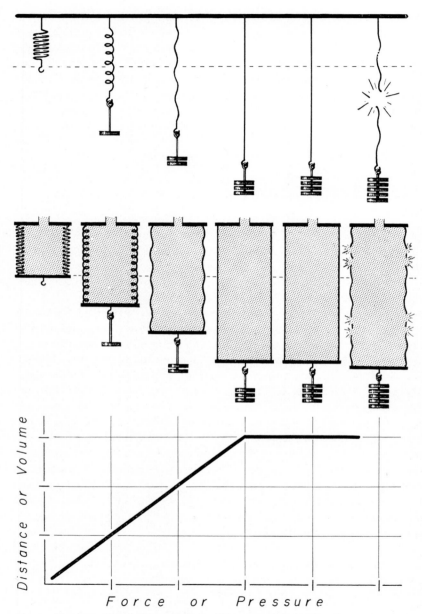

FIG. 43.—HOOKE'S LAW APPLIED TO A SPRING AND TO THE LUNGS

popular usage of the word "resistance," tissues with elastic properties do offer "resistance" to stretch. However, in scientific usage (electricity, aerodynamics), *resistance* involves a relationship between pressure and *flow* and is measured during motion, not under static conditions. Therefore we shall use *compliance* in considering *static* pressure-volume relationships and *resistance* in speaking of *dynamic* pressure-flow relationships (Table 16).

TABLE 16.—MEASUREMENT OF COMPLIANCE AND RESISTANCE

	DEFINITION	UNITS	MEASUREMENTS REQUIRED	CONDITIONS OF MEASUREMENT
Compliance	Volume change produced by a unit pressure change	$L/cm\ H_2O$	Pressure & volume	Static
Resistance	Pressure differential required for a unit flow change	$cm\ H_2O/L/sec$	Pressure & flow	Dynamic

The system pictured in Figure 43 is a single elastic system; it has only one set of "springs." Actually, the elastic forces can be analyzed in terms of the elastic properties of the *lungs* ("lung springs") and the elastic properties of the thoracic cage ("thoracic springs") (Fig. 44). The resting position of the lungs alone (out of the thorax, exposed to atmospheric pressure and with no stretching force applied) is at the minimal air volume, which is less than residual volume. The resting position of the thoracic cage alone (lungs removed and no stretching or compressing force applied) is at a much greater volume, estimated by some to be about 55% of the vital capacity. The resting position of the lungs *and* thoracic cage, held *together* normally by the pleural surfaces, is somewhere between these two positions. This balanced or neutral position is called the *resting expiratory level,* and the contained gas volume at this level is the *functional residual capacity* (FRC). At this position, the "lung springs" are somewhat stretched and the thoracic springs somewhat compressed. Muscular energy is necessary to unbalance the lung-

◄━━━◀ FIG. 43.—For an elastic structure, the increase in length (or volume) varies directly with the increase in force (or pressure) until the elastic limit is reached. This linear relationship applies equally to normal lungs, over the physiologic range.

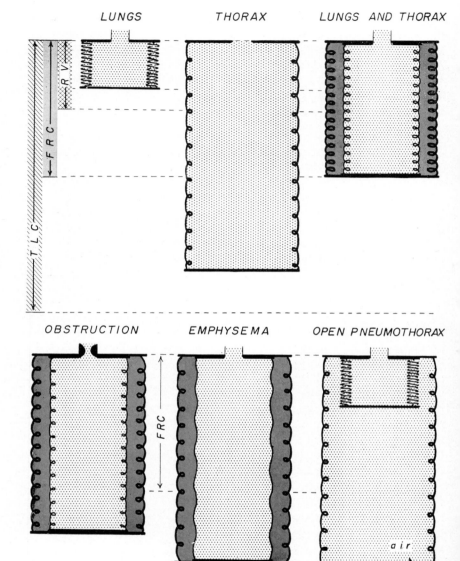

FIG. 44.—ELASTICITY OF THE LUNGS AND THORAX

166

thoracic cage system toward either inspiration or further expiration. When the lungs and thoracic cage are acting together as a unit (as they normally do), they require more force for expansion to a given volume than does either component alone. Thus, if the compliance of the lung is 0.2 L/cm H_2O and that of the thoracic cage is also 0.2 L/cm H_2O, the compliance of the lungs and thoracic cage together (in series) is 0.1 L/cm H_2O

$$\frac{1}{\text{Compliance (total)}} = \frac{1}{\text{Compliance (lungs)}} + \frac{1}{\text{Compliance (thoracic cage)}}$$

MEASUREMENT OF PULMONARY COMPLIANCE

It is possible to determine the elastic pressure acting on the lungs alone by measuring the static "transpulmonary pressure." This is shown in Figure 45, 2, as the pressure differential between the pleural space and the mouth. Transpulmonary pressure must be measured by getting between the lung and the chest wall (inside the chest but outside the lung). Because of the possibility of lung puncture, it is dangerous to measure intrapleural pressure directly in some patients with pulmonary disease, but a satisfactory approximation of changes in intrapleural pressure can be obtained by measuring pressure in the esophagus through a small tube or balloon in the esophagus with the patient sitting or semirecumbent. The esophagus has a slight tone of its own but is sufficiently passive so that the pressure changes follow accurately those outside the lungs but inside the chest wall.

Ideally, transpulmonary pressure should be measured under static conditions (no air flow) at a series of different end-inspiratory volumes. The patient, with an esophageal balloon in the proper location, is asked to inspire a measured volume from a spirometer and then hold his breath while the new intraesophageal pressure is measured (a saline manometer is satisfactory); the procedure is repeated several times at different vol-

---

◀━━◀ FIG. 44.—*Above: Left,* resting position of the lungs alone; *middle,* resting position of the thoracic cage alone; *right,* resting position of the lungs and thoracic cage held together in normal manner by their pleural surfaces. *Below:* Changes from normal resting position of the combined lungs and thoracic cage caused by obstruction, emphysema or open pneumothorax. Dotted areas represent air-containing regions. Inner springs represent elastic tissues of the lungs; outer springs represent elastic tissues of the thoracic cage. Dark gray areas denote contact between visceral and parietal pleura.

WORK OF BREATHING

WORK = PRESSURE x VOLUME

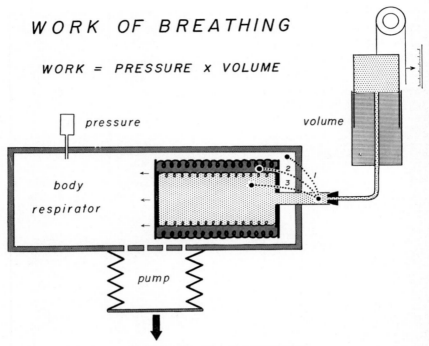

FIG. 45.—THE WORK OF BREATHING

Schematic representation of the lungs and thorax is the same as in Figure 44; here they are enclosed in a body respirator. On inspiration, the pump (bellows) lowers pressure in the body respirator below that of the atmosphere, and air at atmospheric pressure enters the lungs from the spirometer; on expiration, pressure in the respirator falls to atmospheric, and the unopposed elastic pressure of lungs and thorax produces expiration. Volume and pressure are measured continuously. *1*, transthoracic pressure (pressure difference between respirator and mouth); *2*, transpulmonary pressure (pressure difference between pleural cavity and mouth); *3*, transairway pressure (pressure difference between alveoli and mouth).

PRESSURE DIFF.	MEASURES	STATIC MEASUREMENT (if related to change in vol) PROVIDES DATA FOR CALCULATION OF:	DYNAMIC MEASUREMENT (if related to air flow) PROVIDES DATA FOR CALCULATION OF:
3	Transairway pressure		Airway resistance
2	Transpulmonary pressure	Pulmonary compliance	Pulmonary resistance* (tissue and airway)
1	Transthoracic pressure	Total compliance (pulmonary and thoracic)	Total resistance* (pulmonary and thoracic)

*After subtracting pressure to overcome elastic recoil.

168

umes and a pressure-volume curve is constructed. The pressure-volume curve is usually linear over the range normally used (although it is not when very large volumes above or below FRC are used). The compliance computed is, of course, an average value for the lungs. The apparatus is inexpensive, the procedure is simple, and the data are objective. Compliance for individual lungs can be measured during bronchospirometry.

Some investigators measure the elastic recoil of the lung by determining the intrapleural (intraesophageal) pressure at end-expiration (FRC). The technique, unfortunately, is not a precise one because the intraesophageal balloon records pressure *changes* more faithfully than it measures *absolute* intrathoracic pressure. Compliance, measured by the slope of the pressure-volume curve, relates volume *change* to transpulmonary pressure *change,* without respect to the absolute pressure. Sometimes, it is useful to measure both compliance and end-expiratory esophageal pressure. For example, in the aged, compliance measured by the slope of the pressure-volume curve may not change markedly, but the end-expiratory transpulmonary pressure may be only half that of a healthy young adult. This is interpreted to mean that the amount or character of tissues or fluids responsible for elastic recoil has changed with aging.

It is also possible to estimate compliance of healthy individuals by constructing pressure-volume curves during a series of tidal volumes of increasing depth, without breath-holding. Figure 46 illustrates the principle involved; continuous recording of pressure and volume is required. Since compliance, by definition, must be measured under static conditions, values of volume and intraesophageal pressure must be selected only at points when there is no flow. Figure 46 shows points of "no-flow" at end-inspiration and end-expiration. At these points, all of the transpulmonary pressure is used to counteract the elastic recoil of the lung; none of it is necessary to overcome frictional resistance since there is no flow. In healthy man, pressure-volume slopes constructed in this way are quite similar to those constructed by the breath-holding technique; this is true even at rapid rates of breathing.

Unfortunately, in many patients with pulmonary disease, pressure-volume curves constructed *during* breathing, especially at a rapid rate, yield values for compliance that are much lower than those obtained under static conditions. Even though the definition of compliance requires that measurements be made under static conditions, investigators have confused terminology by introducing terms such as "effective," "dynamic," "functional," "fast" and "slow" compliance. What these terms really mean is that in some patients compliance cannot be measured

MEASUREMENT OF LUNG COMPLIANCE
INTRAPLEURAL PRESSURE METHOD

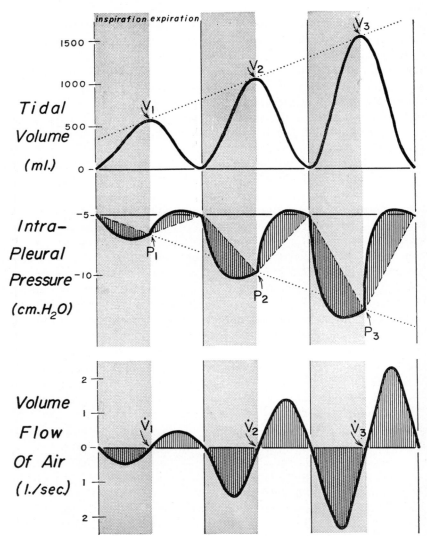

Fig. 46.—Measurement of Pulmonary Compliance
during the Respiratory Cycle

correctly during rapid breathing rates or sometimes even during normal respiratory rates. When "compliance" estimated *during* breathing is lower than compliance measured under *guaranteed static* conditions, abnormal tissue or airway resistance is usually present; this prevents complete filling of air units in the short time allowed.[†]

It seems desirable always to measure compliance during 1–2 sec periods of breath-holding so that air flow from the atmosphere to the alveoli or from some alveoli to other alveoli has actually ceased and mouth pressure is in fact equal to alveolar pressure. If one wishes, *in addition,* to construct pressure-volume curves *during* breathing (slow or rapid rates or both), one may obtain additional information, but it pertains to pulmonary resistance and should not be called compliance.

MEASUREMENT OF COMPLIANCE OF LUNG-THORACIC CAGE SYSTEM

Figure 43 (p. 164) shows schematically how the elastic properties or the compliance of the lungs and thoracic cage may be measured by static pressure-volume measurements at different lung volumes. In actual practice, this measurement can be made in one of three ways:

1. A patient whose breathing has been suspended voluntarily or because of disease is placed in a body respirator (Fig. 45) so that transthoracic pressure (*1* in Fig. 45) can be measured. Measurement of the volume of air inspired at each of several subatmospheric pressure levels around the body yields data for a pressure-volume curve.

[†] If all the airways are markedly narrowed, there is insufficient time for filling of all alveoli; if some are narrowed, there will be uneven ventilation, and poorly ventilated units will receive little gas volume when the respiratory frequency is high.

◄━━◀︎ FIG. 46.—Tidal volume, intrapleural (or intraesophageal) pressure, and volume flow of air are measured continuously and simultaneously, for three breaths, each deeper than the preceding one. At the end of inspiration, there is no air flow ($\dot{V}_1$, $\dot{V}_2$ and $\dot{V}_3$ = zero), and therefore the total transpulmonary pressure is that overcoming elastic resistance. A pressure-volume curve can therefore be plotted from V_1 and P_1, V_2 and P_2, and V_3 and P_3.

If there were no tissue and airway resistance, transpulmonary pressure would be required only to overcome elastic resistance; intrapleural pressure fluctuations during the respiratory cycle would then follow the straight (dashed) lines (if the inspired and expired volumes were linear with respect to time). However, tissue and airway resistances do exist and an additional pressure (that between the straight and the curved lines on the intrapleural pressure record) is required to overcome these (see Fig. 51, p. 192).

2. The chest of an anesthetized patient is inflated through a cuffed endotracheal tube. The tube is occluded and the pressure measured under static conditions in the tube-lung system. The pressure measured is transthoracic (alveolar pressure-atmospheric pressure around the thorax). The volume change above the resting expiratory level caused by this inflating pressure is measured by opening the tube and measuring the volume of gas expired into a spirometer. The procedure is repeated at several volumes and a pressure-volume curve plotted.

3. A normal subject inspires a measured volume of gas from a spirometer, then closes his nose and mouth, opens his glottis and relaxes his muscles of respiration. The elastic recoil of the lungs and thorax is now unopposed by active contraction of the inspiratory muscles; this produces an alveolar pressure (transthoracic) which can be measured by a nasal tube, because in a static system such as this, nasal pressure equals alveolar pressure. Repetition of this procedure several times at different volumes produces a "relaxation pressure curve." Figures for compliance obtained by this method are larger than those for the second method mentioned.

Although the pressure-volume relationship may yield a curved rather than a straight line, a value for compliance (volume change per unit pressure change) obtained over the usual range of tidal volumes may be used to compare the compliance of the lungs and thoracic cage in different individuals.

Measurement of Compliance of the Thoracic Cage

If data are obtained simultaneously for compliance of the lungs alone and of the lungs and thoracic cage together, one can calculate the compliance of the thoracic cage alone, using the equation

$$\frac{1}{C_{total}} = \frac{1}{C_{lungs}} + \frac{1}{C_{thoracic\ cage}}$$

It is also possible to estimate the compliance of the thoracic cage during a relaxed expiration (McIlroy).

Normal Values for Compliance

Normal values for a healthy young man are, approximately:

Pulmonary compliance .... 0.2 L/cm H_2O
Thoracic cage compliance .... 0.2 L/cm H_2O
Total (lungs and thoracic cage) compliance ... 0.1 L/cm H_2O

Values for compliance, to have any diagnostic meaning, must be related to a predicted normal value for a person of the same sex, age, height, weight and lung volumes. Not enough measurements have been made, using standard techniques, on enough individuals with healthy lungs to provide tables of normal data for all age groups and both sexes. The best equations at the present time for predicting normal values are given in Table 34 (p. 329).

Interpretation of Data for Compliance

1. Data for pulmonary compliance can be interpreted properly only when they were obtained under conditions known to be static. Even when compliance is measured at both normal and rapid breathing rates and similar values are obtained, one cannot assume that these values are equal to compliance measured during breath-holding.

2. Effect of lung volume.—Obviously, pulmonary compliance varies with the initial volume of the alveoli which are to be distended by the applied transpulmonary pressure. If a change in transpulmonary pressure of 5 cm H_2O results in a volume change of 1 liter, the compliance of the lungs is $\frac{1}{5}$, or 0.2 L/cm H_2O. However, the volume change in one of the two lungs will be only 0.5 liter (for the same change in transmural pressure), and compliance of one lung will thus be $\frac{0.5}{5}$, or 0.1 L/cm H_2O. For one of the three right lobes, the volume change may be only 0.15 liter and the compliance for one lobe only $\frac{0.15}{5}$, or 0.03 L/cm H_2O. This does not mean that the tissues of one lobe or of one lung are stiffer than those of the two lungs measured together or that they differ in their elastic tissue components; it simply means that compliance is not really a meaningful term unless related to the original lung volume (FRC). If one wishes to compare the elastic properties of the lungs of a newborn with those of a child or adult, one must measure:

$$\frac{\text{Vol. change/original lung vol.}}{\text{Pressure change}} \quad \text{or} \quad \frac{\text{Compliance‡}}{\text{FRC}}$$

The pulmonary compliance of newborn infants, on this basis, is 0.065 L/cm H_2O per liter of FRC and that of adults is between 0.05 and 0.06.

If one wishes to relate the compliance of asthmatic, emphysematous,

---

‡ Compliance/FRC has been termed "specific" compliance.

atelectatic, congested, pneumonic or edematous lungs to that of normal lungs, one must know the FRC in each case, simply because the compliance of normal lungs changes directly with changes in FRC. Obvious though this may be, most of the reported data for compliance in healthy subjects and in patients with disease are *not* related to FRC and hence are useless if one wishes to make inferences regarding the effect of disease on the characteristics of tissues of the lungs. A report that the compliance of the lungs is 50% of normal does not mean that these tissues are stiffer or less distensible unless one knows that the FRC in communication with the airways is approximately normal. Change in position, for example, changes FRC and changes compliance; however, it does not change compliance/FRC. Again, if a foreign body momentarily obstructed a bronchus, pulmonary compliance measured at that instant (without reference to FRC) would be decreased though there was no change in the elastic properties of the lungs.

3. TISSUES WHICH HAVE "ELASTIC RECOIL."—We generally assume that only histologically identifiable elastic fibers, with characteristic staining properties, possess elastic properties. Radford has suggested that, in addition, collagen, the reticulum of the lungs, pleura, bronchi and blood vessels, the surface tension of gas-liquid interfaces, the smooth muscle of bronchi and lungs, the pulmonary blood volume and bronchial mucus may be partly responsible for the elastic properties of the lungs. Similarly, numerous tissues may contribute to the elastic properties of the thoracic cage.

Of particular interest is a surface film lining the alveoli which has remarkable surface tension-lowering properties. The first clue to this film and its properties was Von Neergaard's discovery that saline-filled lungs inflated considerably more for a unit change in transpulmonary pressure than did air-filled lungs. The conclusion was that air-filled lungs have greater elastic recoil than saline-filled lungs and that the difference is due to the surface tension of the air-water interface (this film acts as though it were elastic tissue in this respect). If this alveolar film were pure water or saline with a surface tension of 70 dynes/cm, its surface force would be great enough to cause alveolar instability and collapse. However, alveolar cells appear to produce a phospholipid which lowers the surface tension of this film to extremely low levels (2–8 dynes/cm in the compressed state) and so maintains alveolar stability (Clements; Avery and Mead). The amount or characteristics of this surfactive material can be altered in many ways and in a relatively short time, whereas elastic fibers presumably are less labile. Consequently, when one finds changes in compliance/FRC, one should not infer that these are due to changes in elastic fibers, without studying also the other tissues or materials which contribute to the pressure-volume curve of the lung. We do not know the precise chemical composition of this surfactant and what regulates its formation. The possibility exists that the body can regulate pulmonary compliance by the quantity and type of material formed.

USEFULNESS OF MEASUREMENTS OF COMPLIANCE

1. When pulmonary compliance is abnormal, some pulmonary abnormality is present. The primary abnormality may, of course, be a change in FRC. When compliance/FRC is abnormal, one should suspect a change in the quantity or quality of the tissues of the lung, the presence of pulmonary edema or an alteration in the surfactant lining the pulmonary alveoli.

2. Suitable measurements enable the physician to know whether a decrease in compliance is due to changes in the lungs, in the thoracic cage or in both. This knowledge is useful therapeutically as well as diagnostically. For example, if the patient is unable to provide enough ventilation by his own muscular effort, methods providing much higher positive pressures may be used safely if it is the thoracic cage which is uncompliant. This is because alveoli rupture only when overdistended, and overdistention is caused only by large *trans*pulmonary pressures. Decreased compliance of the lungs is apt to be non-uniform, and a pressure which produces little ventilation of some regions may overdistend and even rupture alveoli in other regions. On the other hand, decrease in thoracic compliance usually affects the whole thorax and prevents grossly uneven alveolar distention at high inflation pressures.

3. Knowledge of the physical characteristics of the lungs and thorax enables the physician to select the proper type of mechanical resuscitator for a patient, and the anesthesiologist to provide the proper controlled ventilation for the lungs (in operations with the thorax open) or for the lungs and thorax (when the thorax is intact).

4. In cases requiring determination of pulmonary disability, measurements of compliance provide objective data on one type of physical basis for dyspnea and disability.

PULMONARY COMPLIANCE IN DISEASE

PULMONARY CONGESTION.—The compliance (uncorrected) is decreased when experimental pulmonary congestion is produced by sudden inflation of a pressure suit around the abdomen and legs or by rapid intravenous infusion of large volumes of fluid. It is likely that compliance/FRC does not vary, because experimental increase in transpulmonary vascular pressure of 16 cm H_2O does not change the compliance of saline-filled lungs.

PULMONARY EDEMA.—Compliance is reduced when edema fluid is present in the alveoli. The decrease is presumably out of proportion to the changes in FRC. Here surface tension forces may be altered because of change in the character of the alveolar phospholipid film or because of changes in the geometric configuration of the air sacs. Froth may block additional bronchioles and prevent expansion of otherwise normal alveoli.

HEART DISEASE.—Whenever heart failure is associated with a decrease in FRC (pleural or large pericardial effusion, ascites or greatly enlarged heart) or with pulmonary edema (with or without subsequent fibrosis), compliance (uncorrected for FRC) is reduced. Mitral stenosis with mild pulmonary vascular congestion does not lead to decrease in compliance. Compliance may be reduced in patients with mitral stenosis during exercise or after repeated bouts of pulmonary edema; presumably vital capacity and FRC decrease at the same time.

RESTRICTIVE DISEASE OF THE LUNGS.—Compliance is reduced in patients with pleural, interstitial, or alveolar fibrosis. It is not known whether this decrease is out of proportion to the reduction in FRC. It is known that collagen and "scar" tissue have length-tension (or pressure-volume) relationships different from those of elastic tissue. If, however, the affected areas receive no ventilation and become airless, FRC is reduced at the same time. Chest-strapping reduces pulmonary compliance but also reduces FRC. Fibrosis or sclerosis of the pulmonary vessels does not appear to alter pulmonary compliance.

EMPHYSEMA.—When compliance is measured by static methods, it is usually increased in patients with emphysema. When measured during breathing, especially during rapid breathing ("dynamic" compliance), it is less than normal. The pressure-volume curve is usually shifted toward the left, which means that less transpulmonary pressure is required to maintain the lungs at FRC (or that normal transpulmonary pressure results in a large FRC). Figure 44, *below, center* (p. 166), shows that if there were complete loss of elastic recoil of the lungs but that of the thoracic cage remained normal, the thorax would enlarge toward its neutral position.

OTHER LUNG DISEASES.—Compliance (uncorrected) is decreased in atelectasis and pneumonia.

CONTRACTION OF BRONCHIOLAR SMOOTH MUSCLE.—The compliance of saline-filled lungs of animals does not change when bronchoconstriction is produced. Presumably the change of smooth muscle to a more contracted state does not change measurably the distensibility of the lung.

When airways are occluded in man by spasm, edema, congestion or mucus, one would expect uncorrected compliance to decrease; and to decrease markedly when measured during rapid breathing. Tubocurarine (known to cause histamine release and bronchoconstriction) may decrease compliance (uncorrected); other muscle relaxants do not.

THORACIC DISORDERS.—Poliomyelitis and kyphoscoliosis are often associated with changes in the lung characterized by decreased compliance (uncorrected); in some cases, compliance/FRC is decreased.

PULMONARY ARTERY OBSTRUCTION.—Pulmonary artery ligation in the dog is followed, in several days, by a pronounced decrease in pulmonary compliance associated with congestive atelectasis; these changes are accompanied by decrease in the activity of the alveolar surfactant (noted as an increase in the surface tension of lung extracts). Compliance returns to normal in several weeks.

ANESTHESIA.—General anesthesia in man is sometimes associated with a decrease in pulmonary compliance, possibly because of closure of alveolar units.

VAGOTOMY.—In animals, bilateral vagotomy is followed by an increase in compliance but no change in compliance/FRC.

HYPOTHERMIA.—In man, no change in compliance was noted after reduction of body temperature to 29°C.

THORACIC CAGE COMPLIANCE IN DISEASE

This may be decreased in patients with kyphoscoliosis (idiopathic, tuberculous, postpoliomyelitic), pectus excavatum, arthritic spondylitis following thoracoplasty, skeletal muscle diseases associated with spasticity or rigidity and in abdominal disorders characterized by marked elevation of the diaphragm (the diaphragm and attached abdominal viscera represent one component of the thoracic cage). It may also be decreased in patients with marked obesity (Pickwickian types).

EFFECT OF DECREASED COMPLIANCE ON THE PATIENT

a) Decreased compliance forces the patient to do more muscular work to achieve adequate alveolar ventilation; this is particularly true when tidal volume is large (p. 191). We do not know whether increased respiratory effort causes hypertrophy of the respiratory muscles, but we do know that increased respiratory muscular effort is often associated with dyspnea and may eventually lead to fatigue and failure of the respiratory muscles.

We have found pulmonary compliance to be as low as 0.01 L/cm H_2O, or 5% of predicted normal value, in patients with severe diffuse alveolar fibrosis and diffuse carcinomatosis of the lungs. In such patients, a pressure differential of 50 cm H_2O would be required to inflate the lungs with 500 ml of air. Such pressures are greater than patients can produce over long periods and in excess of that provided by any approved respirator.

b) Diseases altering pulmonary compliance rarely alter it uniformly throughout the lung. Uneven compliance (assuming that the intrathoracic pressure acting on the lung surface is uniform throughout) must lead to uneven gas tensions in different regions of the lung at end-inspiration; and this contributes to uneven ventilation/blood flow ratios.

c) Because of the increased energy requirement of deep breathing, especially when compliance is reduced, patients with low compliance usually breathe more rapidly and less deeply than do normal subjects (p. 191). As a rule, patients with decreased compliance (and no significant airway obstruction) have a normal or near-normal MVV (MBC; p. 200) until vital capacity is reduced to 50% or less.

B. AIRWAY RESISTANCE

Just as a driving pressure is necessary in the pulmonary circulation to pump blood through the arteriolar, capillary and venular resistances (p. 78), so a driving pressure is necessary during inspiration to pull air through the upper airway, bronchial and bronchiolar resistances into the alveoli and during expiration to push alveolar gas out through these tubes (Fig. 47). The same equation applies as for blood flow:

$$\text{Resistance} = \frac{\text{driving pressure}}{\text{flow}}$$

The driving pressure across the airways is the transairway pressure (*3* in Fig. 45, p. 168), which is atmospheric pressure minus alveolar pressure during inspiration and alveolar pressure minus atmospheric pressure during expiration. The units are cm H_2O/L/sec.

Airway resistance is created by friction between molecules of the flowing gas and between the gas molecules and the walls of the tubes. When

AIRWAY RESISTANCE $= \dfrac{\text{ALVEOLAR PRESSURE}}{\text{FLOW}}$

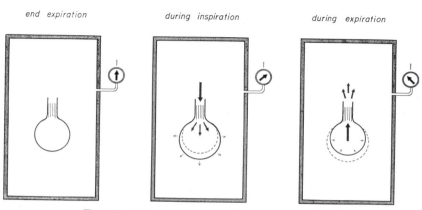

FIG. 47.—MEASUREMENT OF AIRWAY RESISTANCE:
BODY PLETHYSMOGRAPH TECHNIQUE

The rectangle represents the air-tight body plethysmograph. The patient is represented by alveoli and conducting airway, and his airway resistance by parallel lines in the conducting airway. The circle with pointer represents a sensitive gauge which continuously measures pressure in the box around the patient. During inspiration (*center*) the alveoli have enlarged from the original volume (broken line) to a new volume (solid line); during expiration (*right*), the alveoli have returned to their original volume. (See text.)

flow is laminar or streamlined (Fig. 48), airway resistance varies *directly* with the viscosity of the gas and the length of the tubes and *inversely* with the fourth power of the radius of the lumen of the tubes.

$$\text{Resistance to flow through a tube} = \frac{\text{viscosity} \cdot \text{length}}{(\text{radius})^4} \times \frac{8}{\pi}$$

Figure 48 shows the relationship among driving pressure, flow and resistance. If the resistance, R, is small (short, wide tube) and the flow, V̇, is small, only a small driving pressure is required (*above left*). If R is increased (longer or narrower tube), more pressure is required to produce the same flow (*above center*). If a greater flow is now required through the same resistance, more driving pressure is required (*above right*).§

§ As a rule, resistance is measured at flow rates of 0.5 L/sec in order to keep this part of the equation constant.

$$\text{RESISTANCE} \quad = \quad \frac{\text{PRESSURE} \quad \text{DIFFERENCE}}{\text{VOLUME} \quad \text{FLOW}}$$

$$= \quad \frac{\Delta P \; (cm. \, H_2O)}{\dot{V} \; (liters/sec.)}$$

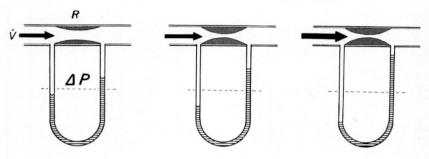

TYPES OF AIR FLOW

LAMINAR

$$P = K_1 \, \dot{V}$$

TURBULENT

$$P = K_2 \, \dot{V}^2$$

TRACHEO-BRONCHIAL

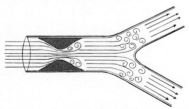

$$P = K_1 \, \dot{V} + K_2 \, \dot{V}^2$$

FIG. 48.—RESISTANCE TO AIR FLOW THROUGH TUBES

Airway resistance also depends on the nature of air flow. Air flow may be laminar (or streamlined) or turbulent (Fig. 48, *below*). As stated before, the pressure required to produce *laminar* flow is proportional to the volume flow ($\dot{V}$) times a constant (K_1), which is related to the *viscosity* of the gas; it is independent of the *density* of the gas. The pressure required for *turbulent* flow is proportional to the *square* of the volume flow ($\dot{V}$)^2 times another constant (K_2), which is related to the *density* of the gas; it is independent of the *viscosity* of the gas.

In smooth, straight tubes, turbulent flow occurs only at high velocities. However, the tracheobronchial tree has hundreds of thousands of branchings, and eddy formations may be set up at these; the pressure required for eddy flow is approximately the same as for turbulent flow. Turbulence (at low flow rates) or eddy formation is particularly apt to occur when there are irregularities in the tubes, such as might be caused by mucus, exudate, tumor or foreign bodies or by partial closure of the glottis. Physicians sometimes administer 80% helium-20% O_2 to a patient with obstructed breathing in the hope that the airway resistance might be decreased by inhalation of a less dense gas. However, the *viscosity* of this mixture is slightly greater than that of air, and so the resistance to laminar flow is increased slightly, if there is any change. Inhalation of 80% helium-20% O_2 *will* decrease resistance when there is *turbulent* flow or eddy formation because the *density* of the gas mixture is low (see p. 296).

MEASUREMENT OF AIRWAY RESISTANCE

Airway resistance must be measured under dynamic conditions, i.e., during air flow. Three measurements must be made simultaneously and continuously in order to calculate airway resistance: (1) alveolar pressure, (2) atmospheric pressure, and (3) instantaneous air flow. Atmospheric pressure and instantaneous air flow (pneumotachograph) are easy to measure; alveolar pressure during flow can be measured with the body plethysmograph.

FIG. 48.—*Above:* Width of the arrow signifies volume flow of air ($\dot{V}$); shaded obstruction, degree of resistance (R) to flow. The U-tube manometer measures the pressure difference (ΔP) across the resistance. As resistance is increased, greater pressure is required to maintain the same flow. When flow is increased, another increment of pressure is needed. *Below:* Pressure required when air flow is turbulent (or when there are eddies) is considerably greater than that when flow is laminar (see text).

INTERRUPTER TECHNIQUE

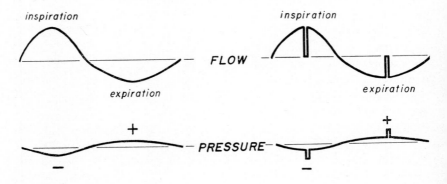

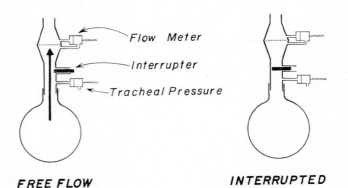

FREE FLOW   INTERRUPTED

$$RESISTANCE \ = \ \frac{PRESSURE}{FLOW}$$

Fig. 49.—Method for Measuring "Airway" Resistance

Simultaneous measurements of trans-airway pressure (pressure difference between alveoli and mouth) and of flow are required to measure airway resistance. Here the subject breathes through a flow meter; air flow can be interrupted very briefly at any time without the subject's knowledge and pressure measured on the tracheal side of the obstruction. At random times during the respiratory cycle, the flow is interrupted momentarily at the mouthpiece by a shutter and static pressure measured (tracheal pressure). In a static system, the mouth or tracheal pressure is equal to alveolar pressure, if the glottis is open. This measurement of "airway" resistance probably includes tissue resistance as well (see text).

Figure 47 (p. 179) shows schematically the principle of the method. The patient (only the lung is pictured) is seated within the air-tight box; pressure is measured continuously in the box around the patient. One would expect that inspiration of 500 ml of air from the box into the patient's lungs would produce no pressure fluctuations in the box (if precautions are taken to prevent changes due to changes in temperature and humidity of the respired gas); actually the box pressure rises during inspiration. This is simply because gas flows only from a point of higher pressure to a point of lower pressure. At the beginning of inspiration, muscular action has enlarged the thorax and lowered alveolar pressure below atmospheric pressure. Throughout inspiration, alveolar gas (previously at atmospheric pressure) is now at subatmospheric pressure and so occupies more volume; this is the same as adding this increment of gas volume (resulting from the decompression) to the plethysmograph and so the pressure rises. The pressure change is registered by a very sensitive manometer. The reverse happens during expiration, when alveolar gas is compressed. From this measured pressure and appropriate calibrations, alveolar pressure can be calculated for any moment in the respiratory cycle. From these simultaneous measurements of alveolar pressure and flow (pneumotachograph), airway resistance can be determined. The method is sensitive, rapid, objective and specific for changes in airway resistance because the values do not include resistances attributable to the chest wall or lung tissues. It may be repeated as often as desired without tiring the patient.

Before the introduction of the body plethysmograph, alveolar pressure was estimated from mouth pressure, which was measured when flow had been stopped momentarily by an electrical shutter (Fig. 49). The assumptions were made that, during the brief period of interruption, mouth pressure equals alveolar pressure and that this static alveolar pressure is identical to that immediately before interruption. Figure 49 shows how the oral pressure rises abruptly to alveolar pressure when flow is abruptly interrupted by a shutter during expiration, and how it falls abruptly to alveolar pressure when flow is interrupted during inspiration. Unfortunately, there are theoretical reasons and experimental data indicating that the pressure during this brief interruption is slightly greater than it was immediately before interruption. Therefore, this "alveolar" pressure probably includes pressure overcoming pulmonary and thoracic tissue resistance. Furthermore, in patients who have an unusually high airway resistance, pressure equilibrium between mouth and alveoli does not occur rapidly.

Other methods (pp. 186 and 196) provide data from which inferences regarding airway resistance may be drawn. For example, if the maximal expiratory flow rate, maximal voluntary ventilation (MVV) and forced expiratory volume are markedly decreased and the pulmonary resistance abnormally high and all return to normal after administration of a drug known to be a bronchodilator, one can infer correctly that the results of these tests had been abnormal because of increased airway resistance rather than because of abnormal pulmonary tissue or thoracic cage resistance.

NORMAL VALUES FOR AIRWAY RESISTANCE

Normal values, using the body plethysmograph, during rapid, shallow breathing range from 0.6 to 2.4 cm $H_2O/L/sec$ (measured at flow rates of 0.5 L/sec) in adults (see Table 35, p. 329).

INTERPRETATION OF DATA

1. EFFECT OF A PREVIOUS DEEP INSPIRATION.—The subject is asked to pant during the measurement for technical reasons. However, panting is advantageous in that it permits measurements to be made near FRC, without a deep inspiration. A full inspiration can, at least temporarily, overcome the very increase in airway resistance that one wishes to measure. It is important to be sure that a deep sigh or full inspiration did not occur within a minute or two of the actual measurement.

2. EFFECT OF LUNG VOLUME.—Airway resistance becomes less as lung volume is increased. The reciprocal of airway resistance (1/R, or conductance) varies linearly with FRC. For this reason it is important to know the FRC at the moment that airway resistance is measured. Fortunately, instantaneous thoracic gas volume can be determined in the body plethysmograph at the moment that airway resistance is tested. For comparative studies, it is well to relate resistance (or better, conductance) to simultaneously measured FRC.

3. EFFECT OF INSPIRATION AND EXPIRATION.—During quiet breathing, airway resistance is slightly less during inspiration (presumably because the inspiratory traction of the pulmonary tissues widens the smaller air-

ways) and slightly greater during expiration. However, the resistance does increase more toward the end of a maximal expiration in normal subjects.

4. EFFECT OF INHALATION OF DUSTS OR SMOKE.—If one wishes to compare the airway resistance of different groups of patients, it is important that no bronchoconstrictor or bronchodilator agents be administered before the test. For example, inhalation of submicronic inert particles (carbon, aluminum, chalk, cigaret smoke) may lead to a 2-fold increase in airway resistance which may last 20–40 min.

5. DETECTION OF ABNORMAL TYPES OF RESISTANCE.—The body plethysmograph method will detect only those types of resistance that are present during panting. It will not detect abnormal resistance due entirely to a check valve (p. 198), which occurs only with a full and forced expiration.

USEFULNESS OF MEASUREMENT OF AIRWAY RESISTANCE

The specific test of airway resistance enables the physician to determine whether a decreased MVV or maximal expiratory flow rate (p. 196) is due to increased resistance in the airway or to numerous other factors. It provides an objective test that is suitable for judging pulmonary disability because the patient cannot voluntarily influence the result of the test. It is also useful in evaluating therapy on an individual basis.

AIRWAY RESISTANCE IN PATIENTS

ASTHMA.—Airway resistance is always increased during the asthmatic attack and may be increased 2- to 3-fold in the symptom-free interval between attacks. The resistance, as in normal individuals, is greater during expiration, but inspiratory resistance is also greater than normal. The asthmatic type of resistance is, except in very severe cases, reversible by vigorous therapy.

EMPHYSEMA.—Airway resistance is usually increased and not reversible by bronchodilator therapy. Much of the increased airway resistance in emphysema appears to be due to collapse of airways during expiration. The finer airways do not have rigid walls and are generally kept open by traction of the elastic tissues of the lung; this traction is diminished in emphysema if elastic tissue is diminished or altered and so the fine tubes collapse during expiration (check valves). Larger airways have their own structural tissue, but this appears to be modified or damaged in emphysema, and even the larger air ducts may collapse during expiration. In addition, during a forced expiration, positive intrapleural pressure is developed because muscular contraction decreases the volume of the thoracic cage faster than air leaves the lungs. This positive pressure exceeds the pressure in the lumen of bronchioles on the tracheal side of the partial obstruction and tends to collapse the walls further. (The pressure required to collapse airways and limit flow is far lower in patients with emphysema than in normal individuals.) Finally, alveoli which have lost varying amounts of their elastic tissue tend to empty in a disorderly manner, and the orifice of the air duct may be closed or may be occluded prematurely by adjacent inflated air sacs.

OTHER OBSTRUCTIVE DISEASES.—Airway resistance is increased in a wide variety of disorders in which fibrous tissue, tumors, effusions, etc. constrict, compress, impinge on or obstruct airways.

ADDED RESISTANCES.—The physician occasionally imposes additional airway resistance (external or internal) on the patient by the use of narrow tracheotomy tubes, long and narrow endotracheal tubes, bronchospirometers, breathing tubes and valves. For example, the resistance to steady flow (at a rate of 1 L/sec) through a no. 9 Magill endotracheal tube is 6 cm $H_2O/L/sec$, which is approximately 7 times the normal resistance to flow through the upper respiratory tract. One patient was wearing a tracheotomy tube which had been inserted because of postthyroidectomy stenosis of the larynx and attacks of asthma. The tracheotomy tube was removed and its resistance to air flow found to be 2.2 cm $H_2O/L/sec$.[‖] When an inner flap was inserted for vocalization, the inspiratory resistance was 9.9, and the expiratory resistance very high because of the flap action. The laryngeal stricture had a resistance of 7.8 cm $H_2O/L/sec$, and flow was turbulent. Patients with weakened respiratory muscles often suffer severe distress with the addition of even small external resistances.

EFFECTS OF INCREASED AIRWAY RESISTANCE ON THE PATIENT

1. EFFECT ON FRC AND RV.—Figure 50 shows that normally expiration is passive and complete in less than 3 sec. If airway resistance were

---

[‖] Resistances were measured at a flow rate of 0.5 L/sec.

to increase abruptly during expiration (as might occur at the beginning of an asthmatic attack), the lung volume might not return to the resting expiratory level in this 3 sec interval. Thus, if expiration is completely passive, expiration will not be complete if only 3 sec is available for it. This means that FRC will be greater at the beginning of the next inspiration.

If more time is permitted for expiration, the chest will return to the original resting expiratory level; however, in some patients the obstruction is so severe that this would require such a slow respiratory frequency that alveolar ventilation would be reduced. There are several other possibilities: (a) The patient may expire actively rather than passively and so increase the pressure differential available for air flow; this has the disadvantage of tiring the patient. (b) As FRC increases (because the time available is not enough for complete expiration), the elastic force at end-inspiration increases, because this varies directly with the volume of the lung (Fig. 43, p. 164). This increases the pressure available for expiration, expiration is then completed in the time available, and inspiratory and expiratory tidal volumes again become equal. Further obstruction will lead to a further increase in FRC and elastic force until a new balance is reached (Figs. 44, p. 166, and 50). For example, a patient had moderately severe asthma with resistance to air flow 5 times normal. His lung volume, measured by the plethysmographic method (p. 20) which includes "trapped air," was 6.5 liters. After bronchodilator therapy, his airway resistance decreased to normal and his lung volume to 4.0 liters.

Patients with severe pulmonary emphysema often present a more serious mechanical problem when anesthetized. These patients normally achieve expiration in the time available by active contraction of their expiratory muscles; under general anesthesia, expiration becomes passive and can be accomplished only by the recoil of elastic fibers stretched during inspiration.

2. DYSPNEA.—A normal resting subject in whom bronchial obstruction is induced experimentally by inhalation of histamine or irritant aerosols does not experience any respiratory symptoms until airway resistance is increased to 3-fold or more. Severe dyspnea may not result until airway resistance is increased 5- to 15-fold. Thus specific tests can detect the presence of abnormal airway resistance before the patient experiences any symptoms.

3. EFFECT ON FREQUENCY OF BREATHING.—Because resistance in-

EFFECT OF INCREASED AIRWAY RESISTANCE

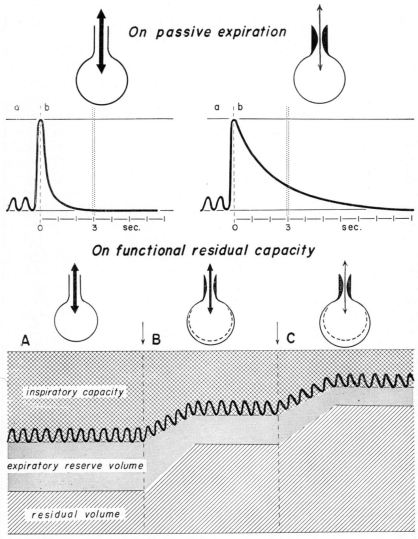

On passive expiration

On functional residual capacity

inspiratory capacity

expiratory reserve volume

residual volume

FIG. 50.—EFFECT OF INCREASING EXPIRATORY RESISTANCE ON AIR FLOW
AND FUNCTIONAL RESIDUAL CAPACITY

creases with the velocity of flow, patients with airway obstruction generally elect to breathe slowly.

4. EFFECT ON MVV.—Airway obstruction of sufficient degree decreases the volume of MVV because the patient is unable to achieve high flow rates.

C. TISSUE RESISTANCE: PULMONARY RESISTANCE

In addition to the frictional resistance caused by the flow of gas molecules through the airways, there is another frictional resistance in the pulmonary and thoracic tissues themselves. This is the result of displacement of the tissues during inspiration and expiration; the tissues involved include the lungs, rib cage, diaphragm and abdominal contents. Like airway resistance, tissue resistance can be measured only during motion; the force needed to overcome it is related to the rapidity or quickness of motion. At the beginning of inspiration, when air flow has not yet begun and the tissues are not moving, resistive force is zero. It becomes maximal at the time of the maximal rate of air flow (even though maximal inspiratory *volume* has not yet been reached). It is zero again at end-inspiration when flow and movement stop; at this point the elastic force is maximal (Fig. 46) because the maximal volume has been reached. At the end of inspiration, the elastic tissues are under stretch and tend to recoil. This elastic or recoil force is available to overcome frictional resistance in tissues and airway resistance. Just as there is friction in the moving tissues during inspiration, so there is friction of motion during expiration, and again the frictional force is greatest at the moment of maximal movement or volume flow. The greater the amount of elastic force dissipated in overcoming frictional resistance in the *tissues,* the less is the elastic force available for overcoming *airway*

◀──◀ FIG. 50.—*Above:* Effect on air flow during passive expiration. *a* represents quiet breathing recorded on a slow kymograph. At *b* the kymograph is speeded and the patient takes a full inspiration and expires passively. *Left,* open airway, rapid passive expiration; *right,* partial expiratory obstruction, slow passive expiration (thickness of arrows signifies *rate* of flow; *volume* expired is the same in both cases). *Below:* Effect on functional residual capacity. *Left to right,* increasing expiratory obstruction leads to increased functional residual capacity if expiration is passive and time for expiration is limited. Dashed lines in lungs *B* and *C* represent the original functional residual capacity of *A,* when no expiratory obstruction was present.

resistance. When the force available for causing air flow is reduced, expiration is slowed.

MEASUREMENT OF TISSUE RESISTANCE

1. PULMONARY TISSUE RESISTANCE ("NON-ELASTIC," "VISCOUS" RE-SISTANCE).—The transpulmonary pressure during flow (Fig. 45, p. 168) overcomes elastic recoil, airway resistance and pulmonary tissue resistance. If one subtracts from the total transpulmonary pressure that which is required to overcome elastic recoil,¶ the remaining transpulmonary pressure is that required to overcome airway and pulmonary tissue resistance. Pulmonary tissue resistance cannot be measured independently. However, if *pulmonary* resistance (which is the sum of airway resistance and pulmonary tissue resistance) and *airway* resistance (body plethysmograph method) are measured simultaneously, pulmonary *tissue* resistance can be calculated by subtraction.

Pulmonary *tissue* resistance in healthy young men is about 20% of the total *pulmonary* resistance, the remainder being *airway* resistance. It is often increased in patients with pulmonary sarcoidosis, pulmonary fibrosis, diffuse carcinomatosis, asthma and kyphoscoliosis. It is rarely increased to the extent of being an important or limiting resistance.

Before specific methods for measuring airway resistance were developed, *pulmonary* resistance (which includes *two* components—airway *and* pulmonary tissue resistance) was often used synonymously with *airway* resistance. In general, pulmonary resistance is 20% greater than airway resistance; normal values are given in Table 35 (p. 329). It is measured by plotting air flow against transpulmonary pressure during flow (with pressure to maintain elastic recoil subtracted).

2. THORACIC CAGE RESISTANCE.—No measurements of this resistance have been made in patients with thoracic disorders.

D. COHESION

In certain abnormal conditions, such as atelectasis and collapse of the lung during thoracic surgery, the surfaces of the smaller air ducts are held together by surface tension forces (cohesion). In such cases, another

---

¶ This requires knowledge of the pressure-volume curve of the lungs and the assumption that it is a straight line. The subtraction can be done electrically, if desired.

factor opposes inspiration, because no air movement occurs until an "opening pressure" has been built up in the airways. Attempts to overcome atelectasis by a high endotracheal pressure are hazardous if some of the airways are open, since the high pressure results in distention of their alveoli and may lead to alveolar rupture. In thoracic surgery, once a lung has been permitted to collapse to "minimal volume," the surfaces of the airways are likely to stick together by cohesion. Probably because of this phenomenon, positive pressure applied to the nose, mouth or endotracheal tube will inflate only the lung in the closed hemithorax, even though the compliance of a lung and its hemithorax is less than for the lung alone (on the open side). Once this opening pressure is exceeded, the lung on the open side will receive more ventilation than the other, if both are inflated by the same pressure.

E. INERTIA

The inertia of the lung-thoracic cage system is so small that it can be neglected.

F. THE WORK OF BREATHING

Work, in the physical sense, is force $\times$ distance, or pressure $\times$ volume. The cumulative product of *pressure* and the *volume* of air moved at each instant is equal to *work* ($W = \int PdV$). If one knows the mechanical work done and the O_2 consumed by the respiratory muscles in doing this work, the efficiency of ventilation can be calculated

$$\text{Efficiency} = \frac{\text{useful work}}{\text{total energy expended}} \times 100.$$

WORK OF MOVING ONLY THE LUNGS.—This is calculated from records of transpulmonary pressure and volume during breathing. The principle is illustrated in Figure 51, which shows a block attached to a wall by a spring. In the upper set of diagrams, the block is resting on a "frictionless" surface such as ice. In this case, as the block is moved by an external force, the distance moved is proportional to the force (*solid arrow*) even during movement, since the only force required is that to stretch the spring. In the lower set of diagrams, the block is resting on a rough surface and two forces are required to move it. One is the force required to stretch the spring; this (solid portion of the *arrow*) depends on the dis-

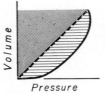

WORK OF BREATHING

Work = *Force* x *Distance*
= *Pressure* x *Volume*

NO FRICTION

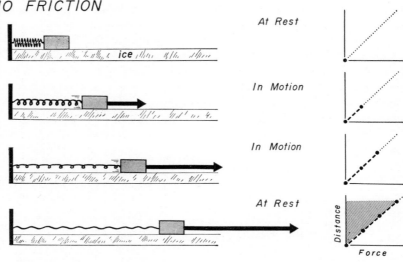

At Rest

In Motion

In Motion

At Rest

FRICTION

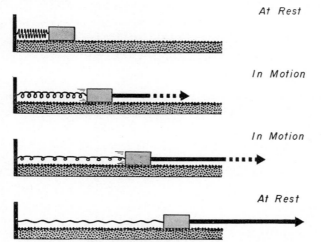

At Rest

In Motion

In Motion

At Rest

FIG. 51.—WORK OF BREATHING DURING INSPIRATION

tance moved and is the same as in the upper diagrams. The other (*broken arrow*) is the force required to overcome friction. This force increases when the speed of movement increases and becomes zero when the block comes to rest. The graphs show the force-length changes corresponding to each movement of the block. When friction is present, the line deviates from the straight line; the shaded area between the straight line and the curve represents the additional *work* to overcome friction during movement.

Similarly, during inflation or deflation of the lungs, the amount of pressure required at any given instant depends not only on the pressure to overcome elastic recoil but also on the pressure to maintain movement of air through the airways and movement of the tissues of the lungs. The greater the rate of volume change (volume flow/min) the greater is the pressure used in overcoming friction. In Figure 51 (*top, left*) is shown a pressure-volume curve during breathing. Since work = ∫ PdV, the shaded area between the diagonal and the ordinate represents the work in overcoming the elastic resistance, whereas the shaded area between the diagonal and the curved line represents the additional work of moving non-elastic tissues and overcoming airway resistance.

WORK OF MOVING THE LUNGS AND THORACIC CAGE.—This is done normally by the muscles of respiration. It is difficult to estimate by direct means. However, if a patient is no longer breathing spontaneously as a result of poliomyelitis, deep anesthesia or the injection of drugs which produce neuromuscular block, his ventilation can be maintained by a body respirator (Fig. 45, p. 168).* This permits measurements of the work required for normal pulmonary ventilation because, under these conditions, the lungs, thorax and gas are moved by the body respirator.

---

* Attempts have also been made to measure the work of breathing in subjects who have been instructed to relax voluntarily all the muscles of respiration while they lie in the respirator; it is not certain, however, that such voluntary relaxation is complete.

◄——◀ FIG. 51.—*Solid arrow* represents the force required to move the block a certain distance when there is no friction and only the elastic resistance of the spring must be overcome. *Broken arrow* shows the additional force required to overcome friction; this is needed only during movement of the block. (See text.) The graphs of force vs. distance are straight lines when there is elastic resistance alone, but are curved when there is frictional resistance as well; the shaded area in the graphs above the diagonal line represents the *work* required to overcome elastic resistance; that below the diagonal line represents work to overcome frictional resistance.

It is easy to measure the work of the body respirator, and the respirator must be doing the amount of work that would have been done by the respiratory muscles under these conditions. The work done by the respirator is calculated from simultaneous measurements of (1) the force acting on the thorax to cause inspiration (the pressure difference between the mouth and the inside of the body respirator; *1* in Fig. 45, p. 168), and (2) the volume of air breathed. Normal values are 0.5 KgM/min during rest. The work of breathing increases disproportionately as the minute volume increases and reaches a maximum of about 250 KgM/min when a subject breathes maximally (about 200 L/min).

O_2 CONSUMPTION OF RESPIRATORY MUSCLES.—The O_2 consumed by the respiratory muscles in a healthy person is normally such a small fraction of the total body metabolism that it is difficult to measure. It does become measurable as the O_2 cost of additional ventilation during performance of the test for maximal voluntary ventilation or when the patient is made to breathe through a known, added resistance. From such measurements and other data, it has been calculated that the mechanical efficiency of the respiratory muscles is low (5–10%), so that 10 or 20 times the O_2 is required to perform the mechanical work as is needed for a similar amount of heat energy. It is difficult to estimate the O_2 cost of additional ventilation if cardiac work is increased simultaneously.

It is certain that the respiratory muscles of many patients with cardiopulmonary disease do more work and require more O_2 than those of resting subjects. It would be interesting and important to determine the mechanical work of breathing, the O_2 consumption of the respiratory muscles and the efficiency of breathing in normal subjects and in patients with respiratory impairment. Some studies have indicated that the "O_2 cost" of additional ventilation (above the resting level) is greater than normal in patients with emphysema and in obese patients.

MINIMAL WORK OF BREATHING.—It is now possible, with our new knowledge of the mechanics of breathing, to offer rational explanations of breathing patterns in patients with pulmonary disease. The optimal rate and depth of breathing should be that which produces the required alveolar ventilation with the minimal amount of work on the part of the respiratory muscles. If the alveolar ventilation required is 4.0 L/min, this can be achieved by rapid, shallow breathing or slow, deep breathing. Some combinations which will give an alveolar ventilation of 4.0 L/min (assuming a respiratory dead space of 150 ml) are:

FREQUENCY, BREATHS/MIN	TIDAL VOLUME, ML	MINUTE VOLUME, L/MIN	ALVEOLAR VENTILATION, L/MIN
10	550	5.5	4.0
15	417	6.3	4.0
20	350	7.0	4.0
30	283	8.5	4.0
40	250	10.0	4.0

If we examine these factors for the best compromise between rate and depth, we see that as the rate increases, the depth decreases, and therefore the elastic forces decrease. However, the minute volume increases (because dead space ventilation/min increases), so that air flow must increase and the resistive forces must be greater.

The best compromise in normal subjects, so that the required alveolar ventilation is obtained by the least sum of these forces, occurs at about 15 respirations per minute. In patients with very stiff lungs (decreased compliance), the best combination occurs at more rapid rates, to minimize the elastic factor. On the other hand, asthmatic patients, who have increased airway resistance as the dominant mechanical problem, do not select rapid respiratory rates because they would require a greater minute volume and therefore higher rates of air flow.

For example, patient G.L. had a respiratory rate of 30–40/min. Lung compliance (esophageal balloon) was 0.013, which is about 1/17 normal. The airway resistance was within the normal range. Autopsy showed pulmonary carcinomatosis, which was the cause of his stiff lungs, but there was no airway obstruction. This patient was breathing frequently because of the greatly increased effort involved in breathing deeply. This phenomenon also occurs in some patients who have pulmonary restrictive disease, pulmonary scleroderma and other lesions restricting or constricting the lungs and chest.

G. MAXIMAL INSPIRATORY AND EXPIRATORY FORCES

These forces are measured under static conditions by having the subject expire or inspire maximally against a mercury or other manometer. The maximal pressure is usually measured by a manometer connected to a stopper in one nostril. The other nostril must be closed to prevent air flow, and precautions must be taken so that the patient does not use his buccal muscles to develop pressure. A normal subject can develop 60–100 mm Hg positive or negative pressure, depending to some extent on lung volume and degree of effort. The test has been used but little clinically, largely because a high pressure is also developed within the middle ear and this causes discomfort.

It is particularly useful in studying patients in whom the MVV is decreased but pulmonary compliance and resistance are normal; reduction in maximal inspiratory or expiratory force may point to muscular weakness as the critical factor causing the decrease in MVV.

TESTS OF OVER-ALL MECHANICAL FUNCTION OF LUNGS AND THORAX

So far, we have discussed compliance and resistance and specific tests to measure specific properties of the lungs and thorax. In general office and hospital practice, it is customary to use relatively simple procedures to test the mechanical function of the lungs. As we shall see, these tests

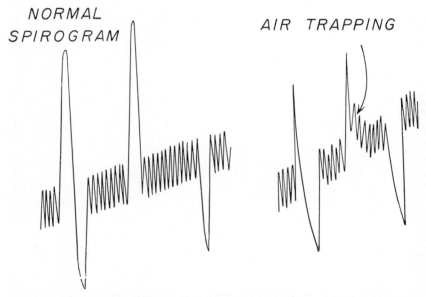

FIG. 52.—SPIROGRAMS OF NORMAL INDIVIDUAL AND PATIENT WITH EMPHYSEMA

In each case, a patient performs the following maneuvers (left to right): (1) vital capacity test, (2) maximal inspiration followed by normal breathing, and (3) maximal expiration followed by normal breathing. *Left,* spirogram of normal individual. *Right,* spirogram of patient with emphysema; note (*a*) slow return to resting expiratory level ("air trapping") following maximal inspiration, and (*b*) prolongation of expiration (the latter shown more clearly in Figure 50, where a rapid kymograph is used).

are not completely objective because they require co-operation of the patient; further they are not analytical because they measure several properties of the lungs and thorax simultaneously. Nevertheless they represent the proper initial approach. They are often diagnostically useful per se; when they are not, the result obtained usually suggests the proper direction for additional, more precise study of the patient.

SPIROGRAMS.—Spirographic tracings of normal breathing, forced inspiration and expiration, and maximal voluntary ventilation made on a rapidly moving kymograph (Figs. 52 and 53) permit analysis of many characteristics of the breathing pattern and provide a permanent record for comparison with later tracings. Some of these characteristics follow:

(1) *Times for normal inspiration and expiration.*—Normally, expiration requires about 1.2 times as long as inspiration. In patients with expiratory obstruction or with disease in which the elastic recoil (which normally aids expiration) is diminished, expiratory time is prolonged.

(2) *Time for return to resting expiratory level.*—If a normal individual inspires maximally and then permits his chest to return passively to the resting expiratory level, all of the inspired air is expelled before the next inspiration occurs (Figs. 50 and 52). In patients with predominantly expiratory obstruction, this maneuver is followed by a slow steplike return to the normal base line, during which several breaths may occur before the resting expiratory level is reached. This phenomenon, called "air trapping," may be noted to an even greater degree in emphysema, partly because of associated obstruction and partly because after rapid overdistention of the lung, the lung returns more slowly to its original volume. This abnormally slow return to the resting expiratory level may also occur after a maximal expiration. If patients with air trapping are taught to breathe out slowly, they can often breathe out more completely. This is one of the rational objectives of breathing exercises.

(3) *One- and two-stage vital capacity* (see p. 7).—The "two-stage vital capacity" refers to the procedure in which the inspiratory capacity and expiratory reserve are determined separately and then added (see p. 7). In asthma and emphysema, the two-stage value may exceed the one-stage by as much as 1 liter. This is because of the air trapping that occurs when maximal expiration follows a maximal inspiration. If the two-stage value is smaller than the one-stage, it is likely that the subject is not co-operating fully.

(4) *Maximal inspiratory and expiratory flow rates.*—Alterations in the pattern of breathing become more apparent when maximal, forced inspiratory and expiratory efforts are made. Figure 53 shows records

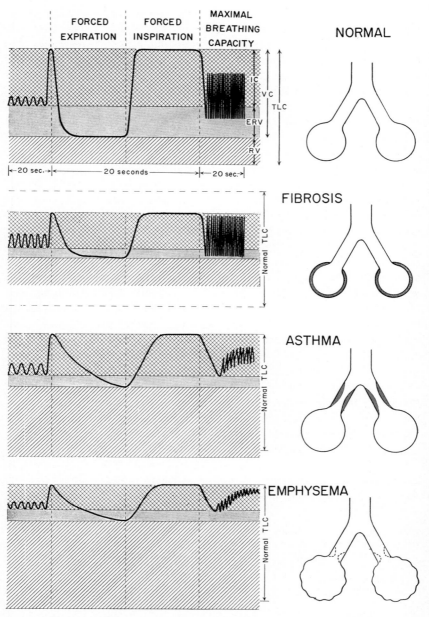

FIG. 53.—SPIROGRAMS OF NORMAL PATIENT AND PATIENTS WITH PULMONARY FIBROSIS, ASTHMA, AND EMPHYSEMA

198

from normal individuals and from patients with pulmonary disease. Quantitative measurements of air flow can be made directly from the spirometer record if a rapid paper speed is used; such values are identical to those using the more expensive electrical flow meter or pneumotachograph, if air flows do not exceed 400 L/min.

At least a dozen different methods have been proposed for the performance, recording and measuring of maximal expiratory flow rates. We prefer the following method because it provides a permanent, easy-to-measure record of both expiratory *and* inspiratory flow rates and because other measurements (forced expiratory volume, maximal mid-expiratory flow rates) can be obtained from the record, if desired. The subject is asked to inspire maximally and then blow out as hard and fast as he can. The first 200 ml of expired gas is disregarded and the flow rate is measured between 200 and 1200 ml of expired gas. The rate of air flow during forced expiration in a healthy young man is initially very rapid (400 L/min), though there is considerable slowing at end-expiration. If he exhales maximally and then breathes in as hard and fast as he can, the air flow is again rapid (300 L/min), but this rate can be maintained during inspiration until the lungs are full (Fig. 53). A marked reduction in flow rates indicates that a mechanical problem exists which may be present during either expiration or inspirations, or both. Flow rates may be reduced to as low as 20 L/min. Such severe reduction in expiratory flow rate is particularly serious because it decreases the patient's ability to cough and so to remove secretions from his airway.

The test does not give information as to the specific mechanical factor involved and does require co-operation of the patient; in these respects, it suffers from the same defects as the maximal voluntary ventilation test (maximal breathing capacity, see below). However, the test is much simpler (portable apparatus is now available), it is less fatiguing, is easily

---

◀———◀ FIG. 53.—In each illustration, the patient (left to right) (*a*) breathes quietly (slow kymograph), (*b*) takes a maximal inspiration, then expires as completely, forcefully and rapidly as he can (rapid kymograph), (*c*) from the position of complete expiration, makes a maximal, forced inspiration (rapid kymograph), and (*d*) performs the maximal breathing capacity test (slow kymograph). Timed vital capacity can be measured from (*b*) and maximal and mean expiratory and inspiratory flow rates can be calculated from (*b*) and (*c*).

The spirogram is shown in proper relation to total lung capacity, vital capacity, functional residual capacity, residual volume, expiratory reserve volume, and inspiratory capacity of each patient. The "lungs" on the right are similar to those pictured in Figure 22, p. 73. "Fibrosis" refers to restrictive types of fibrotic disease.

repeatable and clearly separates inspiratory and expiratory difficulties.

If one measures "intrathoracic pressure" during the test (esophageal balloon technique), one can determine whether the subject is making his maximal effort; if not, lack of comprehension, lack of co-operation or neuromuscular, muscular or metabolic disturbances may be responsible.

(5) *Forced expiratory volume ("timed vital capacity").*[†]—This is a very simple test which measures the volume that is expired by maximal effort in a specified time. The time may be the first second ($FEV_{1.0''}$), or the first 3 sec ($FEV_{3.0''}$), or the interval between 0.25 and 0.75 sec ($FEV_{0.25-0.75''}$). In the United States, $FEV_{1.0''}$ and $FEV_{3.0''}$ are commonly used (1 and 3 sec "timed vital capacity"). The patient makes a forced expiration into a spirometer which has a device that records total expired volume and the volume expired in 1, 2 or 3 sec, depending on the setting of the timer. The volume in 1 sec can be expressed either as per cent of that particular forced vital capacity $\left(\text{i.e., } \dfrac{FEV_{1.0''}}{FVC}\% \right)$ or as per cent of the vital capacity performed without relation to speed $\left(\text{i.e., } \dfrac{FEV_{1.0''}}{VC}\% \right)$. It has sometimes been expressed in terms of per cent of *predicted* vital capacity.

A normal individual can expire 83% of his vital capacity in 1 sec, 94% in 2 sec and 97% in 3 sec, and it makes little difference whether forced vital capacity, vital capacity or predicted vital capacity is used. This is not true in patients with pulmonary disease; a patient with interstitial pulmonary fibrosis may expire 83% or more of *his* vital capacity in 1 sec (because he has a markedly reduced vital capacity) but only 50% of his *predicted* (normal) vital capacity. Because of this, spirograms which permit measurements of actual flow rates (Fig. 53, p. 198) are preferable; a 1 sec volume can be read from the spirogram if desired. The $\dfrac{FEV_{1.0''}}{FVC}$ (in terms of actual vital capacity) is reduced in patients with obstructive pulmonary disease but not in those who have restricted expansion without obstruction.

MAXIMAL VOLUNTARY VENTILATION (MVV); MAXIMAL BREATHING CAPACITY (MBC).—Maximal breathing capacity (MBC) is the maximal volume of gas that can be breathed per minute. Maximal voluntary ventilation (MVV) is the maximal volume that can be breathed per minute by voluntary effort (Fig. 53, p. 198).

---

† See Table 17 for terminology.

TABLE 17.—TERMINOLOGY FOR MEASUREMENTS OF VENTILATORY CAPACITY

MEASUREMENT EXPRESSED IN TERMS OF:	NAME OF TEST (SYNONYMS IN PARENTHESES)	ABBREVIATION	REMARKS
A. Single Breath 1. Volume	Forced vital capacity* (Fast vital capacity)	FVC*	Always refers to *expiratory* effort unless qualified by "inspiratory"
2. Volume in a unit time	Forced expiratory volume* ("Timed vital capacity")	FEV_t*	Must be qualified by a time interval. $FEV_{1.0''}$ = vol. expired in 1 sec; $FEV_{0.25-0.75''}$=vol. expired between 0.25 and 0.75 sec
	Percentage expired* ("% timed vital capacity")	%FEV_t/VC*	Refers to volume of forced expiration (in time specified) related to vital capacity
		%FEV_t/FVC*	Refers to volume of forced expiration (in time specified) related to *forced* vital capacity
3. Volume/time	Maximal expiratory flow rate	MEFR	Refers to L/min for specified portion of a forced expiration; MEFR 200–1200 is flow rate for the liter of expired gas after 200 ml has been expired
	Maximal inspiratory flow rate	MIFR	Refers to L/min for specified portion of a forced inspiration
	Maximal mid-expiratory flow	MMF	Refers to L/min measured for the middle half of FVC
B. Repeated Breaths 1. Volume/time	Maximal breathing capacity	MBC	Usually attained by voluntary effort; occasionally exercise produces greater values
	Maximal voluntary ventilation*	MVV*	Maximal volume obtained by voluntary effort

* New terminology (Gandevia and Hugh-Jones, Thorax 12:290, 1957).

As a rule, maximal ventilation can be attained only by voluntary effort, although in some patients with severe pulmonary disease, exercise ventilation or ventilation induced by inhalation of high concentrations of CO_2 may exceed the MVV, probably because voluntarily forced expiration occludes airways partially or completely.

In the MVV test, the patient is instructed to breathe as deeply and as rapidly as he can through a low resistance system for 15 sec. The patient should be permitted to choose his own frequency and tidal volume; the frequency is usually between 40 and 70/min and the tidal volume is about 50% of vital capacity. Maximal figures are rarely attained by insisting upon repeated performance of the entire vital capacity, because the extremes of inspiration and expiration are performed with undue expenditure of time and energy.

Normal figures for MVV.—Normal figures obtained in different laboratories vary by as much as 30%, according to the type of apparatus used and the resistance it offers to breathing. Until similar apparatus and procedure are employed universally, it seems inevitable that each laboratory must calibrate its own apparatus and secure its own normal standard values. Unfortunately, it is not sufficient to secure normal data only for young healthy adult males, since values in healthy females and elderly males are considerably lower. Because of the large standard deviation, a healthy person may deviate by 25–35% of mean group values; consequently, reduction in MVV must be large to be significant.

Most of the figures for normal MVV have been obtained on healthy medical students. It is not strictly justified to compare values obtained on patients with these, because the test requires the maximal respiratory muscular effort of which the patient is capable and a desire to co-operate even to the point of exhaustion. Not every patient is motivated to this extent and some, especially in compensation cases, may even be malingerers. Cournand has advised that CO_2 be added to the inspired air to detect these. The use of an esophageal balloon to measure changes in "intrathoracic pressure" during the test also aids in evaluating the patient's effort.

Significance of MVV values.—The ability of a patient to breathe at sustained high velocity depends on many factors: the muscular force available, the compliance of the lungs and thoracic cage and the resistance of the airway and pulmonary thoracic tissues. Figure 53 (p. 198) shows that MVV is reduced out of proportion to decrease in vital capacity in patients with obstruction of the airways or with emphysema. This illustration also shows that air trapping and a large increase in functional residual capacity may occur during the test; in extreme cases, this results in an MVV that is less than the exercise or even the resting minute volume.

On the other hand, MVV may be fairly well maintained in some patients with restrictive types of pulmonary restrictive disease, even though there is marked reduction in vital capacity (Fig. 53), because the major defect in these patients is a limitation to expansion of the thorax. Similar values have been obtained in healthy individuals whose chests have been strapped tightly. The addition of as much as 90 lb on the chest and abdomen results in only a slight decrease in MVV in healthy subjects; the effect of such a weight over long periods of time is not known.

A comparison of the vital capacity and MVV in the same individual is often made by calculating the ratio

$$\frac{\% \text{ of predicted MVV}}{\% \text{ of predicted vital capacity}}$$

This ratio is called the air velocity index (AVI). The index may be misinterpreted if it is used without the absolute figures from which it is derived, since an index of *one* (presumably a normal value) may result from proportionate *reduction* in *both* MVV and vital capacity.

Although MVV gives information regarding the mechanics of breathing in many types of cardiopulmonary disease, a low value is not diagnostic of any single disease or disorder. Furthermore, it is a needlessly exhausting test and must not be used in patients with coronary insufficiency. It probably will be replaced eventually by simpler tests utilizing a single-breath or a more specific approach (see p. 197). However, it will continue to be useful whenever a repetitive test of the function of the respiratory muscles is needed, as in myasthenia gravis.

FUNCTIONAL RESIDUAL CAPACITY.—Measurement of the functional residual capacity (FRC) gives information as to the balance of forces in the lungs and chest (see Fig. 44, p. 188).

RESIDUAL VOLUME.—When a patient has a large residual volume, he may be unable to expire fully because of (*a*) increased airway resistance during the expiratory phase, (*b*) inability to exert sufficient force, or (*c*) increased rigidity of the lungs or thorax.

PART TWO

CLINICAL APPLICATIONS

CHAPTER 8

A Practical Approach to Evaluation of Pulmonary Function

THE STUDY of pulmonary physiology has moved in one decade from the pure research laboratory into the hospital cardiopulmonary laboratory, the clinic and the physician's office. This has created several problems: (1) Hospitals, clinics and chest physicians need to know how to develop their own pulmonary function laboratory. (2) The practicing physician needs to know when to refer his patients to a laboratory for studies of pulmonary function, and which studies to request. It is the object of this section to provide at least partial answers to these problems, as we see them.

First, not every chest physician, and indeed not every hospital, can have a "complete" laboratory capable of testing all aspects of pulmonary function (even if pulmonary physiologists could agree on what constitutes "modern" and "complete" testing). Table 18 represents an attempt to classify most of the present tests according to whether they can be performed in (A) the office, clinic or small hospital, (B) in a well-equipped cardiopulmonary laboratory in a medical center, staffed with clinical pulmonary physiologists, or (C) only in the research laboratory. Every patient with known or suspected cardiopulmonary disease should have the studies listed in Column A, just as every new patient presenting himself for any complaint should have a urinalysis and measurement of his blood pressure and hemoglobin. The studies in Column A include radiologic examination of the chest, an electrocardiogram and measurement of the number of red blood cells, hemoglobin concentration and packed

TABLE 18.—CLASSIFICATION OF TESTS OF PULMONARY FUNCTION

(Clinical history, physical findings and radiologic evidence are only mentioned here; they may be of considerable importance in identifying physiologic disturbances, but have been described in great detail in many other books and monographs.)

PROCEDURES USED IN:

For Measurement of:	A. Office, Clinic or Small Hospital	B. Cardiopulmonary Laboratory in Medical Center	C. Research Cardiopulmonary Laboratory
1. LUNG VOLUMES	Vital capacity, inspiratory capacity, expiratory reserve volume	Residual volume, functional residual capacity, total lung capacity, RV/TLC ratio	Thoracic gas volume (body plethysmograph)
2. PULMONARY VENTILATION			
a) Volume	Clinical & fluoroscopic analysis of physical basis for hypoventilation. Spirometric measurement of rate, tidal volume & minute volume; calculation of alveolar ventilation based on above measurements & estimated anatomic dead space	Alveolar or arterial blood P_{CO_2}. Ventilatory response to inhaled 5–10% CO_2 in air	Alveolar ventilation calculated from *measured* anatomic dead space
b) Distribution	Clinical & radiologic examination for uneven expansion of lungs & uneven air flow (uneven breath sounds, percussion notes, chest expansion; uneven radiolucence seen fluoroscopically)	Single-breath N_2 meter test. Pulmonary N_2 elimination rate. Helium distribution test. Calculation of "physiologic" dead space & of effective alveolar ventilation. Bronchospirometry. Rate of oximeter rise during O_2 inhalation	Volume of trapped gas (body plethysmograph). Inhalation of radioactive xenon, CO_2, etc., to determine regional pattern

(Continued)

TABLE 18.—Classification of Tests of Pulmonary Function *(cont.)*

For Measurement of:	A. Office, Clinic or Small Hospital	B. Cardiopulmonary Laboratory in Medical Center	C. Research Cardiopulmonary Laboratory
3. PULMONARY CIRCULATION			
a) Changes in pressure, flow, resistance or volume	Clinical, ECG & radiologic examination for evidence of pulmonary hypertension or congestion; circulation times (?)	Cardiac catheterization & measurement of pressure, flow, resistance & O_2 content at selected points between venae cavae & pulmonary artery	Pulmonary capillary blood volume (CO method). Pulmonary capillary blood flow (N_2O uptake). Injection of acetylcholine or similar vasodilator drug to determine reversibility of increased vascular resistance
b) Distribution..	Radiologic examination for evidence of nonuniform pulmonary vascular markings; listen for bruits	Selective pulmonary angiography. Bronchospirometry (O_2 consumption of right vs. left lung). Arterial O_2 saturation & rate of oximeter rise during inhalation of O_2 (right-to-left shunt?)	Arterial blood— mixed expired alveolar gas CO_2 tension difference. Arterial O_2 tension during inhalation of O_2. "Alveolar" dead space. Measurement of excretion or absorption of radioactive xenon or krypton (given intravenously) or CO_2 (inhaled) to determine regional pattern
4. ALVEOLAR-CAPILLARY DIFFUSION	No specific test but can suspect diagnosis on clinical and radiologic evidence	Diffusing capacity (CO). Arterial O_2 saturation during exercise & during inhalation of O_2 (not specific)	Membrane diffusing capacity (CO). Erythrocyte "resistance" (CO). Diffusing capacity (O_2). Maximal diffusing capacity (exercise)

(Continued)

TABLE 18.—CLASSIFICATION OF TESTS OF PULMONARY FUNCTION *(cont.)*

For Measurement of:	A. Office, Clinic or Small Hospital	B. Cardiopulmonary Laboratory in Medical Center	C. Research Cardiopulmonary Laboratory
5. ARTERIAL O_2, CO_2 AND pH....	Look for cyanosis. Packed cell volume & RBC/cu mm (not specific). Measure change in respiration & pulse rate during inhalation of O_2	Arterial O_2 content, capacity & saturation; arterial CO_2 content & tension; pH. Ear or cuvette oximetric analysis of absolute values & changes in O_2 saturation during exercise or inhalation of O_2	Measurement of arterial Po_2 by O_2 electrode or bubble equilibration technique. Measurement of arterial Pco_2 by CO_2 electrode or bubble equilibration technique. Spectrophotometric analysis for abnormal Hb
6. MECHANICAL FACTORS IN BREATHING	Maximal expiratory & inspiratory flow rates; spirogram; FEV; MVV (all tests performed before and after administration of bronchodilator drugs)	Pulmonary compliance. Total pulmonary resistance. Maximal inspiratory & expiratory pressures (oral & esophageal)	Airway resistance (body plethysmograph). Pulmonary tissue resistance. Compliance of thoracic cage

cell volume as well as of vital capacity and its subdivisions, maximal flow rates and possibly MVV.

The measurement of lung volumes, ventilation and mechanical factors in breathing in the office, clinic or hospital (Group *A,* Table 18) requires the use of a spirometer of 6–9 liter capacity (a water-filled basal metabolism spirometer is satisfactory) preferably writing on a drum which has a slow (0.5–1 mm/sec) and a very fast (30–40 mm/sec) speed (a student laboratory kymograph is ideal). Several spirometer-kymograph units are commercially available for pulmonary function testing; the physician purchasing one of these should make sure that (1) internal and external tubes are wide, (2) valves have low resistance, (3) the bell moves with little friction and has little inertia, and (4) the drum has slow and *fast,* rather than very slow and slow, speeds. Several less expen-

TABLE 19.—Interpretation of Data

Group A Tests* (see Table 18)	Group B & C Tests (see Table 18)
EXAMPLE 1 — All tests normal; no symptoms and no clinical or radiologic evidence of cardiopulmonary disease. Patient is almost certainly normal	No need for further study
EXAMPLE 2 — *All tests normal, but patient has chief complaint of "blueness."* Suspect pulmonary or cardiac venous-to-arterial shunt (p. 243) or abnormal (inactive) Hb	Determine maximal O_2 content and tension of arterial blood drawn after patient has breathed pure O_2 for 15 min (and is still breathing O_2) in posture in which his cyanosis characteristically develops. If blood is not maximally oxygenated (100% saturation, 1.8 ml of dissolved $O_2/100$ ml of blood, or Po_2 of >600 mm Hg), patient has a shunt Cardiac catheterization or angiocardiography may be necessary to determine its location If dissolved O_2 is > 1.8 ml $O_2/100$ ml or Po_2 is > 600 mm Hg, test blood spectrophotometrically for abnormal (inactive) Hb
EXAMPLE 3 — *All tests normal, but patient has chief complaint of shortness of breath.* Suspect neurocirculatory asthenia or pulmonary vascular disorder (embolism, vascular sclerosis, pulmonary hypertension or left heart failure; pp. 246-255)	Do complete pulmonary function studies of ventilation, distribution, diffusion, arterial blood; if no pulmonary disease, measure uniformity of pulmonary capillary blood flow by arterial-alveolar Pco_2 difference; if no uneven distribution, do cardiac catheterization and measure pulmonary vascular pressures and resistance

---

* The pulmonary function studies in Group *A* are vital capacity, spirogram, maximal inspiratory and expiratory flow rates, maximal voluntary ventilation and alveolar ventilation calculated from TV, frequency and estimated anatomic dead space. If abnormal values are found, tests should be repeated after administration of bronchodilator drugs. (Clinical, radiologic, hematologic and electrocardiographic studies also yield valuable *physiologic* data, and these studies should always be performed with this in mind.)

(Continued)

TABLE 19.—INTERPRETATION OF DATA *(cont.)*

Group A Tests*	Group B & C Tests
EXAMPLE 4 *All tests normal except for decrease in alveolar ventilation.* Suspect central lesion near medullary respiratory centers	Test the respiratory center by determining patient's ventilatory response to inhaled 5–10% CO_2 in air
EXAMPLE 5 *Vital capacity normal (or nearly so); maximal expiratory flow rate and MVV decreased.* Suspect obstructive pattern (p. 220) caused by asthma, emphysema, bronchitis or bronchial obstruction. Give adequate bronchodilator therapy (isoproterenol aerosol, epinephrine subcutaneously, aminophylline I.V. or, if need be, adrenal cortical therapy) to determine if there is a reversible asthmatic component	If not reversible and objective or analytical data are necessary, measure distribution of inspired gas, residual volume, total lung capacity, thoracic gas volume, volume of trapped gas, airway resistance and pulmonary compliance
EXAMPLE 6 *Maximal expiratory flow rate normal (or nearly so), MVV normal, vital capacity decreased; alveolar ventilation normal or increased.* Suspect restrictive pattern (p. 238) or pattern of impaired diffusion (p. 232). Look for cyanosis (aggravated during exercise) and radiologic evidence of diffuse pulmonary opacities	Measure arterial blood P_{CO_2} and arterial O_2 saturation at rest and during exercise. Measure pulmonary diffusing capacity, pulmonary and thoracic compliance and pulmonary tissue resistance
EXAMPLE 7 *Vital capacity, maximal expiratory flow rate and MVV decreased; alveolar ventilation normal.* Suspect pattern of obstruction (p. 220), restriction (p. 238), pulmonary vascular congestion (p. 252) or of hypoventilation due to neurologic disorders (p. 220). Repeat tests after adequate therapy for (1) asthma and (2) congestive heart failure	Perform complete pulmonary function studies, including maximal oral and esophageal inspiratory and expiratory pressures as tests of respiratory muscle weakness
EXAMPLE 8 *Vital capacity, maximal expiratory flow rate, MVV and alveolar ventilation decreased.* Suspect pattern of hypoventilation due to neurologic, neuromuscular or muscular disorder (p. 213) or of severe restriction or obstruction	Measure maximal oral and esophageal inspiratory and expiratory pressures, pulmonary and thoracic compliance, pulmonary tissue and airway resistances

sive devices utilize a bellows and pen which provide a written record of vital capacity and maximal expiratory flow rate, without provision for the back-and-forth movement necessary to measure tidal volume, MVV and maximal inspiratory flow rate.

Simple spirometric measurement of vital capacity and maximal flow rates requires no more than 5 min of the patient's time (if the values are normal) and involves no discomfort. When the values recorded are low, the physician should give adequate bronchodilator aerosol therapy over 3–5 min, wait 10–15 min for maximal effect, then repeat the procedures.

Office studies provide permanent records of the status of the patient at the first examination. They often disclose unsuspected pulmonary disorders in patients thought to have heart disease.* They may detect disease early enough to permit effective prevention of its progression and they serve as an objective guide to therapy in the individual patient.

We have recently asked a group of post-doctoral fellows and staff working in pulmonary function laboratories to review the records of several hundred consecutive patients given pulmonary function studies; however, the data for each patient were presented sequentially instead of all at once. Initially the group was given only the data from studies in Column A (history, physical examination and relatively simple pulmonary function studies). In a surprisingly large number of cases, the diagnosis (which finally was based on *all* studies performed) was tentatively or reasonably well established by Group A tests alone. We believe, therefore, that the studies listed in Column A can form the basis for diagnosis when used and interpreted by physicians well versed in pulmonary physiology. When they provide sufficient diagnostic information, no further studies need be done. When they give incomplete or inconclusive answers, the patient should be referred to a cardiopulmonary laboratory for tests in Group B. When the functional diagnosis cannot be made there, it can usually be made in one of the several research institutes studying cardiopulmonary physiology. For these reasons, and because most patients who present diagnostic problems are able to travel to the nearest center, we do not believe that every large hospital should have a "complete" laboratory (Column C) or need even perform all tests listed in Column B.

Table 19 is a guide to interpretation of data obtained from simple (Group A) tests and to possible steps to follow when simple tests do not provide an adequate basis for diagnosis.

---

* Of 60 patients whose final diagnosis was "obstructive pulmonary disease," the diagnosis was made clinically in only 65%; pulmonary function tests were essential for diagnosis in 28% and a combination of the two in 7%.

CHAPTER 9

Patterns of Pulmonary Function in Cardiopulmonary and Respiratory Disorders

PHYSIOLOGIC TESTS measure function. Like the electrocardiogram and the chest film, they do not provide a pathologic or bacteriologic diagnosis of pulmonary disease. True, a cardiologist can say with some assurance that a particular electrocardiographic pattern is highly characteristic of right ventricular hypertrophy; however, this "diagnosis" is possible only because electrocardiographic patterns have been correlated for many years with clinical and pathologic diagnoses of cardiac disease. Again, a radiologist can give his opinion that a certain pattern of diffuse mottling of the lungs represents pulmonary fibrosis. His diagnosis is possible only because of previous correlative studies with other diagnostic methods over many years. The scientific radiologist will not say, "This patient has sarcoidosis," but rather, "On the basis of past experience, the shadows in this film are quite similar to those seen in patients proved by other tests to have pulmonary sarcoidosis."

Likewise, physiologists can determine characteristic *patterns* of altered function and suggest the most likely clinical disease or syndrome compatible with the observed pattern. The physiologist, on the basis of his studies alone, will be unwilling as a rule to make specific pathologic diagnoses. Rather than say, "The patient has obstructive pulmonary emphysema," he will state, "The patient has a pattern characteristic of obstructive ventilatory disease. It is compatible with pulmonary emphysema for the following reasons. . . ." This is not evading his responsibility to make a diagnosis; it is a statement of his belief that physiologic tests usually supplement and do not replace other diagnostic methods, and that a total evaluation of the disease process often requires use of the methods of several disciplines.

Pulmonary function studies have now been performed in patients with many different diseases. However, instead of listing all of these disorders with the physiologic abnormalities reported for each, we shall present *patterns* of altered function. We believe that this approach is more useful because most diseases (including those still to be identified) will probably fit one or more of the following patterns: (1) aging; (2) alveolar hypoventilation; (3) airway obstruction; (4) impaired diffusion; (5) pulmonary or thoracic restriction; (6) right-to-left shunts; (7) uneven pulmonary capillary blood flow; (8) pulmonary vascular congestion; (9) precapillary obstruction.

PATTERN OF AGING*

Elderly "normals" are usually men and women above 50–60 years who have no symptoms of cardiopulmonary disease and have normal lungs on clinical and radiologic examinations. A few persons between the ages of 50 and 90 have pulmonary function comparable to that of healthy young men and women, but these are atypical. Older persons usually have the following pattern:

LUNG VOLUMES.—The vital capacity decreases and the residual volume and functional residual capacity increase (for predicted values based on age, see Table 28, p. 325). Since the total lung capacity does not change, RV/TLC increases to between 35 and 45%.

VENTILATION.—Frequency or tidal volume, and minute volume of breathing increase slightly; anatomic dead space increases probably because of the increase in functional residual capacity; O_2 consumption and CO_2 production per minute decrease. The ventilatory responses to inhaled CO_2 in air and to 100% O_2 are normal.

DISTRIBUTION OF INSPIRED GAS AND BLOOD.—The distribution of inspired gas, measured by the single-breath test, is more uneven than in young persons. Alveolar dead space is increased.

---

* We have included data representative of important *groups* of tests rather than data from all known tests because (1) some laboratories use unique tests or modifications of standard tests, and (2) often several standard tests measure the same aspect of lung function; for example, tests of MVV, maximal flow rates and forced expiratory volume all measure the bellows function of the lung; it is not necessary to perform more than one test of this group.

PULMONARY CIRCULATION.—Pressure, flow and resistance in the pulmonary circulation are normal when the subject is resting.

DIFFUSION.—Resting diffusing capacity (single-breath CO test) is normal. Maximal diffusing capacity for O_2 decreases with advancing age.

ARTERIAL BLOOD.—The arterial blood O_2 saturation (96.5%) is not significantly different from that in young men (97.4%). Arterial blood CO_2 tension and pH are normal.

MECHANICS OF BREATHING.—The MVV and maximal flow rates may be decreased to 50% of normal. Pulmonary resistance is usually increased, but airway resistance (measured in the body plethysmograph during panting) is normal. The elastic tissues of the lungs appear to change with age because pulmonary compliance is increased and the static pressure-volume curve is shifted to the left (the end-expiratory transpulmonary pressure is decreased, even though the lung volume is greater). Muscle force decreases, and this may be responsible for the decrease in flow rates.

The pathogenesis of these changes can only be surmised: (1) The normal aging process may interfere with maintenance, repair and replacement of connective tissue, blood vessels, skeletal and smooth muscles and permit normal changes to go unrepaired; or (2) the pattern is really not the result of physiologic aging but is caused by a succession of unrecognized minor pulmonary infections or injuries incurred during four or five decades.

It is important in evaluating pulmonary function in older men and women to remember that the base line is not the same as for healthy young adults. It is equally important to know that these individuals may have no pulmonary symptoms even though the MVV may be as low as 50% and the RV/TLC ratio more than 40%. However, the changes produced by relatively mild pulmonary disease added to pre-existing changes caused by aging may lead to definite symptoms because of the decrease in reserve.

PATTERN OF HYPOVENTILATION

Hypoventilation can result from so many different causes (p. 45) that the label "hypoventilation syndrome" is meaningless. Hypoventilation may occur in normal individuals during deep sleep, in patients with normal lungs and thorax (depression of respiratory centers, abnormal pattern of rate and depth of breathing, interference with neuromuscular conduction and transmission), in patients with normal lungs but a rigid thorax (kyphoscoliosis) and in patients with very severe obstructive or restrictive pulmonary disease (asthma, emphysema, interstitial fibrosis). Obviously the "diagnosis" of hypoventilation is only the first step toward finding the specific cause.

Some physicians use the term "hypoventilation syndrome" to apply only to grossly obese individuals. Such labeling is also unacceptable because only a small fraction of obese people hypoventilate, and when they do it may be for varied reasons: excessive work load on the respiratory muscles, weakness of skeletal muscle because of fatty infiltration, primary disease of the central nervous system leading to both obesity and depression of breathing, primary polycythemia leading to central embolic phenomena and hypoventilation, or simply because of unrelated pulmonary disease. Furthermore, anoxemia in obese patients may not be due to alveolar hypoventilation at all, but to uneven distribution of gas and blood.

Pulmonary function studies in patients with hypoventilation but no detectable physical abnormality in the lungs and thorax show the following typical results:

LUNG VOLUMES.—These may be normal (see Case 1) or markedly reduced if there is depression or block of neural pathways from the respiratory center to the respiratory muscles.

VENTILATION.—Alveolar ventilation, calculated from tidal volume, frequency and anatomic dead space, is decreased in relation to the patient's metabolic rate.

DISTRIBUTION OF GAS AND BLOOD may be normal, but hypoventilation often leads to airway obstruction (because of the patient's inability to cough effectively), and this in turn to uneven ventilation. Marked obesity may lead to restriction of thoracic and diaphragmatic movements and to scattered alveolar collapse, just as tight thoracic strapping does; this results in uneven ventilation in relation to blood flow.

PULMONARY CIRCULATION.—Normal unless thromboses have occurred because of polycythemia or because of heart failure due to anoxemia.

DIFFUSION.—Normal.

ARTERIAL BLOOD.—Oxygen tension and saturation are always decreased and arterial blood Pco_2 increased if the patient is breathing air. If hypoventilation is not complicated by obstruction, alveolar collapse or previous pulmonary disease, arterial blood O_2 and CO_2 values should return to normal when a normal volume of *air* is breathed. Arterial blood O_2 saturation rises to 100% and Po_2 to more than 600 mm Hg when O_2 is inhaled, even though hypoventilation continues. The Hb concentration and packed cell volume are high (polycythemia secondary to anoxemia).

MECHANICAL PROPERTIES of the lungs and thorax may be normal (see Case 1, following). Maximal flow rates are decreased when there is interference with neuromuscular conduction and transmission.

Case 1 (Hypoventilation)

N. M. is a large man (2.1 M^2 surface area), 63 years of age, with polycythemia of unknown cause. The Pulmonary Function Section was asked to determine whether his polycythemia was secondary to anoxemia of cardiopulmonary origin.

For 17 years, the patient has had frequent attacks of hiccup, sometimes followed by vomiting and blood spitting. A few months previously, he had a severe hemorrhage, possibly originating in esophageal varices. More recently, he has had several attacks of numbness and tingling on the right side of his body and noted that his memory was failing slightly.

The patient is ambulatory and co-operative. He is not dyspneic, but his face has a purplish-red cyanosis with numerous telangiectasias. There is moderate enlargement of the heart and liver, but not of the spleen.

PULMONARY FUNCTION STUDIES
Abnormal values are starred (*)

LUNG VOLUMES

Inspiratory capacity, ml	3930
Expiratory reserve volume, ml	390
Vital capacity, ml	4300
Residual volume (RV), ml	1710
Functional residual capacity, ml	2100
Total lung capacity (TLC), ml	6030
RV/TLC $\times$ 100, %	28
Dead space (anatomic), ml	270*.

VENTILATION

Tidal volume, ml	370*
Frequency, breaths/min	24
Minute volume, L/min	8.8
Alveolar ventilation (calc. on basis of anatomic dead space), L/min	2.4
Minute volume (7.5% CO_2), L/min	22

DISTRIBUTION OF INSPIRED GAS

Single-breath test, % N_2, 750–1250 ml	1.3
Pulmonary N_2 emptying rate (7 min), % N_2	0.3

(Continued)

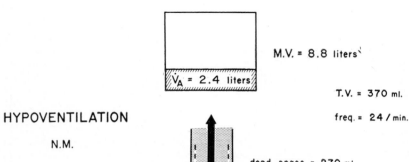

M.V. = 8.8 liters

T.V. = 370 ml.

HYPOVENTILATION

N.M.

freq. = 24 / min.

dead space = 270 ml.

V_A = 2.4 liters

O_2 sat. = 82 %

P_{CO_2} = 62 mm. Hg

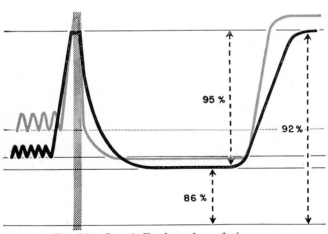

95 %

92 %

86 %

FIG. 54.—Case 1. For legend, see facing page

Figs. 54–59.—Schematic Representations of Pulmonary Function Tests

Above: Pulmonary gas exchange. Symbols are the same as those in Chapter 4. Total area of the large block represents minute volume of breathing. Striped portion represents maximal alveolar ventilation, calculated on the basis of tidal volume, *anatomical* dead space, and frequency of breathing. Arrows in the conducting airways (shaded area) indicate tidal volume entering and leaving the whole lung and its distribution to different regions. Circular areas represent alveoli in different regions (not necessarily in the right vs. the left lung). Small arrows designate the process of diffusion of O_2 and CO_2 across the alveolar-capillary membranes. Width of the blood channel surrounding the alveoli signifies the volume of blood flow to each region; dark gray indicates poorly oxygenated blood; light gray, well oxygenated blood leaving the pulmonary capillaries. Volume of the respiratory dead space has been either measured by the single breath test (Fig. 60) or estimated by reference to standard values (see Fig. 13, p. 42).

Below: Tracings of patient's spirogram, similar to that depicted in Figure 53, p. 198. Vertical cross-hatched bar represents the point at which the kymograph is speeded. Tracing to the left of it is the patient's tidal volume (slowly moving paper). Record to the right represents forced maximal expiration from the maximal inspiratory position followed by forced maximal inspiration from the maximal expiratory position (rapidly moving paper). Tidal volume is shown in its proper relation to the lung volumes, such as residual volume, functional residual capacity, vital capacity, and inspiratory capacity. Vital capacity does not always equal the sum of inspiratory capacity and expiratory reserve volume determined individually (see p. 197). Black tracing represents the patient's spirogram; the gray tracing represents a predicted spirogram for a healthy individual of the same age and physical characteristics. The "per cents" refer to the per cent of predicted normal residual volume, vital capacity, and total lung capacity.

DIFFUSION

Single-breath CO diffusing capacity, ml/min/mm Hg.................. 30

ARTERIAL BLOOD

O_2 saturation (air), %... 82*
O_2 saturation (O_2), %... 100
Dissolved O_2, ml O_2/100 ml blood............................... 1.9
CO_2 tension, mm Hg... 62*
pH 7.20*
O_2 saturation (hyperventilation with air), %...................... 99
O_2 saturation (exercise), %..................................... 58*

MECHANICS OF BREATHING

Max. voluntary ventilation, L/min.............................. 195
Max. expiratory flow rate, L/min............................... 340
Max. inspiratory flow rate, L/min.............................. 205
Forced expiratory volume, % in 1 sec........................... 79

INTERPRETATION (see Fig. 54).—Alveolar ventilation is decreased, arterial blood O_2 saturation is low and arterial P_{CO_2} is increased. These data fit the basic requirements of the pattern of hypoventilation. Although his minute volume is 8.8 L/min, his *alveolar* ventilation (calculated from tidal volume, rate and anatomic dead space) is only 2.4 L/min, or 0.7 L/100 ml O_2 consumption. In this patient, alveolar ventilation is decreased largely because of insufficient tidal volume, but in part because of an increased anatomic dead space.

Because his lung volumes are normal and his maximal voluntary ventilation (195 L/min) is well above the average for a healthy young man, we can eliminate the patterns of obstruction and of restriction. The hypoventilation then must be due to specific depression of the medullary respiratory center because (1) it is present in spite of three potent stimuli (high arterial P_{CO_2}, low arterial P_{O_2} and low arterial pH); (2) his respiratory response to inhalation of 7.5% CO_2 in air is far less than predicted (see Fig. 16, p. 52), and (3) voluntary hyperventilation with air corrects the anoxemia (this eliminates any disease of spinal cord, motor nerves or respiratory muscles).

The remaining tests confirm the diagnosis because they exclude other causes of anoxemia. There is no impairment of diffusion; there is no anatomic venous-to-arterial shunt (during inhalation of O_2, the O_2 dissolved in blood increased to 1.9 ml, equivalent to a P_{O_2} of 630 ml Hg); distribution of gas and blood is uniform, (physiologic dead space calculated from the equation shown on p. 338 was approximately equal to anatomic dead space and tests of distribution of inspired gas were normal).

CONCLUSIONS.—The patient probably has a lesion in the region of his medullary respiratory center; this may be secondary to thrombosis caused by primary polycythemia. A curious feature of this case which requires further investigation is the obvious depression of the respiratory center to normal chemical stimuli at a time when, by his own volition, the patient breathed 194 L/min. This implies that impulses from his cerebral cortex drive his ventilation even when the respiratory center does not respond normally to its usual chemical stimulus or to exercise.

A presumptive diagnosis could be made here simply by measurement of tidal volume and frequency of breathing at rest, and of MVV. More complex tests serve to confirm the diagnosis by eliminating other possible causes.

Attempts at therapy included mechanical hyperventilation, Diamox, respiratory stimulants and breathing exercises. None was beneficial; this suggests that his central nervous system damage is irreversible.

Case 5 (Obstructive Emphysema)

This case is presented on p. 227 as typical of the obstructive pattern in emphysema. However, the patient also has severe hypoventilation; alveolar ventilation, calculated from tidal volume, frequency and anatomic dead space, is only 2 L/min. Arterial O_2 saturation is 90.2% and arterial blood P_{CO_2} 57 mm Hg.

Is this patient's hypoventilation due to primary depression of the respiratory center? This is unlikely. It is probably due to gross abnormalities in the mechanical properties of his lungs, increase in the work of breathing and respiratory muscle fatigue. However, he may have *secondary* depression of the respiratory center caused by chronic anoxemia and CO_2 retention. This could be estimated by noting the maximal ventilation during inhalation of 5–7% CO_2 in air; however, this value is meaningless unless it is related to the MVV, which in this patient is greatly reduced. In general, patients with severe emphysema appear to have normal impulses from the respiratory center and vigorous respiratory muscle contraction (as manifested by changes in esophageal pressure), but this cannot be translated into effective ventilation because of mechanical limitation to movement of the lungs.

Case 2 (Hypoventilation)

S. L., a muscular, moderately obese man (age 28, 5 ft 10 in. tall, 220 lb) received tetanus antitoxin following an injury. Eleven days later his chest felt heavy and he became dyspneic on lying down. He could sleep only in the sitting position. He consulted a physician who thought that the dyspnea was psychogenic. Two weeks later he still had no dyspnea when standing but became cyanotic and dyspneic on lying down. Simple pulmonary function studies showed:

LUNG VOLUMES

Vital capacity (standing), ml... 2400
Vital capacity (supine), ml... 600

VENTILATION

Minute volume (standing), L/min..................................... 13
Minute volume (supine), L/min....................................... 2

Arterial blood was not analyzed, but the oximeter reading declined abruptly when he changed from the standing to the supine position.

In this patient motor neuritis and weakness of his respiratory muscles undoubtedly developed as a reaction to tetanus antitoxin; paralysis of his thoracic muscles was complete and of the diaphragm, partial. When he stood up, his diaphragm was able to produce adequate alveolar ventilation; when supine, the weight of the abdominal contents pushed against the weak diaphragm and prevented adequate inspiration. The patient ultimately made a complete recovery.

This case illustrates pure alveolar hypoventilation due to disease of motor nerves to the respiratory muscles. The diagnosis was made by simple measurements of vital capacity and ventilation with the patient in the posture in which dyspnea occurred.

PATTERN OF DIFFUSE OBSTRUCTION OF SMALL AIRWAYS

Obstruction of smaller airways may occur because of (1) constriction of bronchiolar smooth muscle; (2) mucosal congestion or inflammation; (3) edema of bronchiolar tissues; (4) plugging of the lumen by mucus, edema fluid, exudate or foreign bodies; (5) cohesion of mucosal surfaces by surface tension forces; (6) infiltration, compression or fibrosis of bronchioles, or (7) collapse or kinking of bronchioles due to loss of the normal pull of alveolar elastic fibers on bronchiolar walls or to loss of structural, supporting tissues of the bronchial walls ("weak walls").

The obstructive pattern may be a simple one in which airway obstruction is the only pulmonary abnormality (as in asthma); it may be more complex, e.g., when structural disease of the lung causes the obstruction (as in emphysema), or it may be present as a pattern which complicates a variety of diseases.

Several important concepts deserve emphasis:

1. The airway resistance of healthy individuals is about equal during quiet inspiration and expiration, but it becomes greater during expiration when breathing is forced or deep. However, a pronounced increase in expiratory resistance, with little or no increase during inspiration, is almost certainly due to collapse of airways because of "weak walls" or loss of the traction normally provided by the elastic properties of surrounding tissues. Because of this, the airways open readily during inspiration but collapse early in expiration, thus creating a check valve. Measurement of the maximal inspiratory as well as expiratory flow rate permits diagnosis of this specific type of obstruction.

2. When obstruction is reversed completely and rapidly by therapy, the obstruction must have been due to smooth muscle constriction, mucosal congestion or edema, or plugging of the lumen. Rapid reversal cannot occur when there is organic narrowing of the lumen (as in peribronchiolar fibrosis) or destruction of tissues resulting in a check valve (as in obstructive emphysema). Relief of obstruction by isoproterenol, which is both bronchodilator and vasodilator, suggests that smooth muscle constriction is the mechanism responsible for the obstruction; relief following use of a powerful vasoconstrictor, such as norepinephrine administered as an aerosol, would indicate that vascular congestion is of critical importance.

3. Normal airways may appear to be obstructed when the respiratory muscles are weak or paralyzed. To learn whether low flow rates are due to weak muscular action, one can determine the maximal force that the respiratory muscles are capable of exerting by measuring the maximal oral or intra-esophageal pressures developed during forced expiration.

Pulmonary function studies in the obstructive pattern show:

LUNG VOLUMES.—Vital capacity may be normal if none of the airways is obstructed completely. It is decreased if the obstruction of some airways is complete, or if the narrowing is so severe that the airways close completely during a forced expiration. Both residual volume and functional residual capacity are increased; the greater inflation of the lungs puts more stretch on the airways, may widen their lumens and so facilitate breathing. Thoracic gas volume often exceeds the FRC measured by dilution methods (p. 20), presumably because some airways are completely blocked part of the time and the alveolar gas distal to these is not included in the lung volume measured by gas dilution. Total lung capacity is usually considerably greater than normal in patients with obstructive pulmonary emphysema; since the increase may be as much as 3 liters, it cannot be due simply to loss of alveolar septa or capillaries since the volume occupied by *all* of the lung and its blood is very much less than this.

VENTILATION.—Patients with emphysema may hyperventilate until the disease is almost terminal. Breathing through obstructed airways increases the work of breathing and O_2 consumption of the respiratory muscles and probably contributes to ventilatory failure.

DISTRIBUTION OF GAS AND BLOOD.—Distribution of inspired gas is non-uniform in all types of obstructive airway disease. This is true in asthma and peribronchiolar fibrosis, as well as in emphysema, because the degree of narrowing is never the same in each of the hundreds of thousands of airways. However, patients with pulmonary emphysema usually have far greater maldistribution of inspired air than do patients with other diseases.

PULMONARY CIRCULATION.—There is no constant relationship between the type and degree of airway obstruction and changes in the pulmonary circulation. If pulmonary blood flow is uniform but ventilation is uneven, uneven ventilation/blood flow ratios must occur. If there is widespread destruction of pulmonary capillaries and reduction in the pulmonary vascular bed, pulmonary hypertension, right ventricular hypertrophy and right heart failure may supervene.

DIFFUSION.—Diffusing capacity may be normal, as in patients with bronchial asthma who have no airways completely occluded and in patients with emphysema in whom there is no significant reduction in the pulmonary capillary bed. It is decreased in many patients with advanced emphysema, but this test is not wholly reliable in patients whose distribution of gas is grossly uneven; for example, if part of the patient's lung is perfused but not ventilated, and another region is ventilated but not perfused, the diffusing capacity of these parts is zero even though the alveolar-capillary membranes are normal in thickness and area.

ARTERIAL BLOOD.—Arterial blood O_2 and CO_2 may be normal if blood flow to the poorly ventilated alveoli is reduced in proportion to the air flow (see Fig. 32, p. 102). Arterial O_2 saturation may be decreased and

Pco_2 normal (Case 3) because of uneven ventilation/blood flow ratios. Arterial Pco_2 becomes elevated when a large portion of the lung is poorly ventilated but still has considerable blood flow (Case 17, p. 273) or if actual hypoventilation occurs (Case 5, p. 227).

MECHANICAL FACTORS.—Maximal flow rates (MVV, MEFR and FEV) decrease far more than does vital capacity. If the patient has bronchial asthma, his flow rates return to or toward normal following bronchodilator therapy. If the patient has emphysema or other disease which permits collapse of the medium-size to fine airways, there is little improvement in the flow rates following bronchodilator therapy. Pulmonary resistance and airway resistance are always increased in the obstructive pattern. Muscle force is normal unless chronic hyperventilation has led to fatigue. Pulmonary compliance is normal unless the number of patent airways is reduced by obstruction so that there is considerable air trapping.

Case 3 (Asthma)

S. M. is a student, aged 17, in whom frequent wheezing, coughing and shortness of breath developed following an attack of bronchopneumonia at age 2. The attacks are more severe at night, and on occasion he has found it necessary to sleep in a chair. The Pulmonary Function Section was asked to determine the nature of his physiologic disorder and, in particular, to recommend effective therapy.

When the patient was studied, he had no dyspnea or cyanosis. The thorax appeared to be enlarged, and percussion notes were indicative of hyper-resonance, but no râles or rhonchi were heard. Radiologic examination showed overinflation of the lungs with increased lung markings but no evidence of localized disease.

PULMONARY FUNCTION STUDIES
Abnormal values are starred (*)

LUNG VOLUMES

Inspiratory capacity, ml	2630*
Expiratory reserve volume, ml	920
Vital capacity, ml	2800*
After therapy	3640
Residual volume (RV), ml	3500*
Functional residual capacity, ml	4420*
Total lung capacity (TLC), ml	7050
RV/TLC × 100, %	50*
Dead space (anatomic, estimated), ml	160

(Continued)

Tidal volume, ml...	600
Frequency, breaths/min	16
Minute volume, L/min..	9.6
Alveolar ventilation (calc. on basis of anatomic dead space), L/min.....	7.0

DISTRIBUTION OF INSPIRED GAS

Single-breath test, % N_2, 750–1250 ml............................	3.0*
Pulmonary N_2 emptying rate (7 min), % N_2.......................	2.8*

ARTERIAL BLOOD

O_2 saturation (air), %.......................................	90.5*
O_2 saturation (O_2), %.....................................	100
Dissolved O_2, ml O_2/100 ml blood................................	1.8
CO_2 tension, mm Hg...	38
pH	7.44

MECHANICS OF BREATHING

Max. voluntary ventilation, L/min...............................	60*
After therapy	110*
Max. expiratory flow rate, L/min................................	50*
Max. inspiratory flow rate, L/min...............................	220*

INTERPRETATION (see Fig. 55).—The reduction in vital capacity, increase in residual volume (both in absolute units and as a percentage of total lung capacity), reduction in MVV, maximal inspiratory and expiratory flow rates and uneven distribution of inspired gas are all part of the pattern of obstruction. Because total lung capacity is not decreased, patterns caused by restrictive lesions of the lungs and thorax or by lesions occupying significant amounts of space are ruled out. The increase of 840 ml in vital capacity and 50 L/min in maximal voluntary ventilation after administration of isoproterenol aerosol, epinephrine subcutaneously and aminophylline intravenously indicates that reversible bronchial obstruction is an important feature in this case and suggests that the diagnosis is bronchial asthma rather than other obstructive diseases such as emphysema, peribronchiolar fibrosis or bronchitis. This diagnosis would have been strengthened had tests been repeated after more prolonged and complete antiasthmatic therapy and complete reversibility found (as in Case 4).

The arterial anoxemia might have been caused by hypoventilation, by uneven ventilation in relation to blood flow, by impaired diffusion or by a shunt. Calculations of alveolar ventilation rule out hypoventilation. The presence of full saturation and 1.8 ml of dissolved O_2/100 ml of arterial

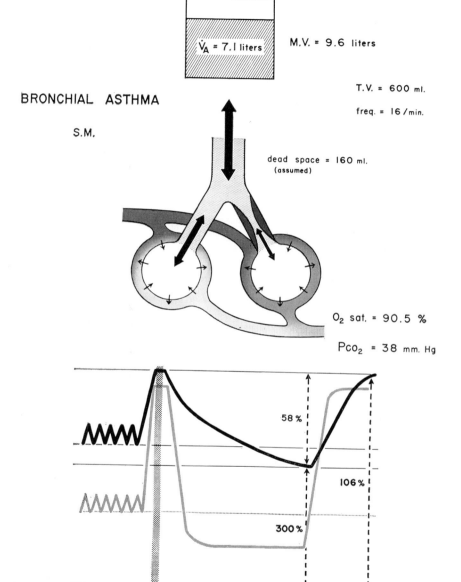

BRONCHIAL ASTHMA

S.M.

$\dot{V}_A$ = 7.1 liters

M.V. = 9.6 liters

T.V. = 600 ml.

freq. = 16 / min.

dead space = 160 ml.
(assumed)

O_2 sat. = 90.5 %

P_{CO_2} = 38 mm. Hg

58 %

106 %

300 %

FIG. 55.—Case 3. For legend, see page 217

225

blood during the inhalation of oxygen eliminates the possibility of any significant shunt. Tests of distribution showed uneven ventilation; anoxemia (completely correctible by O_2 inhalation) would be expected on this account. Since specific tests of diffusion were not available at the time of this study, we cannot rule out some additional impairment of diffusion; one would expect a decrease in diffusing capacity only if the alveolar capillaries were reduced in number and surface area, or excluded from gas exchange by complete obstruction of some airways (this is commonly found in severe emphysema but not in uncomplicated asthma). The arterial Pco_2 is normal, which means that regions with an increased ventilation/blood flow ratio have compensated for regions with a decreased ventilation/blood flow ratio as far as CO_2 is concerned.

CONCLUSIONS.—The diagnosis of asthma was made in this case by simple spirometric measurements repeated after specific, adequate bronchodilator therapy. This case also illustrates how the physician can, by simple office procedures, evaluate therapy for each individual patient with asthma, and prescribe on the basis of objective tests.

This patient had no dyspnea at the time of the study, yet his vital capacity, MVV and maximal flow rates were reduced and improved considerably after therapy. This suggests the need for performing simple tests on *all* patients suspected of having cardiopulmonary disease, even though they may be symptom-free at the time.

Case 4 (Asthma)

J. B. is a 14 year old junior high school student who has had asthma since the age of 2½. He had two or three mild episodes of wheezing, rhinitis and sneezing a month until the age of 7. At this time he had a severe episode of wheezing associated with atelectasis. In the following four years he had severe attacks of airway obstruction weekly, some associated with atelectasis. He was treated during this period with steroids, aminophylline and ephedrine. The severity of his attacks required hospital care for an 18 month period between his eighth and tenth birthday. In the past two years he has had moderately severe attacks twice a week, takes aminophylline and ephedrine daily, requires epinephrine subcutaneously twice a month on the average but has not required steroids. In addition to 18 months of continuous hospitalization, he has had six hospitalizations lasting one to three weeks for asthma associated with pneumonia and/or atelectasis. He has no history of intercurrent bronchitis, sinusitis or bronchiectasis. He has positive skin reactions to house dust and feathers.

SELECTED PULMONARY FUNCTION TESTS

LUNG VOLUMES	ON ADMISSION (SYMPTOM-FREE)	AFTER 1 WEEK OF INTENSIVE THERAPY
Inspiratory capacity, ml	1980	2880
Vital capacity, ml	3225	4150
Residual volume (RV), ml	2385	1990
Total lung capacity (TLC), ml	5620	6140
RV/TLC × 100, %	42	32

DISTRIBUTION OF INSPIRED GAS

Single-breath test, % N_2, 750–1250 ml	7.5	2.5
Pulmonary N_2 emptying rate, % N_2	12.5	1.0

MECHANICS OF BREATHING

Max. expiratory flow rate, L/min	188	500
Max. inspiratory flow rate, L/min	150	300
Forced expiratory volume, % in 1 sec	68	87
Airway resistance, cm H_2O/L/sec	—	1.5

COMMENT.—This case illustrates that asthmatic obstruction in children, no matter how severe, can be corrected completely by vigorous therapy. Therefore, prolonged, repeated overinflation of the lungs caused by predominant expiratory obstruction need not cause tissue destruction and emphysema. This patient illustrates again that a symptom-free asthmatic patient may have considerable airway obstruction in the interval between attacks.

It was not possible to bring the residual volume of this boy back to predicted normal value; it is likely that his thorax is permanently enlarged because of long-continued hyperinflation during his period of rapid growth.

Case 5 (Obstructive Emphysema)

J. G. is a 63 year old man whose chief complaints are cough, considerable sputum on arising and slight dyspnea on exertion. The patient was referred to the Pulmonary Function Section for physiologic diagnosis.

PULMONARY FUNCTION STUDIES
Abnormal values are starred (*)

LUNG VOLUMES

Inspiratory capacity, ml.................................... 1350*
Expiratory reserve volume, ml............................. 500*

Vital capacity, ml... 1730*
 After bronchodilator, ml.. 1780*
Residual volume (RV), ml.. 4400*
Functional residual capacity, ml................................. 4900*
Total lung capacity (TLC), ml................................... 6250*
RV/TLC × 100, %.. 70*
Dead space (anatomic, estimated), ml............................ 150

VENTILATION

Tidal volume, ml... 335*
Frequency, breaths/min 15
Minute volume, L/min... 5*
Alveolar ventilation (calc. on basis of anatomic dead space), L/min..... 2.8*

DISTRIBUTION OF INSPIRED GAS

Single-breath test, % N_2, 750–1250 ml........................... 7.4*
Pulmonary N_2 emptying rate (7 min), % N_2...................... 2.7*

DIFFUSION

Single-breath CO diffusing capacity, ml/min/mm Hg................ 17*

ARTERIAL BLOOD

O_2 saturation (air), %.. 90.2*
O_2 saturation (O_2), %.. 100
Dissolved O_2, ml O_2/100 ml blood.............................. 1.8
CO_2 tension, mm Hg... 57*
pH 7.33*

MECHANICS OF BREATHING

Max. voluntary ventilation, L/min............................... 56*
Max. expiratory flow rate, L/min................................ 19*
 After bronchodilator 22*
Max. inspiratory flow rate, L/min............................... 109*
 After bronchodilator 113*
Forced expiratory volume, % in 1 sec............................ 47*
 After bronchodilator 53*

INTERPRETATION (see Fig. 56).—Practically every value obtained here is abnormal. The decrease in vital capacity, MVV and maximal expiratory flow rate, the increase in residual volume and RV/TLC ratio and the uneven distribution are all characteristic of the *obstructive* pattern. Unlike Cases 3 and 4, antiasthmatic therapy in this case failed to produce any significant change in vital capacity or flow rates; this points

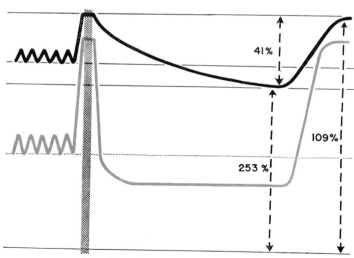

EMPHYSEMA

J.G.

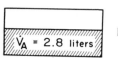

M.V. = 5.0 liters

T.V. = 335 ml.

freq. = 15 / min.

dead space = 150 ml.
(assumed)

O_2 sat. = 90.2 %

P_{CO_2} = 57 mm. Hg

41%

109%

253 %

FIG. 56.—Case 5. For legend, see page 217

229

to an irreversible type of obstruction, and the most common cause of this is chronic pulmonary emphysema.

The obstruction may be due to (1) weak bronchial walls which collapse during expiration (before alveoli empty normally), (2) to flattening of fine air passages because the surrounding tissues no longer pull them open by traction or (3) to plugging by mucus (due either to abnormal secretion or to inadequate mechanisms for removal, e.g., decreased expiratory flow, change in ciliary activity).

Anoxemia in this patient is not associated with impairment of diffusion (the diffusing capacity is normal, at least during rest) or with an anatomic shunt (when the patient breathes O_2 his arterial blood contains almost maximal amounts of dissolved O_2) and must therefore be due to hypoventilation or to uneven ventilation/blood flow ratios. Patients with emphysema usually attempt to hyperventilate until mechanical limitation becomes extreme, but this patient is one of those whose alveolar ventilation is less than normal. This alone, however, does not account for the anoxemia (see Fig. 15, p. 46), and uneven ventilation must account for the rest. The arterial P_{CO_2} is increased because of hypoventilation and uneven ventilation/blood flow ratios due to obstruction; he has respiratory acidosis as a result. This case with obstruction and hypoventilation was selected to show that one patient may display more than one of the patterns of dysfunction.

CONCLUSIONS.—The patient has severe chronic pulmonary emphysema with pulmonary insufficiency for both the oxygenating and carbon dioxide-removing functions of the lung. Mechanical limitation to breathing is severe, but disability is not marked.

The lack of improvement after bronchodilator therapy suggests that there is little to be gained by it. It is unlikely that positive-pressure breathing on inspiration will improve his expiratory flow rate or result in more complete or rapid expiration. Breathing exercises might be tried with some justification, and every attempt should be made to prevent infection, further plugging and atelectasis, which would reduce further his expiratory reserve.

Case 6 (Chemical "Bronchitis")

J. C. is a 39 year old fireman who, as a result of inhalation of irritant fumes, had severe, acute pulmonary insufficiency (arterial O_2 saturation 72%; arterial P_{CO_2} 67 mm Hg; vital capacity and tidal volume each 400 ml). He recovered from this catastrophe; pulmonary function studies were done two and 20 months later.

PULMONARY FUNCTION STUDIES
Abnormal values are starred (*)

LUNG VOLUMES

	AT 2 MO.	AT 20 MO.
Inspiratory capacity, ml	2000	3100
Expiratory reserve volume, ml	1680	1080
Vital capacity, ml	3450*	4120
Residual volume (RV), ml	1770	1760
Total lung capacity (TLC), ml	5220	5880
RV/TLC × 100, %	34	30
Dead space (anatomic, estimated), ml	150	150

VENTILATION

Tidal volume, ml	860*	670
Frequency, breaths/min	22*	18
Minute volume, L/min	18.9*	11.7
Alveolar ventilation (calc. on basis of anatomic dead space), L/min	15.6	9.4

DISTRIBUTION OF INSPIRED GAS

Single-breath test, % N_2, 750–1250 ml	5.5*	2.7

DIFFUSION

Single-breath CO diffusing capacity, ml/min/mm Hg	—	34

ARTERIAL BLOOD

O_2 saturation (air), %	—	95
CO tension, mm Hg	—	38

MECHANICS OF BREATHING

Max. voluntary ventilation, L/min	90*	110*
Max. expiratory flow rate, L/min	170*	300
Max. inspiratory flow rate, L/min	200*	305
Forced expiratory volume, % in 1 sec	66*	91
Pulmonary compliance, L/cm H_2O	—	0.15
Airway resistance, cm H_2O/L/sec	4.3*	2.0

INTERPRETATION.—There is considerable variation in the incidence of chronic bronchitis in different countries (e.g., United States and England). English physicians believe that chronic bronchitis is an important cause of death; American physicians consider chronic bronchitis to be a frequent cause of morbidity but have been unwilling to assign deaths to it unless the bronchitis progresses to obliterative bronchiolitis. We have few data on physiologic function in patients with bronchitis because some investigators have made measurements, for the most part, of the frequency of cough and the volume of sputum and others have not assembled enough well-defined cases for study of function.

This patient had no pulmonary disease before the inhalation of chemical fumes. The acute phase was characterized by necrosis of bronchiolar tissue, airway obstruction and acute hypoventilation. During the recovery phase, gradual repair of bronchi and bronchioles was accompanied by narrowing of the lumen.

This case might therefore be considered typical of "bronchitis"† without complicating alveolar damage or emphysema. It demonstrates that (1) severe obliterative bronchiolitis might cause death by hypoventilation (this patient's life was saved by continuous assisted respiration for several days by an anesthesiologist using an endotracheal tube-bag system), and (2) chronic bronchitis is characterized by a decrease in maximal flow rates (MVV, MEFR and FEV), increase in airway resistance and uneven distribution of inspired gas; these values are influenced little by inhalation of an aerosol of isoproterenol. Significant decrease in vital capacity, total lung capacity or diffusing capacity occurs only when there is complete closure of a significant number of airways.

The obstructive pattern in chronic bronchitis differs from that in asthma because bronchodilator therapy does not cause appreciable or prolonged improvement; it differs from that in emphysema because in bronchitis total lung capacity is normal and airway resistance is increased on both inspiration and expiration.

It is difficult to separate bronchitis *and* emphysema from emphysema alone; we suspect that a large number of patients who "die of chronic bronchitis" have also had emphysema and partial destruction of alveolar walls and their capillary bed.

PATTERN OF IMPAIRED DIFFUSION

Impairment of diffusion may occur because there is (1) a longer diffusion path for O_2 from alveoli to blood, or (2) a decrease in surface

---

† This patient does not have "bronch*itis*" if bronchitis is defined as an infection or inflammation of bronchi: bronchostenosis might be a better designation of the chronic stage of his disease. He differs from ordinary patients with chronic bronchitis in having marked hyperventilation two months after inhalation of the fumes, due possibly to involvement of stretch receptors in bronchiolar walls in the inflammatory or healing process.

area for gas exchange (p. 114). In this section we shall discuss only the first type, commonly known as alveolar-capillary block, in which there is thickening of the alveolar or capillary membranes (or both) or separation of these by transudate, exudate or new tissue growth (fibrous or granulomatous). Among the many diseases producing this pattern are sarcoidosis, beryllium poisoning, Hamman-Rich syndrome, miliary tuberculosis, diffuse carcinomatosis and scleroderma of the lungs; to produce the full-blown pattern, lesions must be widely distributed throughout the whole of both lungs.

The second type of impairment of diffusion (decrease in effective surface area for gas exchange) produces varied patterns because many diseases of the airways, alveoli or blood vessels can produce it. Thus, it may occur in emphysema as a consequence of airway obstruction or destruction of alveoli; in pulmonary vascular disease because of a decrease in the pulmonary capillary bed, or following pneumonectomy because of a decrease in surface area of both alveoli and capillaries. The two types cannot be differentiated by measurements of diffusing capacity but can be by analysis of other studies.

Characteristic pulmonary function findings in this pattern are:

LUNG VOLUMES.—Vital and total lung capacities decrease. Residual volume is normal, but the ratio RV/TLC increases because of the decrease in total lung capacity. Thoracic gas volume equals functional residual capacity measured by dilution techniques because there is no appreciable airway obstruction and gas trapping.

VENTILATION.—These patients characteristically hyperventilate even at rest, largely by an increase in the frequency of breathing. Hyperventilation is due only in part to anoxemia because inhalation of O_2 is not accompanied by much decrease in ventilation. Since arterial P_{CO_2} is low, some stimulus other than high CO_2 or low O_2 must be causing the hyperventilation; this is generally considered to be abnormal pulmonary tissue activating the receptors of the deflation reflex (Hering-Breuer) either directly or indirectly by decrease in alveolar volume.

DISTRIBUTION OF GAS AND BLOOD.—Gas distribution is usually uneven because interstitial edema or fibrosis, though diffuse, is rarely uniform. However, as a rule, the non-uniformity is far less than in patients with obstructive lesions of emphysema, for comparable degrees of disability.

PULMONARY CIRCULATION.—If there is diffuse pulmonary fibrosis there is usually increased resistance to flow through the small pulmonary vessels. This leads to pulmonary hypertension, to increased work of the right ventricle and, in severe cases, to right heart failure.

DIFFUSION.—Carbon monoxide diffusing capacity at rest and during exercise is less than predicted; O_2 diffusing capacity is decreased. In early cases of alveolar-capillary block, a decrease in DCO may be the only detectable abnormality in pulmonary function.

ARTERIAL BLOOD.—Oxygen saturation may be normal in the resting patient because pulmonary reserve is normally great (Fig. 38, p. 126) and also because hyperventilation raises alveolar PO_2; in severe cases, arterial O_2 saturation is decreased in the resting patient. Arterial O_2 saturation and tension decrease during exercise; they reach maximal values when the resting patient inhales oxygen. The alveolar-arterial PO_2 difference may be normal or increased when the patient breathes air; it always increases when he breathes low O_2 mixtures. Arterial PCO_2 is normal or, if the patient is hyperventilating, it is low. There is no problem with outward diffusion of CO_2 even in severe cases of alveolar-capillary block.

MECHANICAL FACTORS.—Maximal voluntary ventilation, forced expiratory volume and maximal flow rates may be normal even when vital capacity is reduced considerably; this is because pure alveolar-capillary block is not associated with airway obstruction and the patient can breathe in and out rapidly. Lung compliance usually decreases and pulmonary tissue resistance may be increased.

Case 7 (Impaired Diffusion)

R. M. is a 32 year old man who, 18 months ago, had "a feeling of something in his lungs." He had no dyspnea, chest pain or cough. A roentgenogram revealed bilateral infiltration of the pulmonary parenchyma.

PULMONARY FUNCTION STUDIES
Abnormal values are starred (*)

LUNG VOLUMES	ORIGINAL STUDY	18 Mo. LATER
Inspiratory capacity, ml	3000	3215
Expiratory reserve volume, ml	1790	1825
Vital capacity, ml	4900	5040
Residual volume (RV), ml	1310	1235
Functional residual capacity, ml	3100	3060
Total lung capacity (TLC), ml	6100	6275
RV/TLC × 100, %	21.4	20
Dead space (anatomic, estimated), ml	150	150

	ORIGINAL STUDY	18 MO. LATER
VENTILATION		
Tidal volume, ml	520	550
Frequency, breaths/min	20*	19*
Minute volume, L/min	10.4*	10.4*
Alveolar ventilation (calc. on basis of anatomic dead space), L/min	7.4*	7.6*
DISTRIBUTION OF INSPIRED GAS		
Single-breath test, % N_2, 750–1250 ml	1.0	1.0
DIFFUSION		
Single-breath CO diffusing capacity, ml/min/mm Hg	19*	30
ARTERIAL BLOOD		
O_2 saturation (air), %	94.2*	97
O_2 saturation (O_2), %	100	100
Dissolved O_2, ml O_2/100 ml blood	1.8	2.0
CO_2 tension, mm Hg	32*	30*
pH	7.48*	7.51*
MECHANICS OF BREATHING		
Max. voluntary ventilation, L/min	183	196
Max. expiratory flow rate, L/min	600	765
Max. inspiratory flow rate, L/min	590	560
Forced expiratory volume, % in 1 sec	83	85
Pulmonary compliance, L/cm H_2O	0.11*	0.21
Airway resistance, cm H_2O/L/sec	0.59	0.61

INTERPRETATION.—All results of the simple tests of pulmonary function (vital capacity and its subdivisions; maximal flow rates) were normal. Nevertheless, despite hyperventilation, the arterial O_2 saturation was low. This could not be due to alveolar hypoventilation, to uneven distribution of gas (normal single-breath test) or to venous-to-arterial shunts (arterial blood was almost maximally oxygenated during inhalation of O_2). The anoxemia could have been due to uneven pulmonary capillary blood flow (due to non-uniform pulmonary vascular disease) or to impaired diffusion. Diffusing capacity was low for a man of his size (2.02 M^2), and pulmonary compliance was about 60% of normal. The pulmonary disorder was therefore identified as impairment of diffusion caused by infiltration of the parenchyma of the lung—probably separating the alveolar-capillary membranes, lengthening the pathway for diffusion of O_2 and stiffening the lungs—but not encroaching at all upon the airways (normal maximal flow rates). Biopsy of the lung showed "chronic pneu-monitis."

This represents a case of uniform pulmonary infiltration, detectable physiologically by tests of diffusion and compliance; results of all other tests were normal except for slight anoxemia and hyperventilation. The impairment of diffusion was completely reversible; 18 months after the initial study, results of all tests were normal except for continued hyper-ventilation, which may be due to apprehension at the time of the studies.

Case 8 (Impaired Diffusion)

D.D. is a 22 year old girl (surface area 1.5 M²) who, when first studied in 1950, had been short of breath since the delivery of her first child four years before. Except for dyspnea and occasional cough, she had no com-plaints. She was hospitalized and studied four times in a six year period. She died in 1957; the pathologist found diffuse granulomatous tissue throughout both lungs.

PULMONARY FUNCTION STUDIES
Abnormal values are starred (*)

LUNG VOLUMES

	PRED. NORMAL VALUES	PULMONARY FUNCTION STUDIES IN:			
		1950	1951	1954	1956
Vital capacity, ml.........	3100	1950*	1920*	1590*	1350*
Residual volume, ml.......	800	850	1290	2040*	1750*
Total lung capacity, ml.....	3900	2800*	3210*	3630	3100*
RV/TLC × 100, %.......	20.5	30	40*	56*	56*

VENTILATION

Tidal volume, ml.........	450	250*	230*	200*	330*
Frequency, breaths/min ...	12	34*	28*	41*	32*
Minute volume, L/min.....	5.4	8.5*	6.4	8.2*	10.5*

DISTRIBUTION OF INSPIRED GAS

Single-breath test, % N₂....	<1.5	—	2	3*	7*

DIFFUSION

CO diffusing capacity (single-breath), ml/min/mm Hg	18	--	—	---	6*

ARTERIAL BLOOD

	PRED. NORMAL VALUES	PULMONARY FUNCTION STUDIES IN:			
		1950	1951	1954	1956
O_2 saturation, %	97.1	98.2	—	94*	90.4*
Pco_2, mm Hg.	40	35*	—	36*	35*
pH	7.40	7.41	—	7.42	7.37

MECHANICS OF BREATHING

Max. vol. vent., L/min.	99	82	86	101	59*
Max. expir. flow rate, L/min	400	—	—	185*	75*
Max. inspir. flow rate, L/min	300	—	—	170*	105*
Forced expir. vol., % in 1 sec	83	—	—	95	72*
Pulmonary compliance, L/cm H_2O	0.2	—	—	—	0.04*
Airway resistance, cm H_2O/L/sec	1.5	—	—	—	1.9*

INTERPRETATION.—At least three patterns of pulmonary function are present here: restriction, obstruction, and impaired diffusion. The *restrictive pattern* was apparent early (1950 and 1951), consisting of a marked decrease in vital and total lung capacities with less decrease in MVV. She was breathing rapidly probably because of lung reflexes (hyperventilation was present before anoxemia developed and later was not reduced by inhalation of O_2). The rapid, shallow breathing may represent an attempt to maintain ventilation with a minimal increase in the work of breathing (p. 194); compliance was only 20% of normal (1956) at a time when airway resistance was increased about 50%.

The *obstructive pattern* developed later in this patient: MVV and flow rates were eventually reduced to low values, owing at least in part to increased airway resistance because lung tissue infiltrated by granulomas will not move or empty rapidly and may encroach on the air passages; they did not increase after administration of bronchodilator aerosols and therefore probably represent organic changes in the tissues. The residual volume increased progressively and distribution of inspired gas became quite uneven.

The *pattern of impaired diffusion* is supported by the decrease in CO diffusing capacity to one third of predicted normal, the low arterial O_2 saturation (1954) and the normal arterial Pco_2. However, some of the decrease in saturation and diffusing capacity may well be due to uneven ventilation (because of uneven compliance of different regions of the lung). The pH of 7.37 (1956) may represent metabolic acidosis due to anoxemia.

CONCLUSIONS.—This patient, like many who have chronic pulmonary disease, had more than one pattern of physiologic disturbance. She had widespread infiltrative disease of both lungs which probably occupied alveolar space (or compressed alveoli), restricted expansion of the lung, caused airway obstruction and led to impairment of diffusion, in part because of alveolar-capillary block and in part because of diminished surface area for gas exchange.

PATTERN OF RESTRICTION

In pure restrictive disease, the characteristic feature is limitation to full expansion of the lungs even though there is no neuromuscular disease. This may be due to diffuse pulmonary disease (such as interstitial fibrosis or scleroderma), to pleural thickening, to pleural effusion or pneumothorax, to disease of the thoracic cage (kyphoscoliosis, ankylosing spondylitis) or to unusual elevation of the diaphragm (large abdominal masses).‡ Obviously, it is incorrect to label this pattern "pulmonary fibrosis" because (1) fibrosis is only one of many causes of the restrictive pattern, (2) peribronchiolar fibrosis causes obstruction rather than restriction, and (3) the physiologist does not "see" increased fibrous tissue by his tests but only records a certain physiologic pattern. It is also incorrect to label this pattern "alveolar-capillary block" because there is none when the restrictive lesion does not involve the alveolar-capillary membranes.

This pattern in its pure form does not include airway obstruction; MVV, performed with quick small breaths, remains normal despite considerable reduction in vital capacity (the same is true in healthy individuals in whom thoracic movement is restricted experimentally by tight elastic strapping of the chest and abdomen). An obstructive pattern may develop later and complicate the pure restrictive pattern. Presumably this occurs because inability to breathe deeply and to cough effectively favors an accumulation of mucus, atelectasis, infection and scattered fibrotic changes. Anesthetized dogs ventilated artificially at a constant tidal volume and prevented from taking deep breaths or sighs do develop changes compatible with closure in some airways; the same changes have been observed in patients narcotized with barbiturates for several days.

---

‡ Space-taking lesions (such as neoplasms) so located that they do not obstruct large airways and cysts uncomplicated by diffuse emphysema also represent a restrictive type of disease. Owing to great pulmonary reserve, radiologically conspicuous lesions of this type may have little effect on function.

Restrictive patterns can be analyzed further to determine whether the limitation to motion is pulmonary or thoracic; if pulmonary, lung compliance is decreased; if thoracic, maximal voluntary effort may produce little change in esophageal pressure. Thoracic restriction may be differentiated from neuromuscular inadequacy by measuring the total compliance of the lungs and thoracic cage.

Characteristic findings in the restrictive pattern are:

LUNG VOLUMES.—Vital capacity, inspiratory capacity and total lung capacity decrease because of limitation to full expansion. Residual volume may decrease (fibrotic shrinkage) or be normal. The RV/TLC ratio may be normal, increased or decreased depending on whether TLC decreases more than RV. An increased ratio, when present, does *not* signify obstruction; in this case it is increased because the TLC is decreased. Body plethysmographic studies show no significant volume of trapped gas except in the presence of pneumothorax or air-filled cysts.

VENTILATION.—This may be normal or increased; when the work required to overcome progressive restriction becomes intolerable, ventilation decreases. Frequency of breathing is usually increased.

DISTRIBUTION OF GAS AND BLOOD.—This is normal in pure cases, but there will be uneven expansion and an abnormal single-breath test (using the N_2 meter) if secondary obstructive changes have occurred. The 7 min pulmonary N_2 emptying rate is often normal because patients with restrictive diseases of the *lungs* characteristically hyperventilate even during inhalation of O_2 and this "washes out" alveolar N_2 rapidly.

PULMONARY CIRCULATION.—This is affected only if there is diffuse interstitial disease of the lung; this can cause increased resistance to flow through the smaller pulmonary vessels and may lead to pulmonary hypertension and right ventricular hypertrophy. Extrapulmonary restrictive disease does not, unless complicating factors arise.

DIFFUSION.—If the disease is pulmonary (interstitial fibrosis or infiltration), the diffusing capacity will be decreased (see pattern of impaired diffusion); if it is pleural, thoracic or diaphragmatic, the diffusing capacity should be normal unless secondary changes in the lungs have occurred.

ARTERIAL BLOOD.—The pure restrictive pattern involves only lung volumes. Whether there are changes in the arterial blood gases depends on whether the disease or its complications have impaired diffusion, caused airway obstruction, shunts (atelectasis) or hypoventilation. Carbon dioxide retention occurs only when the limitation of lung and thoracic movement is so severe that it causes over-all hypoventilation.

MECHANICAL FACTORS.—Maximal voluntary ventilation may be normal or nearly so despite a considerable reduction in vital capacity: if the chest is rigid, the diaphragm can make full rapid excursions; if the diaphragm is crowded into the thorax, the chest cage can still move quickly. If MVV is reduced, it is reduced considerably less than is the vital capacity. Maximal expiratory flow rate is decreased slightly, and rarely to the extent seen in the obstructive pattern. Pulmonary compliance or total thoracic compliance is reduced, but airway resistance is normal.

Case 9 (Sarcoidosis)

W.M. is a 45 year old woman who has had dyspnea and morning cough for 10 years. Although these have been progressive, she is still able to climb one flight of stairs. A biopsy of the cervical node five years ago established the diagnosis of sarcoidosis. She has no chest pain, palpitation, orthopnea or ankle edema.

PULMONARY FUNCTION STUDIES
Abnormal values are starred (*)

LUNG VOLUMES

Inspiratory capacity, ml	1155*
Expiratory reserve volume, ml	335*
Vital capacity, ml	1490*
Residual volume (RV), ml	1720
Functional residual capacity, ml	2055
Total lung capacity (TLC), ml	3210*
RV/TLC × 100, %	54
Dead space (anatomic, estimated), ml	110

VENTILATION

Tidal volume, ml	600
Frequency, breaths/min	18
Minute volume, L/min	10.8
Alveolar ventilation (calc. on basis of anatomic dead space), L/min	8.8

DISTRIBUTION OF INSPIRED GAS

Single-breath test, % N_2, 750–1250 ml	2.0
Pulmonary N_2 emptying rate (7 min), % N_2	2.0

DIFFUSION

† Single-breath CO diffusing capacity, ml/min/mm Hg	4.0*

ARTERIAL BLOOD

O_2 saturation (air), % 91*
O_2 saturation (O_2), % 100
Dissolved O_2, ml O_2/100 ml blood 1.7
CO_2 tension, mm Hg 36
pH 7.43

MECHANICS OF BREATHING

Max. voluntary ventilation, L/min 95
Max. expiratory flow rate, L/min 250
Max. inspiratory flow rate, L/min 200
Forced expiratory volume, % in 1 sec 86
† Pulmonary compliance, L/cm H_2O 0.04*
† Airway resistance, cm H_2O/L/sec 1.90*
† Pulmonary tissue resistance, cm H_2O/L/sec 0.88*

† = performed 3 yr after the other studies.

INTERPRETATION (see Fig. 57).—This patient has both restrictive disease of the lungs and impairment of diffusion. The decrease in vital, inspiratory and total lung capacities, coupled with normal distribution of inspired gas and MVV, fit the *pattern of restriction*. The reduction in pulmonary compliance to one fourth of normal at a time when the total lung capacity was still two thirds of normal means that the lung tissue is stiffer than normal. The large RV/TLC percentage (54) does not mean that this patient has obstructive disease such as emphysema; it is large only because TLC is less than predicted (this is a good example of the dangers in using such *ratios* for diagnostic purposes).

Anoxemia is not due to hypoventilation, to uneven distribution of inspired air or to shunt. It could be due to uneven distribution of pulmonary capillary blood (even with normal distribution of gas), but the specific test of diffusing capacity for CO shows marked impairment; this not only makes the diagnosis but also places the restrictive lesion in the parenchyma of the lung and not in the pleura or thoracic cage.

Arterial P_{CO_2} is decreased because of alveolar hyperventilation.

CONCLUSIONS.—A presumptive diagnosis of restrictive disease could have been made by simple spirometric tests (lung volumes, ventilation and flow rates). However, differentiation of pulmonary from thoracic restrictive lesion required further studies (arterial blood gases, tests of pulmonary compliance and diffusion). In this case the restrictive lesion was due to diffuse pulmonary sarcoidosis.

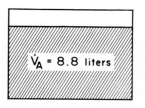

$\dot{V}_A$ = 8.8 liters

M.V. = 10.8 liters

T.V. = 600 ml.

freq. = 18 / min.

SARCOIDOSIS

W.M.

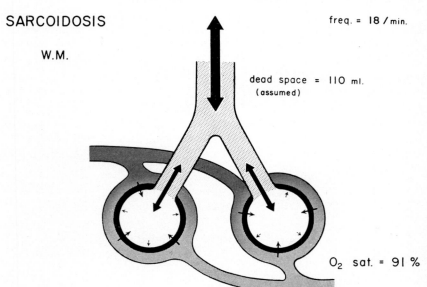

dead space = 110 ml.
(assumed)

O_2 sat. = 91 %

P_{CO_2} = 36 mm. Hg

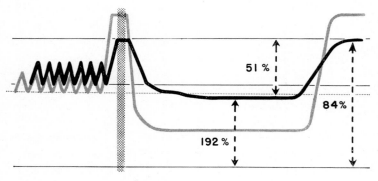

51 %

192 %

84%

FIG. 57.—Case 9. For legend, see page 217

242

PATTERN OF RIGHT-TO-LEFT SHUNT

This differs from the pattern of "non-uniform pulmonary capillary blood flow." In a true *shunt,* a portion of venous, poorly oxygenated blood never comes in contact with ventilated alveoli and the remainder of the mixed venous blood is distributed fairly evenly to the pulmonary capillary bed. Anoxemia occurs in both the "shunt" pattern and in the "non-uniform pulmonary capillary blood flow" pattern. Inhalation of O_2 can be used to differentiate the two; it can never produce maximal arterial O_2 saturation and tension in a patient with a shunt, but always does so in a patient with uneven capillary blood flow. Sometimes the arterial O_2 *saturation* rises to 100% after inhalation of O_2, but the O_2 *pressure* cannot rise to 600 mm Hg or the dissolved O_2 to 1.9–2.0 ml/100 ml blood if a true shunt exists. The equation for calculation of the shunt (p. 343) shows that 20–25% of the right ventricular output can be shunted past the lungs and the arterial O_2 saturation will still rise to 100% during inhalation of O_2. Therefore, when a shunt is suspected, measurements of O_2 saturation alone are not enough; arterial P_{O_2} or dissolved O_2 must also be determined. Measurements of O_2 tension (using an O_2 electrode) are more accurate since in the absence of a shunt the tension changes from 100 to more than 600 mm Hg while dissolved O_2 changes from 0.3 to only 2.0 ml. When a shunt is suspected in a patient with mixed patterns of pulmonary disease, pure O_2 must be breathed for 15–20 min before arterial blood is sampled because that length of time may be required for poorly ventilated parts of the lungs to eliminate N_2 and acquire the maximal alveolar O_2 tension.

The characteristic findings in the "shunt" pattern are:

LUNG VOLUMES.—Normal.

VENTILATION.—Increased, owing to anoxemia.

DISTRIBUTION OF GAS AND BLOOD.—Uniform, unless multiple hemangiomas cause uneven expansion of the lungs.

DIFFUSION.—Normal.

ARTERIAL BLOOD.—Anoxemia is not fully corrected by inhalation of pure O_2. Arterial CO_2 tends to be elevated slightly because of mixture of venous blood (P_{CO_2} 46 mm Hg) with arterial blood (P_{CO_2} 40 mm Hg) but is usually normal or low because of the patient's hyperventilation, caused by decreased arterial P_{O_2} and increased P_{CO_2}.

MECHANICAL FACTORS.—Normal.

Case 10 (Pulmonary Hemangioma)

H.S. is a 38 year old man who had spent three years in a tuberculosis sanatorium for treatment of bilateral apical tuberculosis, although it had never been possible to isolate tubercle bacilli. His chief complaints are dyspnea on exertion and easy fatigability. He has no history of cough, hemoptysis, chest pain, bronchitis, pneumonia, asthma or exposure to unusual dusts or fumes.

The patient has definite cyanosis, but no other abnormal physical findings related to the heart or lungs. Hemoglobin content is 20.1 gm/100 ml, red blood cell count 6,300,000/cu mm and hematocrit 64%. The Pulmonary Function Section was asked to determine the cause of his cyanosis and dyspnea.

PULMONARY FUNCTION STUDIES
Abnormal values are starred (*)

LUNG VOLUMES

Inspiratory capacity, ml	3450
Expiratory reserve volume, ml	950
Vital capacity, ml	4200
Residual volume (RV), ml	2030
Functional residual capacity, ml	2980
Total lung capacity (TLC), ml	6430
RV/TLC × 100, %	31
Dead space (anatomic, estimated), ml	160

VENTILATION

Tidal volume, ml	730*
Frequency, breaths/min	23
Minute volume, L/min	16.8*
Alveolar ventilation (calc. on basis of anatomic dead space), L/min	13.1*

DISTRIBUTION OF INSPIRED GAS

Single-breath test, % N_2, 750–1250 ml	1.5
Pulmonary N_2 emptying rate (7 min), % N_2	1.5

ARTERIAL BLOOD

O_2 saturation (air), %	89*
O_2 saturation (O_2), %	97*
CO_2 tension, mm Hg	32*
pH	7.45*
Alv.-art. Po_2 difference (air), mm Hg	38*
O_2 saturation (11.5% O_2), %	69*
Alv.-art. Po_2 difference (11.5% O_2), mm Hg	12*
O_2 saturation (air, exercise), %	79*
Alv.-art. Po_2 difference (air, exercise), mm Hg	64*

(Continued)

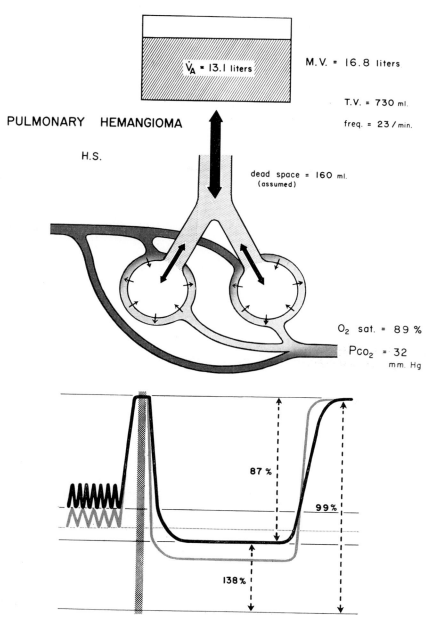

$\dot{V}_A$ = 13.1 liters

M.V. = 16.8 liters

T.V. = 730 ml.

freq. = 23 / min.

PULMONARY HEMANGIOMA

H.S.

dead space = 160 ml.
(assumed)

O₂ sat. = 89 %

P_{CO_2} = 32
mm. Hg

87 %

99%

138%

FIG. 58.—Case 10. For legend, see page 217

245

MECHANICS OF BREATHING

Max. voluntary ventilation, L/min............................. 176
Max. expiratory flow rate, L/min.............................. 390
Max. inspiratory flow rate, L/min............................. 320

INTERPRETATION (see Fig. 58).—This patient had anoxemia which was not corrected fully by inhalation of O_2. This means that whatever else may have been wrong with his lungs, a shunt must be present. Using the equation for calculating the size of a shunt (p. 343) and assuming that his A-V O_2 difference is 4.5 vol %, we find that 40% of his right ventricular output is shunted around ventilated alveoli. Measurements of ventilation, distribution of inspired air and diffusing capacity are unnecessary if this is a pure shunt pattern. (Actually, alveolar ventilation was increased, distribution was normal and diffusion probably normal since the alveolar-arterial O_2 difference decreased from 38 to 12 mm Hg when the patient breathed 11.5% O_2 instead of air; p. 131.)

COMMENT.—The physiologic tests proved the existence of a venous-to-arterial shunt. They could not, however, differentiate an intrapulmonary shunt from an intracardiac one, nor could they disclose whether an intrapulmonary shunt is due to hemangioma or to atelectasis. They did call attention to the existence of a shunt *somewhere*, and a pulmonary angiogram identified the lesions as pulmonary hemangiomas.

This patient had an unusually high O_2 capacity (26.9 vol %) and a hematocrit of 64%; such high values, in our experience, are characteristic in patients with shunts, but not in patients with obstructive or restrictive pulmonary diseases, for comparable degrees of anoxemia. The reasons for the lesser hemopoietic response to anoxemia in chronic pulmonary disease are not known, but may be related to the depressant effects of pulmonary infection or of CO_2 retention on the bone marrow.

PATTERN OF UNEVEN PULMONARY CAPILLARY BLOOD FLOW

This represents the physiologic disturbance pictured in Figure 30 (p. 98), in which alveolar ventilation is uniform but pulmonary capillary blood flow is not, so that some areas of the lung have a low ventilation/blood flow ratio (areas with increased blood flow) and others have a high ratio (areas with decreased blood flow). In its pure form, this pattern includes only diseases of the pulmonary circulation, such as thrombosis or embolism from any cause and nonuniform obstructive lesions of pulmonary vessels.

The characteristic findings in this pattern are:

LUNG VOLUMES.—Normal.

VENTILATION.—This may be increased (anoxemic reflexes).

DISTRIBUTION OF INSPIRED GAS.—Normal.

DISTRIBUTION OF PULMONARY CAPILLARY BLOOD.—Uneven (arterial P_{CO_2} exceeds mixed expired alveolar P_{CO_2}; p. 105).

PULMONARY CIRCULATION.—The pulmonary artery pressure and pulmonary vascular resistance need not be increased in a resting patient unless more than half of the small pulmonary vessels have marked restriction of their blood flow.

DIFFUSION.—Diffusing capacity is decreased if large areas of ventilated alveoli have relatively few capillaries in contact with them (decreased surface area of alveolar capillaries).

ARTERIAL BLOOD.—There is anoxemia which can be corrected completely by inhalation of O_2.

MECHANICAL FACTORS.—Normal.

Case 11 (Pulmonary Embolism)

C.K. is a 68 year old cigar maker who has had several attacks of fever with cough and sputum (sometimes blood tinged) in the past six months. Shortly before study, dyspnea and palpitation developed on exertion and were becoming progressively more severe.

He has a large chest. The percussion notes are hyper-resonant and breath sounds distant. There are no râles. Radiologic study shows marked pulmonary emphysema with no evidence of localized disease; fluoroscopic examination reveals that the pulmonary artery branches are larger and more pulsatile than normal. Clinical diagnosis: emphysema. The pulmonary function tests were performed as a routine study.

PULMONARY FUNCTION STUDIES
Abnormal values are starred (*)

LUNG VOLUMES

Inspiratory capacity, ml	2860
Expiratory reserve volume, ml	1330
Vital capacity, ml	4280
Residual volume (RV), ml	3000
Functional residual capacity, ml	4330
Total lung capacity (TLC), ml	7190
RV/TLC × 100, %	42
Dead space (anatomic, estimated), ml	180

VENTILATION

Tidal volume, ml.. 500
Frequency, breaths/min 15
Minute volume, L/min... 7.5
Alveolar ventilation (calc. on basis of anatomic dead space), L/min..... 4.8
Minute volume (7.5% CO_2), L/min.................................... 48

DISTRIBUTION OF INSPIRED GAS

Single-breath test, % N_2, 750–1250 ml.......................... 0.5
Pulmonary N_2 emptying rate (7 min), % N_2...................... 1.5

ARTERIAL BLOOD

O_2 saturation (air), %... 90*
O_2 saturation (O_2), %.. 100
Dissolved O_2, ml O_2/100 ml blood............................... 1.9
CO_2 tension, mm Hg... 39
pH 7.40

MECHANICS OF BREATHING

Max. voluntary ventilation, L/min.................................... 118
Max. expiratory flow rate, L/min..................................... 320
Max. inspiratory flow rate, L/min.................................... 270

INTERPRETATION (see Fig. 59).—The only abnormality in this man is arterial anoxemia. We do not regard the increased residual volume and RV/TLC percentage of 42 as abnormal for a man of 68 since this is part of the pattern of aging (see p. 212). On the basis of clinical examination (large chest, hyper-resonance and distant breath sounds) and radiologic diagnosis, we expected to find an obstructive pattern. However, MVV and maximal flow rates were excellent for a man of 68, and distribution of inspired gas was normal.

The anoxemia cannot be due to hypoventilation (calculated alveolar ventilation is normal), to uneven ventilation (normal single-breath test) or to a shunt (arterial blood contained 1.9 ml dissolved O_2/100 ml blood when he breathed O_2). By exclusion, it must be due to impairment of diffusion or to uneven distribution of pulmonary capillary blood. At the time this patient was studied, specific tests of diffusing capacity and of uneven blood flow were not available. The patient died six weeks later, and autopsy revealed multiple pulmonary emboli but no evidence of alveolar capillary block. Today the diagnosis could have been made during life by finding a normal diffusing capacity and a high arterial P_{CO_2} relative to mixed expired alveolar P_{CO_2}.

M.V. = 7.5 liters

V̇$_A$ = 4.8 liters

PULMONARY   EMBOLISM

C.K.

T.V. = 500 ml.

freq. = 15 / min.

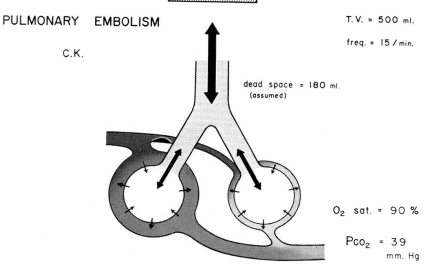

dead space = 180 ml.
(assumed)

O$_2$ sat. = 90 %

P$_{CO_2}$ = 39
mm. Hg

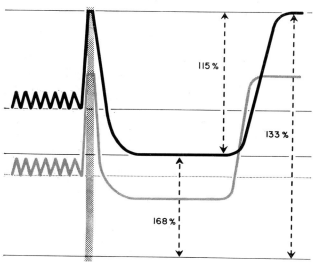

115 %

133 %

168 %

FIG. 59.—Case 11. For legend, see page 217

COMMENT.—The studies done on this patient emphasize: (1) The clinical diagnosis of emphysema may be in error. This patient could not possibly have had pulmonary insufficiency due to emphysema (he had no mechanical difficulties with breathing and no uneven distribution of gas), but an eminent clinician refused to accept the evidence from the pulmonary function studies because the patient had a large chest, hyperresonance, distant breath sounds and dyspnea. (2) The radiologic diagnosis of emphysema is often in error, especially if flat films are relied on. (3) Pulmonary embolism need not lead to characteristic radiologic findings; one does not always find a "wedge-shaped infarct" from occlusion of pulmonary arteries by emboli. (4) In a patient with anoxemia and uniform ventilation, one can diagnose non-uniform circulation by a process of excluding the patterns of hypoventilation, of impaired diffusion and of venous-to-arterial shunt.

Case 12 (Pulmonary Artery Obstruction)

M.U. is a 38 year old man (surface area 2.1 M²) whose chief complaint is shortness of breath which began 15 years ago but has become more noticeable in the past six years.

PULMONARY FUNCTION STUDIES
Abnormal values are starred (*)

LUNG VOLUMES

Inspiratory capacity, ml	3480
Expiratory reserve volume, ml	1100
Vital capacity, ml	4580
Residual volume (RV), ml	2960*
Functional residual capacity, ml	4060*
Total lung capacity (TLC), ml	7540*
RV/TLC × 100, %	39
Dead space (anatomic, estimated), ml	140

VENTILATION

Tidal volume, ml	710*
Frequency, breaths/min	17
Minute volume, L/min	12*
Alveolar ventilation (calc. on anat. dead space), L/min	9.7*

DISTRIBUTION OF INSPIRED GAS

Single-breath O₂ test, % N₂, 750–1250 ml	4.0*
Pulmonary N₂ elimination rate (7 min), % N₂	1.0

PULMONARY CIRCULATION

Pulmonary artery pressure, mm Hg	112/35*
Pulmonary blood flow, L/min	5.8
Pulmonary vascular resistance, mm Hg/ml/sec	10*

DIFFUSING CAPACITY

Dco (rest), ml/min/mm Hg	17.3*
Dco (exercise), ml/min/mm Hg	19.8*

ARTERIAL BLOOD

O_2 saturation (air), %	88*
O_2 saturation (O_2), %	100
Po_2 (O_2), mm Hg	589
CO_2 tension, mm Hg	38
(CO_2 tension, end-expired gas)	(25)*

MECHANICAL FACTORS

Max. expiratory flow rate, L/min	285
Max. inspiratory flow rate, L/min	375
Forced expiratory volume, % in 1 sec	60*
Airway resistance, cm H_2O/L/sec	1.20

BRONCHOSPIROMETRY

	RIGHT	LEFT
O_2 uptake, %	7*	93*
Ventilation, %	60	40
Vital capacity, %	56	44
End-tidal Pco_2, mm Hg	11*	27*
Anatomic dead space, ml	55	70

INTERPRETATION.—The most marked physiologic disturbances in this patient are in the pulmonary circulation. The pattern of non-uniform pulmonary capillary blood flow is well-defined because: (1) the arterial blood Pco_2 is 38 mm Hg at a time when the end-expired alveolar gas Pco_2 is 25 mm Hg; this large difference (13 mm Hg) indicates that some alveoli received little or no pulmonary capillary blood flow (p. 105) and that ventilation of these is essentially wasted. (2) The patient's anoxemia is almost entirely corrected by inhalation of O_2. The bronchospirometric data placed the major lesion in the right lung because it takes up only 7% of the O_2 even though its ventilation is 60% of the total. However, there must be considerable vascular obstruction in the left lung as well because (1) pulmonary arterial pressure and vascular resistance would be increased little or not at all by complete occlusion of only the right pulmonary artery if the left was normal, (2) although the arterial-alveolar CO_2

difference is 27 mm for the right lung, it is 11 for the left, so that the left lung also has uneven ventilation–blood-flow ratios and (3) the diffusing capacity for CO is low at rest and rises little during exercise.

Note the presence of hyperventilation and dyspnea even though airway resistance and maximal flow rates are normal.

CONCLUSION.—Cardiac catheterization and angiographic studies showed almost complete obstruction of the right pulmonary artery. When and how the obstruction(s) occurred is not known and the train of events following occlusion of a pulmonary artery in man is still obscure. Presumably there is initial bronchoconstriction, caused by low PCO_2 in the ventilated alveoli that receive no pulmonary capillary blood flow. This may be followed by a hemorrhagic type of atelectasis and later by restoration toward normal when bronchial blood begins to perfuse alveolar capillaries in adequate amounts. There is no proof that block of the pulmonary circulation causes additional narrowing by inducing reflex pulmonary arteriolar constriction; presumably the widespread obstruction in this patient is mechanical in origin.

PATTERN OF PULMONARY VASCULAR CONGESTION

This is seen characteristically in mitral stenosis, left ventricular failure, left-to-right shunts (septal defects, patent ductus arteriosus) and in hypervolemia (e.g., polycythemia vera). No pattern is characteristic of all of these varied conditions; pulmonary blood flow is greatly increased in shunts and not in the others; pulmonary capillary pressure must rise in mitral stenosis and left ventricular failure but not necessarily in the other conditions; the viscosity is much greater in polycythemia vera but not in the others. For this reason, the pattern presented here will be that of pulmonary congestion caused by mitral stenosis or left ventricular failure, which is fairly uniform; in certain stages it closely resembles the patterns of "impaired diffusion" and "restriction."

Characteristic findings in this pattern are:

LUNG VOLUME.—Vital capacity and total lung capacity are decreased; residual volume is normal. There is no gas trapping.

VENTILATION.—Hyperventilation is present, usually with increased rate of breathing.

DISTRIBUTION OF GAS AND BLOOD.—This may be uniform or slightly non-uniform.

PULMONARY CIRCULATION.—Pulmonary venous, capillary, arterial and right ventricular pressures are increased, as are pulmonary blood volume and pulmonary capillary blood volume. Pulmonary blood flow is normal in the resting patient (decreases with severe failure), with less than normal increase when the patient exercises. The pulmonary circulation time increases.

DIFFUSION.—This may be normal, increased (capillary congestion and increased area) or decreased (if pulmonary capillary pressure rises sufficiently to produce interstitial or intra-alveolar edema fluid). Diffusing capacity does not increase as much as expected during exercise because pulmonary blood flow is limited.

ARTERIAL BLOOD.—Arterial O_2 is normal until pulmonary edema occurs; arterial Pco_2 is decreased if alveolar hyperventilation results from pulmonary stretch reflexes.

MECHANICAL FACTORS.—Flow rates, forced expiratory volume and MVV may be normal until pulmonary edema develops. Pulmonary compliance is decreased and pulmonary tissue resistance increased. Airway resistance is normal.

PATTERN OF PRECAPILLARY OBSTRUCTION IN PULMONARY CIRCULATION

This is caused by diseases which increase the resistance to flow of blood between the right ventricle and the pulmonary capillary bed, such as pulmonic valvular stenosis, pulmonary artery stenosis and diffuse pulmonary arteriolar obstruction due to sclerosis, endarteritis or foreign bodies. It is assumed here that the obstruction affects the pulmonary circulation uniformly; patients with non-uniform obstruction fall into the pattern of uneven pulmonary capillary blood flow.

Characteristic findings in this pattern are:

LUNG VOLUMES.—Normal.

VENTILATION.—Normal.

DISTRIBUTION.—Normal.

PULMONARY CIRCULATION.—Pulmonary artery pressure must rise if normal pulmonary blood flow is to be maintained; right ventricular and pulmonary artery systolic pressures and calculated pulmonary vascular resistance can exceed systemic pressures and resistance. Right ventricular strain, hypertrophy and failure may occur. High right heart pressures may cause right-to-left shunts through a patent foramen ovale. Pulmonary capillary blood volume is normal.

DIFFUSION.—Normal at rest. If the right ventricular output is limited, Dco will not increase when the patient exercises.

ARTERIAL BLOOD.—Normal. Even severe pulmonic stenosis with reduced pulmonary blood flow causes no arterial anoxemia if the lesion is pure and not associated with a right-to-left shunt. If reflex hyperventilation occurs, there is a decrease in arterial P_{CO_2}.

MECHANICAL FACTORS.—Normal. Pulmonary vascular lesions do not affect significantly pulmonary compliance, pulmonary tissue resistance or airway resistance.

Case 13 (Pulmonary Vascular Obstruction)

G. McC. is an 18 year old male student in whom dyspnea increased over a six month period; he is now incapacitated by shortness of breath. Recently he has also had intermittent attacks of substernal pain during exercise and episodes of nausea and vomiting, especially at night.

PULMONARY FUNCTION STUDIES
Abnormal values are starred (*)

LUNG VOLUMES

Inspiratory capacity, ml	3780
Expiratory reserve volume, ml	2090
Vital capacity, ml	5870
Residual volume (RV), ml	1380
Functional residual capacity, ml	3470
Total lung capacity (TLC), ml	7250
RV/TLC × 100, %	19
Dead space (anatomic, estimated), ml	150

VENTILATION

Tidal volume, ml	430
Frequency, breaths/min	24*
Minute volume, L/min	10.3*
Alveolar ventilation (cal. on basis of anatomic dead space), L/min	6.7*

DISTRIBUTION OF INSPIRED GAS

Single-breath test, % N_2, 750–1250, ml	1.5
Pulmonary N_2 emptying rate (7 min), % N_2	0.5

PULMONARY CIRCULATION

Pulmonary artery pressure, mm Hg	97/48*
Pulmonary blood flow, L/min	2.7*
Pulmonary vascular resistance, mm Hg/ml/sec	1.3*
Volume of blood in pulmonary capillaries, ml	59

DIFFUSION

Single-breath CO diffusing capacity, ml/min/mm/Hg   27

ARTERIAL BLOOD

O_2 saturation (air), %   96
O_2 saturation (O_2), %   100
O_2 tension (O_2), mm Hg   622
CO_2 tension, mm Hg 28*
pH 7.43

MECHANICS OF BREATHING

Max. expiratory flow rate, L/min   600
Forced expiratory volume, % in 1 sec   88

BRONCHOSPIROMETRY

	O_2 UPTAKE	VITAL CAPACITY	TIDAL VOLUME
Right lung	50%	52%	53%
Left lung	50%	48%	47%

COMMENT.—All studies of lung volumes, distribution, diffusion, mechanics of breathing and arterial blood showed normal values. The only abnormalities were a 15-fold increase in pulmonary vascular resistance, high pulmonary arterial pressure and low cardiac output. The right and left lungs had a normal distribution of ventilation and O_2 uptake so that blood flow appears to be reduced evenly throughout both lungs. This was confirmed by pulmonary arteriography. The cause of the obstructive vascular disease in this patient is unknown.

The patient had severe dyspnea with completely normal pulmonary function (pulmonary and thoracic compliance were not measured, but it is not likely that compliance can be decreased in the presence of normal vital capacity and total lung capacity). In cases such as this, pulmonary vascular disease is a possible cause of dyspnea; the sensory receptors and neural pathways responsible for this type of dyspnea are unknown.

CHAPTER 10

Pulmonary Disability

DEFINITION.—Pulmonary disability is considered by some to exist when the patient is unable to perform his present job because of pulmonary disease. If this definition is used, the degree of functional impairment of the lungs will vary considerably among "disabled" patients because of the different work requirements of different occupations (heavy laborers vs. accountants). Some recognize the existence of disability only when the patient is unable to perform *any* gainful occupation. Even here the degree of functional impairment will vary within a group of totally disabled patients because (1) a laborer would be considered disabled if he did not have the training to do a desk job even though physically able to do so, and (2) an individual with functional impairment and dyspnea equal to that of the laborer would not be "disabled" if his job involved only mental work and no physical activity.

CAUSES OF PULMONARY DISABILITY

1. PULMONARY INSUFFICIENCY.—Whenever the lungs cannot maintain arterial O_2 pressure and saturation at normal levels, pulmonary insufficiency exists for the oxygenating function. Whenever they cannot prevent arterial P_{CO_2} from rising above normal, pulmonary insufficiency exists for the CO_2 eliminating function. Pulmonary insufficiency and pulmonary disability are sometimes used interchangeably, though they are not synonymous. Some patients are severely disabled without pulmonary insufficiency for the exchange of O_2 and CO_2; others with moderate or severe anoxia do not complain of disability. Chronic anoxemia, unless very severe, is rarely incapacitating by itself if it develops slowly and the patient becomes acclimatized to it. Natives living at high altitudes can do considerable work despite arterial hypoxemia. However, anoxia may in-

256

capacitate some patients by causing or by contributing to coronary insufficiency or congestive heart failure or by producing cerebral symptoms, such as confusion and lethargy. Most patients with chronic pulmonary disease have an arterial O_2 saturation in excess of 85% and few symptoms due to their hypoxemia.

Carbon dioxide retention does not necessarily occur along with insufficiency for the oxygenating mechanism. This is evident in patients with alveolo-capillary block in whom hyperventilation has lowered arterial Pco_2 below normal. On the other hand, pulmonary insufficiency for CO_2 may be present without pulmonary insufficiency for O_2 when the inspired air is rich in O_2. Insufficiency for CO_2 rarely causes incapacitating symptoms if it develops gradually over long periods of time; one patient, maintained on continuous O_2 therapy because of severe emphysema, had arterial Pco_2 between 80 and 140 mm Hg for more than a year and was mentally alert throughout. However, an *abrupt* increase in arterial Pco_2 may lead to coma (p. 314).

It is difficult to define pulmonary insufficiency satisfactorily. Many patients with cardiopulmonary disease would have pulmonary insufficiency for the exchange of O_2 or CO_2 if their ventilation remained at "normal" levels. However, they avoid "insufficiency" for O_2 and CO_2 by hyperventilation. Strictly speaking, they do not have pulmonary insufficiency at this time, but only because of increased ventilation and additional work by their respiratory muscles.

2. COUGH, EXPECTORATION, HEMORRHAGE.—Patients with chronic pulmonary disease may be so incapacitated by an almost constant cough and expectoration of sputum that they cannot work with others on this account. Some are prevented from accepting gainful employment because of the infectious nature of their pulmonary disease. Others are not permitted to work because of an increased tendency to pulmonary hemorrhage.

3. DYSPNEA.—The most frequent cause of pulmonary disability is dyspnea—difficult breathing. Because the evaluation of dyspnea enters into any judgment of pulmonary disability, it is important that the physician have an understanding of what is meant by dyspnea.

DYSPNEA

WHAT IS DYSPNEA?

Is it a symptom or a sign? We use the word dyspnea to connote a *symptom,* a sensory experience which, like pain, can be perceived and judged only by the patient. Use of the term "objective dyspnea" (a decrease in ventilatory reserve below the range of healthy persons when compared at the same level of activity) is inadvisable because it implies that the important factors in the causation of dyspnea have been identified and relate to a specific decrease in ventilatory reserve. This is not necessarily true.

Other terms sometimes confused with dyspnea are hyperpnea (increased breathing), hyperventilation (breathing in excess of the metabolic needs of the patient), tachypnea (increased rate) and polypnea (rapid, shallow breathing). Special types of dyspnea are orthopnea (breathing which can be accomplished best in the upright position) and trepopnea (dyspnea which occurs only in a lateral position).

It might be profitable to compare the symptom, *dyspnea,* with the symptom, *pain.* Pain can be characterized by an instructive variety of terms such as stabbing, throbbing, aching, burning, oppressive and bursting. However, the patient's description of *respiratory* distress is channeled by most physicians into two terms: "dyspnea" and "shortness of breath." More precise recording of the patient's own characterization of his difficulties in breathing might lead to better correlation of these with objective tests of pulmonary function or with mechanisms responsible for the dyspnea. Is the respiratory discomfort experienced in acute respiratory obstruction, emphysema, congestive heart failure, pulmonary embolism, acute neuromuscular paralysis, anemia, acidosis, neurocirculatory asthenia and pulmonary fibrosis really identical in each? How much of the distress is pain, how much fatigue or exhaustion, how much muscular aching, and how much is apprehension or fear?

Some physicians believe that the dyspnea of a healthy athlete is quite different from that of the asthmatic patient in whom there is hard gasping combined with panic and exhaustion and that of the cardiac patient whose breathlessness is associated with profound exhaustion as well as anxiety and fear. There is little precise information on different types of dyspnea in specific diseases.

WHAT IS THE ORIGIN OF DYSPNEA AS A SENSORY EXPERIENCE?

If dyspnea is a symptom, there must be a neuroanatomic basis for it, just as there is for pain; it is improper to say that "dyspnea is due to a loss of functioning lung tissue" or "inability to breathe sufficient air" or "the need of the body for more O_2" without identifying the mechanisms involved.

Like pain, there may be only a central basis or there may be both peripheral and central components. Therefore we must look for the sensory receptors, sensory pathways and thalamic or cortical centers which are responsible for the perception of respiratory discomfort and for the reaction to these unpleasant stimuli. Again, just as some patients have little pain (minimal sensory stimulation) but suffer greatly (maximal central response), or have much pain and suffer little, some patients may have little respiratory difficulty and much dyspnea, or much respiratory difficulty and little dyspnea.

For example, a patient had severe pulmonary insufficiency (arterial O_2 saturation 60%, arterial P_{CO_2} 68 mm Hg, vital capacity 690 ml, total lung capacity 2250 ml and MVV only 11 L/min) but never complained of dyspnea, even during exercise on a treadmill. At the other extreme, patient T.S. (p. 268) complained of dyspnea, but results of modern pulmonary function tests were completely normal.

What and where are the sensory *receptors* which initiate afferent impulses leading to dyspnea? Are they the same mechanoreceptors or chemoreceptors that are involved in the normal processes of breathing— those which regulate the rate and depth of respiration? Is dyspnea caused by a barrage of impulses from these directed to the medullary respiratory center which, when in excess, spill over into the areas of consciousness? Is it caused by the activation of special receptors, not normally active, which send impulses directly to the centers of consciousness and not primarily to the respiratory center? Or is it caused by a change in the pattern of impulses—too few of some, too many of others or an asynchrony of several (cf. dysesthesia)? Are these receptors located in the tissues surrounding the airway, in the alveoli, the pulmonary circulation, the pulmonary parenchyma, the pleura, the bones, joints or ligaments of the thoracic cage or in the muscles of respiration? Are they receptors for touch, change in temperature, in pressure or tension, in stretch, distention, volume or position or in chemical composition? Do their afferent fibers run centrally in the vagi, in the sympathetic nerves or in the somatic nerves?

It is time that we discover the location of the receptors, pathways and centers which are responsible for the perception of the original stimulus, the conduction of the impulses and the reaction to these, because treatment of excessive dyspnea may ultimately depend on this knowledge.

THEORIES OF CAUSES OF DYSPNEA

Attempts to determine the nature and origin of dyspnea have usually centered on correlation of the estimated severity of dyspnea with something that can be measured in man; e.g., dyspnea in relation to vital capacity, MVV, breathing reserve, arterial blood gases, minute volume of ventilation, the degree of inflation of the lungs, pulmonary capillary pressure or O_2 consumption. Many investigators have attempted to conceive a unitarian explanation, but none of these is free from major criticism if it is intended to represent the sole or important cause of all or most types of dyspnea. Three theories of the cause of dyspnea are of special interest.

1. INCREASED WORK OF BREATHING.—Many patients with dyspnea either have mechanical hindrances to breathing (airway obstruction or pulmonary or thoracic restriction) or are ventilating far more than normal because of anoxemia, acidosis, shock or fever. It is reasonable to believe, therefore, that dyspnea occurs when the muscles of respiration perform either an unusual amount or an unaccustomed type of work. This concept is similar to Sir Thomas Lewis' explanation of intermittent claudication, that exercise in the presence of ischemia results in the accumulation of chemical products of metabolism which cause excitation of sensory nerve endings and produce afferent nerve impulses and pain. This concept is an attractive one when applied to the respiratory muscles, because it could explain dyspnea associated with all cardiopulmonary conditions in which the work of breathing is definitely increased. It could also explain the dyspnea that anemic or anoxic patients experience during mild exercise, if the supply of O_2 to respiratory muscles is insufficient. However, no one has reproduced the pain of claudication without drastic reduction in blood flow to working limb muscles, and there is no reason to believe that blood flow is restricted to the respiratory muscles during periods of increased activity. Perhaps the symptom, dyspnea, should be compared to the symptom of fatigue rather than to the pain of claudication, but ignorance regarding fatigue is even more profound.

It is difficult to substantiate this theory because it is impossible to measure blood flow to respiratory muscles and difficult to measure their work. The work of moving the *lungs* (p. 191) is not the total work of breathing; in patients with restrictive disorders of the thoracic cage, the work of moving the thorax may be very large. In addition, muscle *work,* using the strict definition of the physicist, cannot be correlated well with dyspnea because "work" involves both force and the distance through which it acts. Thus, violent breathing efforts against a completely obstructed airway would involve little or no "work" (little or no distance) even though the O_2 consumption of the muscles would rise sharply. Until the physicist devises an acceptable term for work which includes static effort, it is probably better to relate dyspnea to the *force* acting on the lung and the length of its action or to the extra O_2 consumption caused by respiratory effort. Even then, this concept cannot explain all types of dyspnea.

2. UNINTERRUPTED EXCITATION OF THE RESPIRATORY CENTER.—Dr. George Wright believes that breathlessness may be caused by undue intensity and prolongation of the discharge of the medullary inspiratory neurons. The intensity could result from unusually strong, continuous stimuli bombarding the center and the prolongation from abnormally weak inhibitory impulses from stretch receptors in the lungs which normally interrupt the inspiratory neurons rhythmically. Breath-holding in full inspiration or expiration does not lead to immediate dyspnea, so dyspnea is not caused simply by an extreme inflation or deflation of the thorax or lungs. However, breath-holding extended to the breaking point causes unpleasant respiratory distress which is relieved promptly by a deep inspiration even when the gas inhaled is N_2 or 7.4% CO_2 in air. The same is true of exercising patients with mechanical limitation to full inspiration, induced by strapping of the thorax; their dyspnea is also relieved by full inspiration. This concept implies that continuous excitation of the inspiratory center ultimately showers the centers of consciousness with impulses which cause dyspnea.

There are several weaknesses in this theory: (*a*) The effectiveness of the inhibito-inspiratory Hering-Breuer reflex in adult man has been questioned, though it is known to be active in the newborn infant and in common laboratory animals. (*b*) Trained individuals can breath-hold for longer periods if they employ any maneuver which causes inhibition of the respiratory centers such as repeated swallowing movements; in other words, stretch of the lungs may be a nonspecific way of prolonging breath-holding.

3. LENGTH-TENSION APPROPRIATENESS.—Dr. Moran Campbell believes that dyspnea may arise from an imbalance between the demand of the respiratory centers for ventilation and the actual ventilation produced. This means that some center of consciousness is continuously relating the request for more ventilation to the actual ventilation produced. The demand for ventilation ideally might be measured as the activity of the respiratory centers or the impulse traffic from them to the respiratory muscles, in response to direct and reflex stimuli which excite the centers. The demand for ventilation could also be measured as the tension developed by the respiratory muscles. The actual ventilation accomplished could be sensed by stretch receptors within the lungs (sensing a change in lung volume) or by joint receptors and muscle spindles (which can

sense a change in thoracic volume). Tendon receptors could signal change in muscle tension, but these are not necessary if the respiratory centers or the control systems influencing the respiratory centers have direct access to centers of consciousness. The latter could receive information then even when central activity cannot cause an increase in peripheral muscle tension (poliomyelitis, neuromuscular block). Campbell believes that the sensing of change in ventilation is a function of thoracic wall and not of pulmonary receptors. The perception of increased ventilatory loads would, according to this concept, be due to imbalance between the demand for ventilation (muscle tension developed) and its fulfillment (change in muscle length).

Several conditions remain unexplained by any theory that has been proposed:

1. Patients with severe weakness of the respiratory muscles caused by poliomyelitis, intercostal neuritis and myasthenia gravis may suffer intense dyspnea at times when their respiratory muscles are doing little or no work and exerting little or no force on the lung. Further, they may be dyspneic even when a body respirator has produced tidal volume and rate of breathing that are equal to or greater than normal (alveolar P_{CO_2} less than 40 mm Hg).

2. Patients receiving curare to the point of paralysis of the respiratory muscles may experience dyspnea even when rhythmic pulmonary ventilation achieved by a positive pressure to the airway is greater than normal.

3. Patients undergoing high spinal anesthesia may have a sensation of dyspnea at a time when superficial thoracic sensations are lost, but voluntary movements of the thoracic cage appear to be unimpaired. Such patients, because of their sensory loss, may fail to appreciate the depth of respiration (so that there is "length-tension inappropriateness"), but the same could not be true in patients with poliomyelitis or myasthenia gravis or in curarized patients who have no sensory impairment.

4. Patients with neurocirculatory asthenia complain of dyspnea, although no significant alteration in the mechanical factors in breathing have been demonstrated in them.

5. Dyspnea may be severe if a breathing tube is occluded abruptly without warning to the patient, but may be inconsequential if the patient is asked to occlude the tube himself for the same period of time.

6. Patients with acute embolism of a pulmonary artery may suffer severe dyspnea, although the ischemic type of pulmonary embolism theoretically should not be associated with significant changes in the mechanical properties of the lungs.

There is an amazing lack of precise information regarding the origin of dyspnea—one of the commonest symptoms encountered in clinical practice. Theories of the genesis of dyspnea should be supported or disproved by more direct experimentation. This might be achieved by the study of patients who require, for some proper medical reason, interruption of nervous pathways by surgical means or by blocking procedures; this might include patients subjected to thoracic sympathectomy or operations on the central nervous system for the relief of pain. It might be aided by more complete study of those unfortunate individuals who have various motor and sensory paralyses affecting the thorax. It might even involve the study of action potentials in respiratory muscles, the use of differential spinal anesthesia, temporary vagal nerve block or anesthetization of the airways by aerosols (with full realization of the dangers involved) in an attempt to learn more about the nervous pathways for dyspnea.

One might predict that study will reveal eventually that there are multiple factors in the causation of dyspnea and that in certain cases dyspnea will exist with no measurable changes in the physical properties of the lungs by present tests. One might also predict that in the great majority of patients with dyspnea, the physiologist will be able to identify and quantify alterations in the mechanical factors in breathing, and that more widespread use of the newer tests of pulmonary function will bring us nearer to an understanding of dyspnea in most patients with cardiopulmonary disease and disability.

COMPENSATION FOR PULMONARY DISABILITY

Until recently, medical-legal matters involving pulmonary disability were settled by measurement of vital capacity or examination of roentgenograms of the chest, neither of which evaluates function. Yet there may be gross roentgen changes in the lungs of patients with completely normal function (e.g., silicosis) and minor anatomic roentgen lesions in the lungs of patients who have severe disturbances of function (e.g., emphysema). Therefore in the evaluation of disability, tests of function of the lungs should replace tests which estimate only anatomic change in the lungs.

Function tests can determine on an objective basis: (1) the presence or absence of functional impairment, (2) the nature of any impairment (pattern of obstruction? restriction?), (3) the severity of the disturbance, and (4) whether the degree of abnormality is compatible with the claim of disability. The physiologist cannot, of course, declare that the patient is 25%, 50% or 75% disabled, and no reasonable person would request such an estimate.

Can the physiologist determine when a patient is malingering? If he uses tests requiring full co-operation of the patient (MVV, maximal flow rates), normal values settle the issue; abnormal values may be trustworthy if the data and patterns are highly reproducible. In general, compensation cases should be settled by objective tests, such as airway resistance, pulmonary compliance, arterial blood studies, thoracic gas volume and diffusing capacity, which do not require the claimant's co-operation.

Can the physiologist deny the claim of dyspnea and disability when function tests are normal? Neither the physician nor the physiologist can conclude (in view of our present ignorance) that the dyspneic patient does not in fact have dyspnea; it is possible that rather elusive factors may be responsible for the patient's complaints, such as chronic irritation of nerve endings somewhere in the respiratory tract or the existence of some alveoli with decreased compliance and consequent underinflation. The diagnosis of hysteria or psychosomatic disease should be made reluctantly, and patients given such a diagnosis should be followed regularly to determine its long-term validity.

CAUSE-AND-EFFECT RELATIONSHIPS BETWEEN DISEASE AND OCCUPATION.—A patient and his physician are expected in some instances to show that the disability is due to exposure of the patient to a hazard in his occupation. This is often difficult to do. Patients working in hazardous trades may develop pulmonary disease completely unrelated to the employment. For example, individuals in the older age group may have pulmonary emphysema without any exposure to dust or fumes. An epidemiologic approach is really required to decide whether a specific disease is much more common in employees in a particular trade than in the general population, and to establish a cause-effect relationship; this has been done for the soft coal miners in Wales.

It is hoped that industry will perform routine screening studies of pulmonary function on all employees who will be exposed to occupational hazards involving the lungs. The industrial physician should then examine each patient exposed to dust or fume hazard annually with the hope of detecting pulmonary disease early and preventing its progression. Small changes in pulmonary function occurring in any one individual over a period of months or years are more meaningful than the response to a single test compared to normal values collected from healthy individuals. Objective tests sometimes reveal the existence of mechanical problems in breathing even before the patient complains of dyspnea. Here, then, is an opportunity to detect pulmonary disease in its early stage and to give the patient the full benefit of preventive medicine.

Case 14 (Pulmonary Disability)

A. B. is a 47 year old man who was a chipper in a steel mill for five years, during which time he had considerable exposure to silica dust. He left that job 10 years ago and worked as a laborer for five years. Shortness of breath developed five years ago; this has become increasingly severe and he has been unable to work for three years. The patient's physician referred him to the Pulmonary Function Section to obtain objective data regarding the nature of the pulmonary disease.

PULMONARY FUNCTION STUDIES
Abnormal values are starred (*)

LUNG VOLUMES

Inspiratory capacity, ml	2390*
Expiratory reserve volume, ml	1540
Vital capacity, ml	3500
Residual volume (RV), ml	2530*
Functional residual capacity, ml	4070*
Total lung capacity (TLC), ml	6460
RV/TLC × 100, %	40
Dead space (anatomic, estimated), ml	150

VENTILATION

Tidal volume, ml	370*
Frequency, breaths/min	14
Minute volume, L/min	5.2*
Alveolar ventilation (calc. on basis of anatomic dead space), L/min	3.1*

DISTRIBUTION OF INSPIRED GAS

Single-breath test, % N_2, 750–1250 ml	11.5*
Pulmonary N_2 emptying rate (7 min), % N_2	5.0*

DIFFUSION

Single-breath CO diffusing capacity, ml/min/mm Hg	7.0*

ARTERIAL BLOOD

O_2 saturation (air), %	86*
O_2 saturation (O_2), %	100
Dissolved O_2, ml O_2/100 ml blood	1.7
CO_2 tension, mm Hg	49*
pH	7.32*

MECHANICS OF BREATHING

Max. voluntary ventilation, L/min	56*
Max. expiratory flow rate, L/min	42*
Max. inspiratory flow rate, L/min	170*
Forced expiratory volume, % in 1 sec	32*

INTERPRETATION.—The low vital capacity and MVV, large residual volume and very poor distribution of inspired gas are compatible with the obstructive pattern which occurs in many diseases, including silicosis.

The arterial saturation is low. This is not part of the shunt pattern because the hemoglobin and plasma become maximally oxygenated when the patient breathes O_2. It might be part of the pattern of impaired diffusion because the diffusing capacity is low. However, the anoxemia cannot be due entirely to the impaired diffusion because arterial CO_2 tension is high. The data indicate the presence of at least two additional patterns of abnormality which raise arterial CO_2 and lower O_2 saturation: (1) hypoventilation, and (2) uneven ventilation/blood flow.

This patient then does not fit one pattern in pure form. The question arose as to whether the findings could have been due to a compensation neurosis. The abnormalities in the lung volumes and in the mechanics of breathing could have been due to unwillingness to co-operate. But changes in blood gases of this degree are almost impossible of achievement by voluntary hypoventilation. And the results of distribution and diffusion tests are beyond voluntary control.

The obstructive pattern was not reversed by bronchodilators. This irreversible obstruction is compatible with a diagnosis of emphysema, which is often associated with silicosis.

CONCLUSIONS.—The patient has pulmonary disease and pulmonary insufficiency. The ventilatory defect fits the obstructive pattern. The arterial blood O_2 and diffusing capacity are part of three patterns: hypoventilation (due to mechanical limitation), impaired diffusion, and obstruction. These studies cannot establish a causal relationship between the previous occupational hazard and the present pulmonary insufficiency.

Case 15 (Pulmonary Disability)

V. G. is a 42 year old employee of a steel company. About 17–20 years ago, he had three years of exposure to silica dust when he was sandblasting. Following that, he worked crushing rock and had mild dust exposure to silicon dioxide and manganese for 12–13 years. Five years ago, a routine chest film showed some pneumoconiosis (probably silicosis) and he was given another type of work. Recently he has complained of pain in his upper thoracic area and has noticed slight dyspnea on climbing stairs. The plant physician requested pulmonary function studies as a guide to the type of position the worker should have.

PULMONARY FUNCTION STUDIES
Abnormal values are starred (*)

LUNG VOLUMES

Inspiratory capacity, ml..	3520
Expiratory reserve volume, ml......................................	1520
Vital capacity, ml..	4620
Residual volume (RV), ml...	1200
Functional residual capacity, ml...................................	2720
Total lung capacity (TLC), ml......................................	6240
RV/TLC × 100, %..	21
Dead space (anatomic, estimated), ml...............................	180

VENTILATION

Tidal volume, ml...	600
Frequency, breaths/min	19
Minute volume, L/min...	11.4
Alveolar ventilation (calc. on basis of anatomic dead space), L/min.....	8.0

DISTRIBUTION OF INSPIRED GAS

Single-breath test, % N_2, 750–1250 ml...........................	0.6
Pulmonary N_2 emptying rate (7 min), % N_2.....................	0.5

DIFFUSION

Single-breath CO diffusing capacity, ml/min/mm Hg..................	20

ARTERIAL BLOOD

O_2 saturation (air), %..	96
O_2 saturation (O_2), %..	100
Dissolved O_2, ml O_2/100 ml blood.............................	1.8
CO_2 tension, mm Hg..	38
pH	7.38

MECHANICS OF BREATHING

Max. voluntary ventilation, L/min..................................	170
Max. expiratory flow rate, L/min...................................	530
Max. inspiratory flow rate, L/min..................................	300
Forced expiratory volume, % in 1 sec...............................	82
Pulmonary compliance, L/cm H_2O..................................	0.2
Airway resistance, cm H_2O/L/sec.................................	1.9

INTERPRETATION.—Results of all pulmonary tests are normal. The normal lung volumes, MVV, forced expiratory volume and maximal flow rates (all of which require the patient's full co-operation) prove that the man is making his best possible effort and objective tests are not necessary. However, the objective tests of distribution, diffusion, airway resistance and compliance substantiate the lack of a physical basis for dyspnea.

CONCLUSIONS.—Despite radiologic evidence of pneumoconiosis, there are no changes in pulmonary function detectable by present methods. (The silica dust present in his lung may conceivably lead to detectable change in a later decade, but it will be difficult to differentiate such change from the changes to be anticipated because of physiologic aging alone.) There is no contraindication, so far as pulmonary function is concerned, to the patient's returning to work not associated with silica dust. The completely normal function tests should allay the patient's anxiety about becoming a respiratory cripple, although the physician should continue to search for a cause of the thoracic pain.

Case 16 (Unexplained Dyspnea)

T. S. is a 54 year old executive (surface area 1.92 M^2) who two years ago, had two episodes of "virus pneumonia" in two months. Since then he has had persistent shortness of breath and occasional anterior chest pain particularly noticeable at high altitudes; dizziness occurs with exertion and sustained talking. He has noted hyperesthesia of his fingers for four or five years. Roentgenograms show localized densities (scar tissue?) about 2 cm in diameter in the right hilar region. He is not interested in disability compensation; he wants to be able to work harder, unhampered by dyspnea.

PULMONARY FUNCTION STUDIES
Abnormal values are starred (*)

LUNG VOLUMES

Inspiratory capacity, ml	3180
Expiratory reserve volume, ml	1210
Vital capacity, ml	4390
Residual volume (RV), ml	1400
Functional residual capacity, ml	2610
Total lung capacity (TLC), ml	5790
RV/TLC × 100, %	24
Dead space (anatomic, estimated), ml	170

VENTILATION

Tidal volume, ml...	930*
Frequency, breaths/min	13
Minute volume, L/min..	12*
Alveolar ventilation (calc. on basis of anatomic dead space), L/min....	9.9*

DISTRIBUTION OF INSPIRED GAS

Single-breath test, % N_2, 750–1250 ml...........................	2.0
Pulmonary N_2 emptying rate (7 min), % N_2......................	0

DIFFUSION

Single-breath CO diffusing capacity, ml/min/mm Hg................	35

ARTERIAL BLOOD

O_2 saturation (air), %..	98.4
O_2 saturation (O_2), %......................................	100
O_2 tension (O_2), mm Hg....................................	619
CO_2 tension, mm Hg..	27*
pH	7.52*

MECHANICS OF BREATHING

Max. voluntary ventilation, L/min...............................	150
Max. expiratory flow rate, L/min................................	360
Max. inspiratory flow rate, L/min...............................	440
Forced expiratory volume, % in 1 sec............................	79
Pulmonary compliance, L/cm H_2O..............................	0.15
Airway resistance, cm H_2O/L/sec..............................	2.3

COMMENT.—This patient at the age of 54 has pulmonary function comparable to that of a healthy young man of 20; values for lung volumes, distribution of gas, diffusing capacity, arterial blood O_2 and mechanics of breathing are within normal limits for *young* men. However, he is hyperventilating at rest, and this causes decreased arterial blood P_{CO_2}, respiratory alkalosis and probably dyspnea.

We did not catheterize the right ventricle to learn whether he has increased pulmonary vascular resistance and pulmonary hypertension; the normal ECG and cardiac contours made this diagnosis unlikely.

Something is causing this man to hyperventilate: Sensitization of pulmonary stretch receptors by fibrous tissue from previous lesions? Respiratory center abnormally sensitive to incoming regulatory impulses? Respiratory neurosis? Since the pulmonary changes seen on the roentgenogram are unilateral, temporary block of the vagus trunk on that side might relieve the hyperventilation if it is caused by sensory impulses from the lungs.

In any case, the physician can reassure the patient that he has unusually good pulmonary function and ask him to learn to live with his symptom and gradually to exercise voluntary control over his hyperventilation.

PREOPERATIVE EVALUATION OF PULMONARY FUNCTION

The surgeon wishes to know in advance of a lobectomy or pneumonectomy whether his patient will survive the anesthesia, operation and postoperative period. Further, he wants to know whether the patient will merely survive and be a respiratory cripple (confined to bed or chair), or whether he will be able to return to a useful existence which, in some cases, requires a considerable degree of activity.

What do we know about the amount of lung tissue that can be removed safely, assuming that the remaining lung is healthy? Some animals can live a long, active life after removal of more than three fourths of their lung tissue. Man has less reserve, but young men have continued to be vigorous athletes after a pneumonectomy and one boy has remained active after removal of both lower lobes, right middle lobe and the lingula of the left upper lobe.

In general, young people have better pulmonary function following a pneumonectomy than older patients. Assuming that there is no *specific* disease of the remaining lung, this means that a "normal" lung of an older man is not in fact functionally equivalent to the healthy lung of a young adult (p. 212) or that young persons have the capacity to grow new pulmonary capillaries and alveoli and so create additional surface for gas exchange and more tubes for gas and blood flow; both explanations are probably correct, although we have little information on man's capacity for regeneration of pulmonary tissue in different decades of life.*

Theoretically, how should pulmonary function change following lobectomy or pneumonectomy?

a) If the lung removed had no ventilation or circulation. In this case there would be no additional ventilation or blood flow through the remaining lung and there should be no additional work of the right ventricle or respiratory muscles. Pulmonary function might *improve* if the excised lung had compressed healthy alveoli or the airways to these. Pulmonary function might gradually become *poorer* if pneumonectomy leads to distention *and* structural damage of the remaining lung.

---

* Not enough time has elapsed to know how well the one remaining lung functions 30 or 40 years later, when the pattern of aging becomes well developed.

"Overdistention" requires further comment. If a lung is removed, the space it previously occupied in the thorax must fill with something such as air, blood, plasma or fibrous tissue or by elevation of the diaphragm, sucking in of soft tissues of the thorax or displacement of the mediastinum. The last leads to overinflation of the remaining lung; i.e., it now has a larger functional residual capacity. However, a clear distinction must be made between further inflation of a normal lung and the production of emphysema. Case 4 (p. 226) proves that long-continued overinflation need not lead to any permanent irreversible changes such as destruction of alveolar septa or bronchiolar walls, loss of pulmonary capillary bed and changes in elastic fibers of the lung. It might be better if we stopped using the term "compensatory emphysema" (which connotes a destructive disease of the lung) and talked instead of overinflation, which causes no more functional impairment than does a deepened breath.

b) *If the lung removed had both ventilation and blood flow.* Postoperatively, there will be more blood flowing through the vessels of the remaining lung and more air flowing through its airways. If existing blood channels dilate and new channels open, the resistance to blood flow need not increase (see Chapter 4). The work of breathing will increase because either the tidal volume of the remaining lung must increase, e.g., from 250 to 450 ml, or the frequency of breathing must increase; if the tidal volume increases, the muscles of that hemithorax (and probably of the whole thorax) must do more work, and in either case more air flows each minute through the tubes of one lung. However, if functional residual capacity of the remaining lung increases, the airways become wider because of the increased tension of lung tissue. Pulmonary function should be adequate, however, and the patient symptom-free if the remaining lung is healthy.

c) *If the lung removed had considerable ventilation and no blood flow.* Postoperatively the total ventilation will decrease. The work of breathing, measured as pressure $\times$ volume, should diminish because useless ventilation has been eliminated. The O_2 consumption of the muscles of the hemithorax with no lung is not known.

d) *If the lung removed had considerable blood flow and no ventilation.* Excision eliminates a venous-to-arterial shunt and should raise arterial O_2 saturation toward normal. Relief from anoxemia may lead to reduced cardiac and respiratory muscle work. However, the entire right ventricular output must now flow through the vascular bed of one lung, and this can lead to an increased load on the right heart if the remaining pulmonary vascular bed is not normal.

e) If the lung removed had little or no pulmonary blood flow but a large bronchial arterial blood flow. The bronchial arteries enlarge and develop new channels when pulmonary arterial blood flow is restricted or absent; eventually some of the bronchial arterial blood flows through alveolar capillaries via precapillary anastomoses. Bronchial arterial blood may lose CO_2 into ventilated alveoli but takes up O_2 only if the O_2 saturation of systemic arterial blood is low. The quantity of gas exchange is probably not crucial, and removal of a lung with excessive bronchial blood flow may relieve the left ventricle of some unnecessary work.

In practice, the surgeon decides to operate or not on the basis of:

a) The nature of the pulmonary disease. If the patient has carcinoma of the lung both the surgeon and the patient are willing to accept more risk than for non-malignant disease such as tuberculosis or bronchiectasis.

b) Clinical judgment. Some surgeons estimate the degree of the patient's dyspnea at rest or during exercise and use this as a basis for prediction. This is not reliable for many reasons (see p. 257); two important ones are: (1) dyspnea is related more to mechanical difficulties in breathing than to insufficiency for gas exchange, and (2) dyspnea on exertion is common in many patients without pulmonary disease if they are not physically fit because of a long period of inactivity.

c) The function of the lung to be removed. The evaluation of its function requires either bronchospirometry or the use of techniques employing radioactive gases. Bronchospirometry permits a comparison of the ventilation, O_2 uptake, CO_2 output, arterial-alveolar P_{CO_2} differences, maximal flow rates and diffusing capacity of the right vs. the left lung; it can also give some information about the function of individual lobes. As an example, the data in Case 12 indicate that a large portion of the total ventilation (60%) goes to the right lung, which has practically no O_2 uptake (7%). This demonstrates clearly that there is little or no pulmonary blood flow to the right lung and that pneumonectomy should not lead to further right ventricular work.

If scintillation counters are positioned over the upper, middle and lower parts of both the right and the left hemithorax and a radioactive gas (such as labeled CO_2) is inhaled, the initial distribution of gas (amount of ventilation) and rate of removal (pulmonary blood flow) can be used to compare ventilation and blood flow to different regions of the lungs. (Or radioactive xenon, dissolved in saline, can be injected intravenously and the regional patterns of its elimination can be compared.)

These techniques are new, expensive and used at present in only a few research laboratories. Their chief advantage is that they avoid the unpleasant procedure of bronchial intubation.

d) Function of the remaining lung:

(1) Evaluation of over-all function of the two lungs: If obstructive or restrictive disease is so severe that unilateral disease could not possibly account for the decrease in pulmonary function, the remaining lung must be diseased. For example, when arterial Pco_2 is well above the normal upper limit, there must be bilateral involvement of the lungs because hyperventilation of one normal lung should be able to maintain arterial Pco_2 at normal levels despite hypoventilation of the other lung. If the pulmonary arterial pressure is abnormally high preoperatively, the resistance to blood flow through the "normal" lung must be unusually high. If the Dco is very low, there must be bilateral disease.

Surgeons like to be given a number for the simpler tests of MVV or vital capacity, below which the patient will not survive and above which he will; this is difficult to do because these tests measure only part of the function of the lungs.

(2) Physiologic "removal" of one lung: If the lung to be removed has considerable pulmonary blood flow, the physiologist can block this preoperatively using a pulmonary artery catheter with inflatable cuff; if the pressure in the main pulmonary trunk does not rise or rises only slightly (25%) or temporarily, the vascular bed of the other lung is distensible enough to accept the total right ventricular output readily and there will be little or no right ventricular strain postoperatively.

This technique of temporary unilateral pulmonary artery occlusion does not mimic pneumonectomy completely because it does not stop ventilation or bronchial arterial blood flow to the lung. However, bronchoconstriction resulting from the low alveolar Pco_2 usually shifts most of the ventilation to the other side so that simultaneous occlusion of a bronchus is probably not necessary.

Case 17 (Preoperative Evaluation)

J. K. is a 64 year old man in whom a diagnosis of carcinoma of the upper third of the left lung has been established. Because of a history of bilateral apical tuberculosis and radiologic evidence of emphysema in both lower lung fields, the Pulmonary Function Section was asked to study him before lobectomy.

PULMONARY FUNCTION STUDIES
Abnormal values are starred (*)

LUNG VOLUMES

Inspiratory capacity, ml.. 1210*
Expiratory reserve volume, ml.................................. 1020
Vital capacity, ml... 2185*
Residual volume (RV), ml...................................... 3655*
Functional residual capacity, ml.............................. 4675*
Total lung capacity (TLC), ml................................. 5955
RV/TLC × 100, %... 61*
Dead space (anatomic, estimated), ml.......................... 180

VENTILATION

Tidal volume, ml.. 530
Frequency, breaths/min 21
Minute volume, L/min.. 11.1
Alveolar ventilation (calc. on basis of anatomic dead space), L/min..... 7.4

DISTRIBUTION OF INSPIRED GAS

Single-breath test, % N_2, 750–1250 ml...................... 5.6*
Pulmonary N_2 emptying rate (7 min), % N_2................ 4.0*

ARTERIAL BLOOD

O_2 saturation (air), %..................................... 90.2*
O_2 saturation (O_2), %................................... 100
Dissolved O_2, ml O_2/100 ml blood........................ 1.7
CO_2 tension, mm Hg... 53*
pH 7.39

MECHANICS OF BREATHING

Max. voluntary ventilation, L/min............................. 50

INTERPRETATION.—The small vital capacity, large residual volume and functional residual capacity, decreased MVV and uneven distribution are characteristic of the obstructive pattern. Because of the patient's age and because bronchodilator therapy did not help him, we believe that the pattern is that of chronic obstructive pulmonary emphysema.

Because he has a tumor, a space-occupying lesion, within the thorax, we should see a reduction in the patient's total lung capacity; however, there is no decrease. Radiologically obvious tumors may occupy a relatively small part of the thoracic space so that total lung capacity is not decreased measurably. On the other hand, it is possible that the increased total lung capacity so characteristic of emphysema may have been reduced to a normal value by the effect of the tumor.

The arterial O_2 saturation is low and the P_{CO_2} is high. Total alveolar ventilation is not reduced and he does not have a venous-to-arterial shunt (dissolved O_2 value is normal when he breathes O_2). No test of diffusing capacity was made, but the high arterial P_{CO_2} eliminates impaired diffusion as the sole cause of anoxemia. The low O_2 saturation and high P_{CO_2} are probably due to uneven ventilation/blood flow ratios. A high arterial P_{CO_2} from this cause indicates a very widespread pulmonary disturbance; the few remaining areas of normal lung are usually scattered throughout both lungs, making it difficult to remove diseased lung without also excising some of these normal portions. However, if the carcinoma could be removed without sacrificing much normal lung, the chance of survival without serious pulmonary disability would be worth the risk.

At operation it was impossible to remove the mass without removing the whole left lung. Pneumonectomy was performed and the patient died 24 days later.

CONCLUSIONS.—No definite criteria have yet been developed for preoperative evaluation of candidates for lobectomy or pneumonectomy, and it is likely that a co-operative study will be required over a period of years to establish such criteria. Extensive bilateral disease is a contraindication to any extensive surgery on the lung, particularly when there is pulmonary insufficiency for the CO_2 eliminating function. This is particularly true when the maximal expiratory flow rate is reduced preoperatively; this rate may be lowered to a critical degree *post*operatively because of incisional pain. Inability to cough, with consequent inhalation of mucus, reduces pulmonary reserve even further.

Bronchospirometry is often useful to determine the function of the lung to be spared, but it does not measure the function of this lung as it would exist with the other lung removed and the entire cardiac output routed through the circulatory bed of one lung. For this, measurements of pulmonary arterial pressure during unilateral pulmonary arterial occlusion are helpful.

CHAPTER 11

Respiratory Problems before, during and after Anesthesia

1. BEFORE ANESTHESIA.—Ideally, the anesthetist should know the pulmonary status of patients with cardiopulmonary disease who are about to receive anesthesia. In particular he should know the type of disease (obstructive? restrictive?) and its severity (pulmonary insufficiency?) and satisfy himself that, in elective cases, maximal therapeutic improvement has been achieved preoperatively.

The main risk involved before anesthesia is in preoperative medication. Of the substances commonly given before anesthesia, some are respiratory depressants (barbiturates, morphine, Demerol) and can cause or aggravate respiratory acidosis and anoxemia; others (atropine and scopolamine) decrease respiratory tract secretions but presumably thicken them so that the patient has greater difficulty in coughing up mucus.

2. DURING ANESTHESIA.—All of the general anesthetic agents known depress the response of the medullary respiratory centers to CO_2. Not all anesthetic agents, however, cause hypoventilation. Some initiate another respiratory drive (usually reflex) which maintains or even increases minute ventilation. For example, ether, by stimulating sensory receptors in the lower respiratory tract (and possibly elsewhere), causes a reflex respiratory drive. Inhalation of nitrous oxide can cause respiratory stimulation *indirectly;* it is not a stimulant per se, but when administered in too high a concentration (85–90%) it causes anoxemia, and this can initiate a reflex chemoreceptor drive. Other anesthetic agents (intravenous barbiturates and cyclopropane), always used with adequate concentrations of O_2, provoke no reflex drive and produce pure respiratory depression.

Spinal anesthesia, by depressing or blocking conduction through motor nerves innervating the abdominal and intercostal muscles, can also cause hypoventilation.

General anesthesia that is deep enough to depress the respiratory centers usually depresses active expiration before it depresses active inspiration. Therefore, if active expiratory effort is required to deflate the lungs of a patient with cardiopulmonary disease, this effort will be diminished or lost during general anesthesia. Some anesthetic agents (ether, cyclopropane) may sensitize the inhibito-inspiratory member of the Hering-Breuer reflexes so that inspiration is checked much earlier than usual and rapid shallow breathing results.

Neuromuscular blocking agents (tubocurarine, succinylcholine, decamethonium, etc.) given in dosage sufficient to produce relaxation of abdominal or skeletal muscles usually depress neuromuscular junctions of the respiratory muscles as well. Further, certain types of manipulation during an operation may excite visceral receptors and cause reflex depression of breathing.

Bronchial constriction may occur because of (1) the action of anesthetic gases (cyclopropane), (2) liberation of histamine by drugs such as tubocurarine or (3) inhalation of fine chemical dust from the CO_2 absorbent.

Bronchial obstruction may occur if irritant anesthetic gases (such as ether) cause excess respiratory tract secretion at a time when the cough reflex, active expiratory effort and ciliary activity have been depressed by general anesthesia.

We know relatively little of the effect of inhaled anesthetic gases or vapors on the pulmonary vessels; ether is believed to increase resistance to blood flow through the pulmonary bed. Many general anesthetic agents depress ventricular function.

Theoretically, the anesthetist should have little problem in maintaining normal arterial blood gas levels during an operation. General anesthesia decreases metabolic processes, the tissues require less O_2 and form less CO_2, and the need for ventilation should decrease. Also, the anesthetist can control or assist ventilation to supply any necessary volume of air and can use a cuffed endotracheal tube and suction to maintain an open airway. Nevertheless, many anesthetized patients do have increased arterial P_{CO_2} and decreased P_{O_2}. The reasons for this are not completely clear. It may be that the "educated hand" of some anesthetists does not judge tidal volume with accuracy, that the anesthetist is distracted by events in the operating room and does not maintain a proper frequency of ventilation, that increased ventilation is needed because of uneven distribution, or that pulmonary and thoracic compliance is decreased so that a greater inflating force is needed. Some anesthetists may ventilate the patient sufficiently to keep the skin pink, forgetting that they have added O_2 to the inspired gas and that this will keep arterial blood well oxygenated even though hypoventilation and respiratory acidosis are developing.

Anesthesiologists agree that it is unwise to permit accumulation of CO_2 and the development of respiratory acidosis because (1) it seems to induce dangerous arrhythmias in some patients and (2) there is the danger of abrupt hypotension at the end of the operation when the arterial P_{CO_2} falls abruptly. The best way of determining whether alveolar ventilation is adequate during surgical procedures is to measure the alveolar CO_2 tension continuously or frequently by an infra-red CO_2 analyzer or rapid, simple chemical methods.

Conditions other than hypoventilation may cause abnormal levels of arterial blood gases. Uneven ventilation in relation to blood flow may occur for many reasons: the position of the patient on the table; unusual pressure on the thorax or abdomen by the surgeon and his assistants; the development of scattered areas of alveolar collapse (possibly resulting from the action of inhaled vapors on the phospholipid alveolar lining which normally maintains alveolar stability); pulmonary hypotension with pressure in smaller pulmonary vessels below the critical closing pressure, and an open hemithorax in operations on the heart and lungs.

3. AFTER ANESTHESIA.—The major risk from anesthesia in patients with cardiopulmonary disease is in the postoperative period when the anesthesiologist is not present to control or assist ventilation and to maintain an open airway. The danger is due to a number of factors that can reduce ventilation postoperatively: The pre-anesthetic medication has probably been reinforced by postoperative injections of morphine to relieve pain. The neuromuscular blocking agent or the anesthetic agent itself may have an unaccountably prolonged effect. The patient with emphysema has poorly ventilated areas of the lungs and eliminates gaseous anesthetics slowly. Postoperative incisional pain may reduce the will to cough up secretions even though the patient may be awake. The effect of the atropine or scopolamine on secretions has worn off and mucous glands begin secreting material which cannot be flushed out of the airways by weak ciliary activity or cough; secretions accumulate, block the airway and lead to atelectasis and pulmonary infection. Vomitus may be inhaled into the respiratory tract.

In some cases the patient leaves the operating room with a high concentration of O_2 in his alveoli. If some of the alveoli are poorly ventilated, the O_2 may be removed by capillary blood flowing past these alveoli and atelectasis may result.

Case 18 (CO_2 Retention during Cyclopropane Anesthesia)

F. J., a 52 year old man, was undergoing a thoracic operation under cyclopropane-oxygen anesthesia. Analysis of his arterial blood showed CO_2 tension to be 90 mm Hg (normal, 40 mm Hg), and O_2 saturation to be 100%.

INTERPRETATION.—1. Does the increased CO_2 tension indicate metabolic alkalosis or respiratory acidosis? Simultaneous measurement of pH showed this to be 7.14; therefore the elevated CO_2 is definitely due to CO_2 retention and represents respiratory acidosis.

2. How can the CO_2 be elevated at a time when the arterial O_2 saturation is 100%? Cyclopropane is administered with 70–80% O_2; the high O_2 tension in the inspired gas results in full saturation of hemoglobin, even though alveolar ventilation is inadequate for CO_2 elimination (see p. 48).

3. Why is the CO_2 tension elevated?

a) *Impairment of diffusion* does not result in accumulation of CO_2, and this can be ruled out.

b) *Hypoventilation* could explain the CO_2 retention. As a result of preoperative sedation with barbiturates, morphine or Demerol, the respiratory center is almost certainly depressed as far as the direct stimulant effect of CO_2 is concerned. Furthermore, every general anesthetic agent depresses the responsiveness of the medullary respiratory center to CO_2. These agents should result in definite hypoventilation and accumulation of CO_2. However, the anesthesiologist, by assisting the patient's own respiratory efforts, can correct this. In this case, the respired volumes were:

```
Tidal volume, ml.........................  400
Frequency, breaths/min ..................   23
Minute volume, L/min.....................   9.2
Alveolar ventilation (based on est. anatomic
    dead space of 150 ml), L/min..........   5.75
```

Figure 15 (p. 46) shows that alveolar ventilation of 5.75 L/min (assuming an O_2 consumption of 250 ml/min) is more than adequate to maintain normal arterial P_{CO_2}. Therefore hypoventilation of the whole lung is not responsible for the P_{CO_2} of 90 mm Hg.

c) Venous-to-arterial shunt.—If blood flow continues through the capillaries of the exposed lung and this lung receives no ventilation, arterial P_{CO_2} would tend to rise. However, even a large shunt could not produce a P_{CO_2} in this range in view of the increased alveolar ventilation. Further, the arterial blood could not be maximally saturated with O_2 when 70% O_2 was breathed if large venous-to-arterial shunt were present.

d) Uneven alveolar ventilation in relation to pulmonary capillary blood flow.—Even though *total* alveolar ventilation is normal, accumulation of CO_2 may result from variation in ventilation/blood flow ratios throughout the lungs. Several possibilities exist: (1) The functional residual capacity of the "down" lung is less than that in the "up" lung when the patient is in the lateral position and the thorax is closed. This is due to the effect of gravity on the abdominal viscera, the heart and the pulmonary blood. The blood volume of the "down" lung is probably greater than that of the "up" lung. These changes undoubtedly lead to alterations in alveolar ventilation in relation to blood flow in the two lungs. (2) Regional accumulation of mucus may lead to obstruction and to uneven ventilation. (3) Because expiration is passive when breathing is assisted by positive pressure, some regions (with partial obstruction or loss of elasticity) may empty more slowly than others and lead to uneven distribution. (4) The compliance of the lung alone is much greater than that of the lungs *and* thorax. Application of positive pressure to the trachea might therefore result in the delivery of most of the air to the lung in the open hemithorax and only a small part to the lung in the closed hemithorax. If most of the blood is flowing through the hypoventilated lung, accumulation of CO_2 must result. (5) If the lung in the open hemithorax is deliberately compressed manually, a certain pressure will be required to open airways held together by cohesion (surface tension). If the positive pressure applied to the trachea is less than the opening pressure of these alveoli, most of the air will be directed to the lung in the closed hemithorax. If considerable blood flows through the hypoventilated lung in the open hemithorax, CO_2 will accumulate. At present there is not sufficient information regarding the occurrence of one or more of these five factors.

CONCLUSIONS.—Respiratory acidosis occurring during surgical operations may be due to hypoventilation or to uneven alveolar ventilation in relation to pulmonary capillary blood flow. The identification of the responsible factors in any individual patient requires a thorough knowledge of pulmonary physiology and careful measurements of a number of factors. No conclusions can be attempted without complete data.

CHAPTER 12

Physiologic Therapy

WE HAVE NO means at present for substituting good lungs for bad ones, for reconditioning damaged lungs, for initiating or accelerating the growth of new alveolar septa, elastic fibers or capillaries, or for removing fibrous tissue. We can ensure, however, by rational, physiologic approaches to therapy that the patient has the benefit of maximal function from the pulmonary tissues that he does have.

Two types of disorders require physiologic therapy. The first are the *respiratory* disorders in which the chief problem is apnea or serious depression of breathing. The second are the cardiopulmonary diseases that are physiologically characterized by: (1) Inadequate alveolar ventilation, due to airway obstruction or to abnormal physical properties of the lungs or thorax. (2) Uneven distribution of gas and blood, due primarily to uneven ventilation or to uneven pulmonary capillary blood flow or to both. (3) Impairment of pulmonary diffusing capacity, due to a block between gas and blood or to decreased surface area of contact. (4) Abnormality of the pulmonary circulation, such as a pathologic shunt or increased resistance to flow.

Ideally, the physician should plan therapy to correct the abnormalities; if this is impossible, he should attempt to lessen and counteract the specific effects of these abnormalities.

I. Respiratory Disorders with Apnea or Severe Alveolar Hypoventilation

Apnea or severe hypoventilation occurs when the respiratory muscles fail to receive the proper signals from the brain, do not respond to these or are not powerful enough to achieve adequate ventilation because of increased resistance or decreased compliance of the lungs or thorax. The causes of hypoventilation are listed in Table 3 (p. 45).

A. SPEED IN INITIATING THERAPY

Irreversible brain damage usually occurs after 5 min of complete asphyxia. Therefore, whatever method of providing ventilation is *immediately* available is the method of choice. In the operating room, this will probably be a mask-bag system; elsewhere, it may be mouth-to-mouth insufflation or a manual method of artificial respiration. A mechanical device may be used when it is available, but never should one postpone action until a shiny, expensive automatic machine arrives on the scene.

Speed is also essential in starting a stopped heart or correcting serious hypotension. Well-oxygenated blood in the pulmonary capillaries does not help the patient; the blood must be moved to the left ventricle and through the coronary and cerebral capillary beds to be effective in resuscitation.

B. OPEN AIRWAY

All methods of resuscitation (p. 284) fail if the airway is obstructed. Immediate attention should be given to relieving the obstruction. Airway obstruction is common in the unconscious apneic patient because of relaxation of soft tissues of the pharynx, falling back of the tongue or block of airways by mucus or vomitus. However, the apnea may also be *due* to airway obstruction and the consequent asphyxia and medullary depression.

The non-narcotized patient with acute airway obstruction usually increases his respiratory effort. As a result, intrathoracic and intraalveolar pressures fluctuate widely during the respiratory cycle, but alveolar ventilation remains inadequate. Later, because of asphyxia and resultant arterial anoxemia and CO_2 retention, the medullary respiratory center is depressed and ventilatory effort is diminished or absent. At this stage, the medullary vasomotor centers are also likely to be depressed and the patient's systemic blood pressure is low; prompt attention must be given first to eliminating the obstruction (Table 20) and then to correcting both the apnea and the low blood pressure. We have seen a superb diagnostician giving vigorous artificial respiration to an apneic patient who became more cyanotic each moment. An anesthesiologist instantly recognized that there was complete airway obstruction and that the obstruction was in fact *causing* the apnea; the patient had inhaled a plug of mucus. The anesthesiologist aspirated the mucus, *then* ventilated the lungs, and the patient recovered promptly.

TABLE 20.—MEASURES TO BE CONSIDERED IN ACUTE, SERIOUS
AIRWAY OBSTRUCTION

1. Postural drainage: this is particularly important in asphyxia of the newborn and in patients who have inhaled foreign bodies.
2. Mechanical clearing: mucus, food or foreign bodies in the oropharynx may often be removed quickly by the fingers.
3. Oropharyngeal airway (pp. 283 and 302).
4. Proper position of head and neck to avoid mechanical obstruction of airway pp. 285 and 301).
5. Aspiration with syringe, or suction tube (p. 284).
6. Bronchoscopic examination and aspiration.
7. Removal of gastric contents to prevent inhalation of vomited material.
8. Tracheotomy (p. 302).
9. 80% He–20% O_2 therapy (p. 296).
10. Bronchodilator drugs (p. 291).
11. Antifoam agents (p. 298).
12. Antibiotic therapy (p. 297).

When respiratory obstruction is complete or almost complete, the physician must be prepared to institute adequate therapy, no matter how drastic it may seem. The plastic oropharyngeal airway devised by Safar should be part of the emergency equipment of every physician; it can be used both to correct oropharyngeal obstruction and as a tube for mouth-to-mouth insufflation. However, if the obstruction is in the larynx, tracheotomy is necessary.

In addition to its usefulness for by-passing laryngeal obstruction, *tracheotomy* is of value for other reasons. For example, an unconscious patient cannot cough, but his mucus glands may continue to secrete, so that obstruction and infection are likely. A patient with anterior horn cell paralysis cannot breathe and therefore cannot cough; tracheotomy, to permit frequent and efficient aspiration, may be life-saving. A patient with bulbar poliomyelitis or myasthenia gravis cannot swallow properly; tracheotomy may prevent fatal inhalation of food.

True, a tracheotomy does pose new problems (the patient's inability to cough, and by-pass of normal mechanisms for warming, filtering and humidifying inspired air), but these can usually be met by adequate nursing care. Regular aspiration of secretions from the bronchial tree is required. The catheter used should be sterilized to prevent additional

infection; its lumen should be large, so that thick secretions will not occlude it; it should have a curved tip (and a means of identifying the direction of the curve from the visible end), so that the left as well as the
right bronchial tree can be aspirated; it should be removed promptly,
since it reduces the lumen of the airway available for alveolar ventilation.

C. NON-MECHANICAL METHODS FOR PRODUCING PULMONARY VENTILATION

Within the past decade, official organizations in the United States have
recommended first the Schafer prone-pressure, then the Holger-Nielsen
arm-lift back-pressure, and now mouth-to-mouth insufflation as the preferred method for emergency artificial ventilation. Why? First came the
realization that although most manual methods can produce adequate
pulmonary ventilation in a healthy subject who has voluntarily suspended
his breathing, the Schafer method was totally inadequate in apneic
patients in actual need of artificial respiration. Most of these patients
have mechanical problems in breathing and require an additional inflating
force to produce adequate tidal volume. The Schafer method cannot provide this extra force for several reasons: (1) The patient is prone. The
operator first pushes air out of the lungs by pressure on the rib cage; when
he releases this pressure, the thorax and lungs recoil to their original resting volume. The maximal tidal volume obtainable with this technique is
the expiratory reserve volume; this is much smaller, even in normal persons, than the inspiratory capacity. (2) The expiratory reserve volume
in the prone position is smaller than normal because the weight of the
body forces the diaphragm up and compresses the rib cage; it may be
even less because of pre-existing disease or obstruction of some of the air
passages. (3) The pressure-volume curve of the lungs and thorax is such
that more pressure is required to move 500 ml of the expiratory reserve
volume than 500 ml of the inspiratory capacity.

After a clear demonstration of the inadequacy of the Schafer method
in apneic patients, the arm-lift back-pressure (Holger-Nielsen) and the
Silvester methods became popular. These methods provide better ventilation because they include a phase in which the thorax is expanded actively ("pulled") into the inspiratory capacity range as well as compressed by manual pressure; they are "push-pull" methods instead of just
"push." The Silvester method has the disadvantage that the patient is
supine, and this position favors airway obstruction. There may also be
serious mechanical obstruction of the airway when the Holger-Nielsen
method is used, because of the position of the head and neck.

Safar has studied airway patency in anesthetized, spontaneously breathing patients and found that when the head was flexed (chin toward the chest) the airway was obstructed in prone or supine patients with or without an oropharyngeal airway. When patients were supine with the head extended (chin up), half of them had an open airway and the other half required, in addition, forward displacement of the mandible or the insertion of a pharyngeal airway or both. This emphasizes the fundamental point that no method, no matter how powerful, is effective if the airway is obstructed.

MOUTH-TO-MOUTH BREATHING (MOUTH-TO-MOUTH OR MOUTH-TO-NOSE INSUFFLATION; EXPIRED-AIR INFLATION).—Can this method provide a sufficient volume of air for the patient? Yes, because most persons, by expiratory muscle effort, can develop an air pressure equal to or greater than the pressures that mechanical respirators are now permitted to provide. What of the *composition* of the gas provided? For a 500 ml tidal volume, the first 150 ml would come from the anatomic dead space of the operator and therefore would be fresh air; the next 350 ml would be alveolar gas (approximately 14% O_2 and 5.6% CO_2), but only 200 ml of this would enter the patient's lungs, the last 150 ml filling his anatomic dead space. The mean composition of the "fresh air" entering the patient's alveoli would be about 17% O_2 and 3.2% CO_2 (instead of 21% and 0%). The operator could bring the composition of this gas closer to that of air by inspiring deeply (this raises his own alveolar P_{O_2} and lowers his alveolar P_{CO_2}), but this, carried too far, could lower the operator's arterial P_{CO_2} so much that he himself might suffer from cerebral vasoconstriction.

The advantages of the mouth-to-mouth method are: (1) No equipment is required (the plastic airway designed by Safar is desirable, however, because it improves the effectiveness of the method, provides an airway and a breathing tube and makes the method aesthetically more acceptable*). (2) The operator can see the degree of inflation of the chest. (3) He can sense obstruction of the airway. (4) He will probably stay within safe inflating pressures, since he provides his own force.

D. MECHANICAL METHODS FOR PRODUCING PULMONARY VENTILATION

By the time a machine for artificial respiration reaches the patient the issue whether he will survive acute apnea has usually been decided by the application of simpler methods. However, in some patients with polio-

---

* A plastic airway may induce vomiting if used in a conscious patient.

myelitis, cerebral lesions or neuromuscular block, artificial respiration may be required for long periods; here mechanical methods are desirable.†

GENERAL CONSIDERATIONS.—The lungs cannot be inflated unless the air pressure at the mouth is greater than that in the alveoli. The amount of this difference in pressure determines the tidal volume, if other factors remain the same. The same flow of air will occur when mouth pressure is 760 and alveolar pressure 755 mm Hg (natural, negative-pressure,‡ breathing) as when mouth pressure is 765 and alveolar pressure is 760 mm Hg (positive-pressure breathing); in each case the pressure difference is 5 mm Hg. As far as ventilation is concerned, there is no difference between the methods; all that matters to the lungs is that a proper *trans-airway* pressure be created, by either "pushing" or "pulling." Why, then, is natural, or negative-pressure, breathing considered superior to positive-pressure breathing? Because natural breathing favors return of venous blood to the right side of the heart. This is evident if we consider the pressure difference responsible for returning blood to the right atrium. If the pressure in the venules in the legs is +10 mm Hg and the pressure in the great veins in the thorax is —3 mm Hg, the pressure difference for venous blood flow is 13 mm Hg. If the peripheral venular pressure is +10 mm Hg and the intrathoracic pressure is +3 mm Hg, "pushing pressure" is only 7 mm Hg.

What happens to the circulation during positive-pressure breathing? (1) The mean intrathoracic pressure of the respiratory cycle rises; this decreases the pressure gradient and reduces venous return to the right heart.§ (2) Patients with good circulatory responses react to positive-pressure breathing by increased peripheral venous blood pressure. This

---

† These same mechanical methods have other uses. One is to provide rest for fatigued inspiratory muscles of patients with chronic pulmonary disease and dyspnea. Another is to increase ventilation in patients with serious hypoventilation and respiratory acidosis (p. 303).

‡ Intrathoracic pressure is "negative" or, correctly, subatmospheric.

§ The mean intrathoracic pressure need not rise much if the inspiratory (positive-pressure) phase is brief and the expiratory phase is long. Actually, the mean intrathoracic need not rise at all if the inspiratory positive-pressure phase is followed by negative pressure applied to the mouth during expiration. A negative-pressure phase is not recommended for general use because it adds little to ventilatory volume and requires more complex apparatus than does positive pressure alone. In some conditions, it may actually decrease ventilation by reducing lung volume so that cohesion of respiratory surfaces occurs and extra energy is needed to open the airways. If extra positive pressure is needed to overcome airway obstruction, this pressure need not impede venous return, because it is dissipated while the air flows down the tracheobronchial tree, never reaching the alveoli or pleural space.

restores the driving pressure for venous flow, and the cardiac output returns to previous values. This response requires an active sympathetic nervous system and is absent or reduced when spinal anesthesia or ganglionic or peripheral sympathetic blocking agents have been used or when deep narcosis is present. Therefore, positive-pressure breathing may cause or aggravate hypotension in specific circumstances.

BODY RESPIRATOR (DRINKER RESPIRATOR; TANK RESPIRATOR; "IRON LUNG").—This method was conceived as a natural "negative-pressure" method of producing pulmonary ventilation. The patient is supine and all but his head is enclosed in a rigid tank; a rubber diaphragm around his neck seals the tank. The pressure around the body is lowered below the atmospheric; this enlarges the thorax, lowers intrathoracic and intra-alveolar pressure and causes inspiratory gas flow. The pressure then returns to atmospheric and permits elastic recoil of the lungs and thorax and expiratory flow. The cycle is then repeated at the desired frequency.

For years the body respirator method enjoyed the reputation of aiding circulation by creating a negative pressure around the thorax. Whittenberger has pointed out that since the body respirator encloses the whole body from the neck down, its negative-pressure cycle lowers the pressure not only in great veins of the thorax but also in the veins in the legs and all over the body (except in the head). Therefore the effect of a tank respirator on the circulation is approximately the same as "positive-pressure" breathing; the effects would be identical if only the patient's face protruded from the respirator instead of his whole head. In the body respirator, the head and neck are at atmospheric pressure when the body is below atmospheric; in a positive-pressure device, the face is at a pressure greater than atmospheric and the body is at atmospheric. However, the body respirator, like pressure breathing, does not ordinarily decrease the patient's cardiac output and systemic blood pressure, particularly if he is not narcotized and has active cardiovascular reflexes.

CUIRASS RESPIRATOR.—This operates on the same principle as the body respirator, but it encloses the chest and abdomen or the chest alone. The chest cuirass respirator can produce about 50 per cent, and the chest-abdomen cuirass about 60 per cent of the ventilation produced by the body respirator; thus they lack the power and reserve of the body respirator. However, they do provide adequate ventilation in some completely apneic patients and assist the respiration of those whose paralysis is not complete; they permit change in position and environment of a completely paralyzed patient, facilitate nursing care and improve the patient's morale.

TILTING METHOD (EVE, ROCKING OR GRAVITY METHOD).—This method makes use of the piston-like, back-and-forth movements of the diaphragm in the thorax. When the patient is tilted feet down, the abdominal viscera slide down, pulling the diaphragm with them, and cause inspiration; when the patient is tilted head down, the abdominal viscera slide headward, pushing the diaphragm up, and cause expiration. It is a non-mechanical method only when used in an infant or child who can be tilted up and down while held on an adult's arms; it can be used in adults only when a well-balanced tilting apparatus with proper straps to prevent sliding of the patient is at hand. Mouth-to-mouth breathing is superior to the tilting method as an emergency procedure in apneic infants.

POSITIVE-PRESSURE APPARATUS.—Positive-pressure breathing may be produced by hand pressure on an anesthesia bag or bellows or by automatic cycling machines. Several practical aspects of their use deserve emphasis:

1. The physician must not place full reliance on the "machine." He must treat the whole patient and not merely the lungs.

2. Machines, even at maximal positive pressure, may not produce adequate ventilation if the patient's compliance (lungs and thoracic cage) is very low. Such a patient poses a serious problem. "Safe" inflation pressures are generally given as 20–30 mm Hg. Should the operator exceed this range and risk alveolar rupture or stay within recommended limits and risk the patient's death from hypoventilation? The decision is usually to exceed "safe" pressures; since machines are set so that "safe" pressures cannot be exceeded, a bag or bellows must be used. We have seen patients who were inadequately ventilated by the maximal permissible ventilator pressures kept alive for several days by intermittent hand pressure on a bag-mask system; they ultimately recovered. Day has suggested using very high pressures for exceedingly brief periods to overcome atelectasis of the newborn in whom there might be cohesion of air ducts. Since lungs rupture only when distended to a certain volume, they cannot rupture if not enough time is allowed for a large volume of air to enter the alveoli. Difficulty arises, however, if a few alveoli have open airways and preferentially receive a large volume of air despite the short time; these may rupture. Rupture may also follow repeated inflations of alveoli whose airways close during expiration, because of collapse or kinking. Clearly we need more information about the bursting pressure and volume of the weakest alveoli in infants and adults with many kinds of pulmonary disorders.

3. Machines, set to inflate lungs to a certain pressure and then reverse to permit expiration, cycle back and forth rapidly when the airway is obstructed. This is because the volume required to raise pressure in the trachea or upper airway alone is very small. This "chattering" is a signal to find and relieve obstruction.

4. How much ventilation is enough? Figure 15 (p. 46) shows that a moderate reduction in alveolar ventilation raises alveolar and arterial Pco_2 but changes blood O_2 content only slightly. Therefore when artificial respiration is to be continued for more than a few minutes, arterial, alveolar or end-tidal Pco_2 serves as the best guide. An infra-red CO_2 analyzer is ideal for this, but inexpensive, quick CO_2 analyzers are also useful. Repeated analyses of CO_2, for example, show that in a completely apneic patient, a greater initial alveolar ventilation is needed to "blow off" excess CO_2 than is needed thereafter to maintain Pco_2 at near normal levels. For this and other reasons (p. 33) there is no "normal" value for alveolar ventilation, and arterial or alveolar Pco_2 values are a better guide than a measurement of the volume of gas breathed.

E. STIMULATION OF THE RESPIRATORY CENTER

The only centrally acting, specific respiratory stimulant is CO_2. Whenever there is apnea or severe depression of breathing, there must be an increase in arterial Pco_2 (if metabolism is not decreased) and an additional physiologic stimulus to the respiratory center. Will a further increase in arterial Pco_2, achieved by adding 3, 5 or 7% CO_2 to the inspired air, be helpful? Probably not, for several reasons: (1) The dangers of hypoventilation lie in CO_2 excess as well as in O_2 lack; the addition of CO_2 will aggravate the respiratory acidosis. (2) Carbon dioxide in high concentrations is an anesthetic. Although inhalation of 10% CO_2 tremendously stimulates breathing in healthy persons, it may produce some stupefaction even in them; inhalation of 25–30% CO_2 produces surgical anesthesia. Inhalation of less than 10% CO_2 may depress the brain of a patient suffering from chronic anoxia and CO_2 retention.

Inhalation for a few minutes of 7–10% CO_2 in air may be a useful test to gauge the severity of narcotic depression of the respiratory center in cases of poisoning by morphine or barbiturates: if respiratory depth increases noticeably, narcosis is not excessive and the patient will probably recover if given good nursing and medical care. Inhalation of 5–10% CO_2 in air is also useful for 1–2 min intermittently in patients who are hypoventilating postoperatively.

There is also a rationale for its use in combating the action of gaseous poisons, notably CO: if inhalation of 7–10% CO_2 in O_2 increases the depth of breathing, it should hasten the elimination of CO from the lungs and blood. From the practical point of view the inhalation of pure O_2 is recommended because of its ready availability and because it is safer in the hands of inexperienced physicians.

Some physicians use analeptic agents to stimulate breathing in narcotized patients with apnea or severe hypoventilation. Drugs such as Metrazol, picrotoxin and Coramine are potentially useful only in narcotized patients (poisoning with barbiturates or morphine) and have the potential danger that excessive use may actually depress the brain and respiratory center. It is true that anesthetized animals do awaken more rapidly if these agents are given than if they are not. The same may be true for patients under light to moderate narcosis. There is no proof, however, that analeptics increase the recovery rate of deeply narcotized patients who have had severe hypoventilation and anoxia for several hours. Nalorphine, though a mild respiratory depressant itself, does seem to increase the pulmonary ventilation of patients narcotized by morphine.

The analeptics may be used in patients with narcotic depression of the respiratory center, but several rules should be followed: (1) The arterial blood should be well oxygenated because these drugs increase the metabolic activity of the central nervous system. (2) The physician should wait for the effects of the first dose before giving the second. (3) The drug should be stopped at the first sign of increased excitability of the central nervous system. Convulsions, drug-induced or otherwise, are followed by postconvulsive depression; it is desirable to avoid this.

One can and should relieve medullary depression due to asphyxia by restoring CO_2 and O_2 to near-normal levels by artificial or assisted respiration. In patients with high intracranial pressure, removal of some cerebrospinal fluid may improve ventilation. Sometimes a patient hypoventilates because of thoracic or abdominal pain, tight binding or an unfavorable position for breathing; correction of these problems may increase ventilation. Relief from pain is often followed by improved ventilation, and morphine may be used cautiously in patients with serious hypoventilation due to pain.

Diamox, by increasing the renal excretion of $NaHCO_3$, lowers arterial blood CO_2 but at the same time makes the blood more acid; the beneficial effects of Diamox may be related more to its diuretic action and relief of congestive heart failure and cerebral congestion and edema than to its effect on arterial blood P_{CO_2} or pH.

II. Cardiopulmonary Disease

A. THERAPY FOR INTERMITTENT OR CHRONIC BRONCHIOLAR OBSTRUCTION

Bronchiolar *obstruction* is a general term connoting decrease in the lumen of bronchioles. Airways may be obstructed by many mechanisms (p. 220). Because constriction of bronchiolar smooth muscle is only one of these, we do not use the term broncho*constriction* or bronchiolar *constriction* synonymously with bronchial *obstruction*. Careless terminology may lead to careless thinking, and the physician may think only of smooth muscle relaxants when confronted with a problem of airway obstruction. Actually, there is no direct evidence that even bronchial asthma is caused primarily by contraction of bronchiolar smooth muscle. Allergic manifestations in man are associated typically with *edema* (urticaria, vaso-

---

TABLE 21.—MEASURES TO BE CONSIDERED IN MANAGEMENT OF INTERMITTENT OR CHRONIC BRONCHIOLAR OBSTRUCTION

1. Bronchodilator drugs (by inhalation or systemically).
2. Avoidance of bronchoconstrictor drugs or environment.
3. Positive-pressure breathing; control of breathing pattern.
4. Therapy designed to clear airways.
5. Anticongestive and antiedema therapy.

---

motor rhinitis, angioneurotic edema); by analogy, some believe that the airway obstruction in human asthma is also caused by perivascular congestion and edema. The strongest evidence that smooth muscle contraction is an important factor is that isoproterenol, which relaxes both bronchiolar and vascular smooth muscle, relieves a typical asthmatic attack, but norepinephrine, which is a potent vasoconstrictor but a poor bronchodilator, is relatively ineffective. However, the fact that relief of dyspnea in bronchial asthma coincides with the expectoration of bronchial casts (Curschmann's spirals) is taken by some to indicate that secretions and their retention in the chest are the major cause of dyspnea in this disease.

BRONCHODILATOR DRUGS.—These generally are sympathomimetic agents that actively enlarge the lumen of bronchioles by effects on bronchiolar smooth muscle. (Drugs which increase the lumen by other mechanisms have also been called bronchodilator agents.) They may be given locally or systemically. Except in emergencies, the physician should first try local administration of drugs as aerosols. If the desired objective improvement is not evident, he should try them systemically as well. Aerosol administration achieves a high concentration of the drug locally, with minimal systemic absorption and few undesired effects. The aerosol, however, goes only where the inspired gas goes and does not reach blocked areas of the lung; therefore it goes preferentially where it is needed least. On the other hand, a bronchodilator drug given systemically reaches all bronchioles through their systemic bronchial arterial circulation, whether the corresponding airways are occluded or not. Systemic administration has the disadvantage that the concentration of the drug is lower than that achieved locally by inhalation. However, isoproterenol, settling on the bronchial mucosa from an aerosol, may not diffuse into large, thick-walled bronchioles as effectively as it does in fine terminal air passages, whereas systemically administered drugs reach all bronchial smooth mus-

TABLE 22.—BRONCHODILATOR AEROSOLS

PARTICLE SIZE, μ	PREDOMINANT AREA OF SETTLING
>8	Mouth and oropharynx
3–8	Trachea and main bronchi
1–3	Bronchioles
0.3–1	Alveoli (but behave like vapor and most are expired)

cle through the bronchial capillary circulation. Systemic and aerosol therapy may thus reinforce each other; previously ineffective aerosol therapy may become effective once the airways are *partially* opened by systemic therapy, because an aerosolized bronchodilator drug can now reach affected areas.

Inhalation of bronchodilator drugs.—Where liquid particles in aerosols settle in the respiratory tract depends largely on their size (Table 22). If deposition on bronchiolar mucosa is desired, the particle size should be 1–3 microns and a nebulizer certified to deliver in this range should be used. (It is difficult to produce an aerosol in which all particles are of identical size and all settle in one anatomic region; some will be larger and settle in the upper airways.)

Only the drug delivered to the inspired gas reaches bronchioles; that delivered during expiration is wasted. The most economical method, therefore, is to deliver the drug (by squeezing the hand bulb or by using compressed air) from early inspiration to end-inspiration and to request the patient to hold his breath at end-inspiration for 3–4 sec to ensure the settling of aerosol particles on the bronchiolar mucosa. Deep inspirations not only cause a greater volume flow past the bronchioles and increase the total dose deposited locally but also open some airways by increased traction on their walls; however, they also cause more drug to reach the alveolar capillaries and increase the opportunity for systemic absorption.

If no undesirable symptoms occur, the patient should use as much aerosol as is needed to overcome obstruction. He should inhale the aerosol during five or six inspirations and then stop for a few minutes until the extent of improvement or of systemic effects becomes apparent. If improvement is not maximal, he should repeat the cycle. If side effects occur, he should wait longer between cycles. Therapy should not stop simply because the patient feels relieved; *symptoms* of airway obstruction may disappear at a time when airway resistance is still two to three times normal. The proper amount of drug is that which produces maximal *objective* benefit, i.e., optimally opened airways determined by some objective test that indicates change in airway resistance (maximal expiratory flow rate, MVV, vital capacity or airway resistance); improvement may result from opening of completely occluded airways (increase in vital capacity), widening of narrowed tubes (decrease in airway resistance) or both.

Isoproterenol (isopropylarterenol, Isuprel, Isonorin, Aludrine, Norisodrine) may be the natural neurohumoral substance released at sympathetic postganglionic terminations in the bronchioles. It is more effective as a bronchodilator aerosol than epinephrine. A combination of isoproterenol and a potent vasoconstrictor (norepinephrine) might be superior to either alone. The physician must remember that isoproterenol, although sympathomimetic, lacks the vasoconstrictive properties of epinephrine and norepinephrine. It is a vasodilator and, if absorbed systemically through the pulmonary capillaries, causes *hypo*tension and compensatory, as well as direct, tachycardia; the resulting palpitation may be quite unpleasant. Heart disease is not a contraindication to the *proper* use of isoproterenol in the treatment of bronchial obstruction.

Systemic use of bronchodilator drugs.—Effective oral doses of bronchodilator drugs for severe asthma usually produce undesired side effects (ephedrine, excitation of central nervous system; isoproterenol, palpitation; aminophylline, gastric irritation). Oral administration may be satisfactory in patients with mild asthma. Antihistaminics are not particularly useful in the treatment of bronchial obstruction. Some physicians believe that they may be harmful because of their atropine-like activity which, though it suppresses secretion, seems to make it more tenacious. Adrenal cortical steroids (prednisolone, prednisone, hydrocortisone, cortisone) and corticotrophin may relieve obstruction when other agents fail and seem to potentiate the effect of the other bronchodilators; presumably they act by diminishing the response of the bronchial mucosa to allergens and by decreasing capillary permeability and the inflammatory processes in bronchioles. The hazards of adrenal cortical therapy are well known. They include dissemination of latent infection, inhibition of wound healing, perforation of peptic ulcer, salt retention and aggravation of congestive heart failure.

Aminophylline, given intravenously, is often helpful when other bronchodilators have failed. Large doses, 250–500 mg, are required. There have been fatal or near-fatal accidents after its use. It is not generally known that aminophylline injected into fluid perfusing an isolated heart can increase the rate and amplitude of contraction as much as epinephrine. If this follows rapid intravenous administration in man, the abrupt increase in cardiac work may be responsible for occasional cardiovascular catastrophes, particularly if the patient is anoxemic; the heart muscle would then be forced to do more work when its O_2 supply was reduced. It would appear sensible to give aminophylline *slowly* by vein and to give it only when anoxemia has been corrected, at least temporarily, by the inhalation of O_2.

AVOIDANCE OF DRUGS OR ENVIRONMENT THAT CAUSE BRONCHIOLAR OBSTRUCTION.—If the bronchial obstruction is caused by specific allergens, these should be removed from the patient's environment. The patient should avoid the use of known bronchoconstrictor drugs given in the treatment of other disorders (cholinergic and parasympathomimetic agents) and of anticholinesterase agents such as insecticides used in garden sprays.

Nicotine, known to stimulate ganglion cells in both sympathetic and parasympathetic nervous systems, could produce bronchiolar dilatation (upon reaching sympathetic ganglia after systemic absorption) or bronchiolar constriction by a direct action on submucosal parasympathetic ganglion cells in the airway. Inhalation of an aerosol of nicotine (2 mg/ml) does not detectably increase airway resistance in man. However, inhalation of cigaret smoke does increase airway resistance moderately in healthy subjects and in patients. Presumably this is caused by the fine smoke particles rather than by nicotine, since inhalation of fine particles of inert materials such as carbon and aluminum causes similar changes. This effect can be prevented or reversed by the inhalation of 0.5% isoproterenol aerosol. It is not known whether repeated inhalation of fine particulate matter in smoke or smog causes chronic bronchial obstruction. It seems wise at present to ask patients with obstructive pulmonary disease to avoid inhalation of dusts, smokes, fumes and irritating vapors, though admittedly our knowledge of this subject is incomplete.

PRESSURE BREATHING.—Increase in the depth of breathing normally widens the bronchioles. A deep breath may be helpful in relieving bronchial obstruction in several ways: (1) A maximal inspiration can temporarily overcome bronchoconstriction such as that induced experimentally by inhalation of smoke or aerosols of histamine. (2) A deep inspiration can aid in clearing the lumen of mucus. If the bronchiolar lumen is bridged by mucus, the air trapped behind the obstruction is absorbed; the breaking of fluid bridges by bronchodilatation permits air to pass the obstruction and provides the alveolar gas necessary for effective coughing.‖

Deep breathing can be induced by inhalation of 5–7% CO_2 in air or O_2 or by pressure-breathing machines. The latter apply external pressure at the nose and mouth during inspiration, expiration or both. Some physicians believe that positive pressure applied during inspiration (intermittent positive-pressure breathing; IPPB) actually forces the airways open during inspiration. Positive inspiratory pressure does, of course, provide a pressure across the bronchial wall that tends to widen the airways, but so does natural inspiration. Pressure breathing does *not cause greater widening than the forces exerted in natural breathing for the same tidal volume*. A transbronchial pressure of 10 mm Hg achieved by *in*creasing pressure *within the airway* (by positive-pressure breathing) is not different from that achieved by *de*creasing the pressure *around the airway* (by natural negative intrathoracic pressure). Thus, inspiratory positive-pressure breathing causes bronchial dilatation only if it causes breathing to be deeper than natural breathing.

Positive-pressure breathing is used widely as a means of delivering bronchodilator aerosols. Physicians judging its value by the patient's subjective improvement are impressed by it; those who have used objective tests believe that pulmonary ventilation is increased in some patients with emphysema and that their blood gases revert toward normal *during* the period of positive-pressure breathing. Voluntary hyperventilation will achieve the same result if the patient is able to maintain the same pulmonary ventilation. In patients with obstructive pulmonary disease, such

---

‖ Expectoration of large quantities of mucus or sputum often follows bronchodilator therapy.

hyperventilation requires considerable work by the respiratory muscles; the positive-pressure apparatus relieves the inspiratory muscles of much of this work.

On the other hand, the patient with airway obstruction usually has more difficulty breathing *out* than in because of the narrowing of the airways in expiration. This expiratory problem is particularly serious in patients with obstructive emphysema; their airways often have "weak walls" which collapse during expiratory effort. The use of positive pressure *during* expiration has the disadvantage of making the patient use additional energy in expiring against this imposed pressure; it may have the advantages of achieving slower and more orderly emptying of the alveoli and increasing the patient's functional residual capacity with consequent widening of the airways.

In general, the natural breathing pattern of patients is that which requires least energy, considering the physical properties of the lungs and airway (p. 194). Some patients appear to benefit from a change in their natural pattern. Obviously, if tests show that gas is "trapped" during a forced expiration in a patient with obstructive emphysema, and if this patient naturally breathes out quickly, there should be some advantage in training him to breathe in more quickly and breathe out more slowly. (Breathing exercises are discussed further on p. 302.)

HELIUM-OXYGEN THERAPY was proposed some years ago as physiologic therapy for obstructed breathing, because the *density* of 80% He–20% O_2 is much less than that of air or O_2. Table 23 shows, however, that the *viscosity* of 80% He–20% O_2 is actually greater than that of air.

TABLE 23.—RELATIVE DENSITY AND VISCOSITY OF
HELIUM AND OXYGEN

	REL. DENSITY, AIR = 1.000	REL. VISCOSITY, AIR = 1.00
80% He–20% O_2...........	0.332	1.11
100% O_2	1.105	1.13

These figures suggest that inhalation of 80% He–20% O_2 would be useful only in those conditions in which a decrease in gas *density* might be beneficial; such a decrease permits greater flow for the same driving pressure when air flow is turbulent. This occurs only where flow is most rapid or where irregularities in the lumen of air passages cause eddy currents (e.g., glottic narrowing, foreign bodies); inhalation of He–O_2 mixtures may permit increased ventilation for the same effort in such cases (Fig. 48, p. 180). A general increase in air velocities, as during an MVV test, increases the degree of turbulence in the air passages; for this reason the MVV is greater while the patient is breathing He–O_2.

Because the trachea subdivides terminally into hundreds of thousands of fine air passages with a large total cross-sectional area, the velocity of flow through any one small airway is extremely low. Therefore, flow is streamlined in smaller tubes unless unusual obstructions exist. Inhalation of He–O_2 might actually be disadvantageous because its greater viscosity compared to air should require more driving pressure (and hence more effort) to achieve streamlined flow through the small airways.

THERAPY DESIGNED TO CLEAR AIRWAYS.—All physicians agree that it is desirable to clear the airways of secretions, exudates, transudates, froth and cellular debris. Many have suggested ways of accomplishing this. Few have evaluated such therapy objectively in man.

Man has natural mechanisms for keeping his airways clear. Transudate (water and molecules of low molecular weight) in the alveoli is readily absorbed into the pulmonary capillary blood unless there is capillary hypertension or capillary damage. Larger molecules and fine particles enter the pulmonary lymphatics. Mucus is secreted, coats the air ducts and traps foreign particles. Cilia sweep the enmeshed material and mucus from the deeper parts of the lung into the larger passages. Sensory receptors in the latter signal the presence of irritating substances and initiate an explosive expiratory effort (cough). The high-velocity air stream so produced dislodges sputum and expels it from the respiratory tract. The physician's responsibilities are clear: he must encourage fullest use of these natural mechanisms and do as little as possible to hamper them.

Antibiotics are of value in the management of obstructive pulmonary disease when airway obstruction is due in part to exudates or to inflammatory swelling of bronchiolar mucosa; exudates originating from either the alveolar or the bronchiolar capillaries can enter and occlude airways. Prompt and vigorous antibiotic or chemotherapy that controls infection permits clearing of the airways. Although we recognize the importance of identifying the organisms and determining their susceptibility to chemotherapeutic agents, we must occasionally use broad-spectrum antibiotic agents in the emergency treatment of certain patients with severe pulmonary insufficiency, before bacteriologic studies can be completed or even instituted. Dramatic relief of pulmonary insufficiency may follow antibiotic therapy in patients with chronic pulmonary disease even when the characteristic signs of infection (fever, leukocytosis, rapid sedimentation rate) are minimal or absent. Antibiotics should be administered *systemically* and not by aerosol.

Antifoam agents.—Some physicians have reported that dramatic relief of airway obstruction follows the use of aerosols of antifoam agents such as alcohol. Unfortunately, no well-controlled experiments in man support these impressions and the usefulness of these agents should be further documented. The physician must also know whether the antifoam agent is itself an irritant and therefore capable of causing bronchoconstriction and more bronchial obstruction. Further, he should consider the problem of how froth, if converted by antifoam agents into fluid, is eliminated from the respiratory tract. Does the fluid enter the *lower* respiratory tract and create new problems such as impaired alveolar capillary diffusion or lower respiratory airway obstruction? Finally, he should consider whether an antifoam that reaches the alveolar lining may displace or inactivate the normal surfactant there and lead to alveolar collapse.

Cough.—Effective coughing requires a deep inspiration of reasonably dense gas (air rather than 80% He–20% O_2), closure of the glottis, a build-up of pressure by forced expiration and then sudden glottic opening that permits high-velocity air flow. Tight thoracic binders and chest pain prevent the deep preliminary inspiration. The use of 80% He–20% O_2 decreases gas density to one-third. Tracheotomy by-passes the necessary closure and opening of the glottis. Excessive use of opiates and sedatives depresses the cough reflex. Binders, He–O_2, tracheotomy and pain relief are often necessary and are legitimate therapeutic measures for patients with pulmonary disease, but the physician should use them with clear recognition of their effect on cough and be prepared to eliminate secretions in some other way.

In addition, he should teach his patient the importance of frequent coughing when it has a reasonable chance of clearing airways. The question has been raised whether "cough machines" can improve on or replace the natural mechanism. Barach has introduced several devices designed to simulate coughing by producing high expiratory flow rates. One of these is a modified body respirator. The tank pressure is decreased to —40 mm Hg so that the patient's lungs are inflated fully; a large port then opens quickly, destroying the vacuum so that the lungs and thorax recoil quickly to the resting expiratory level, and a rapid expiratory flow is thus created. The other device builds up pressure in a face mask to +40 mm Hg; this is then reduced abruptly by an automatic switch to a negative mask pressure (—40 mm Hg). These "cough machines" are useful in treating an unconscious patient or one with respiratory paralysis but theoretically should be less effective than a natural cough in a conscious patient, unless his respiratory muscles are too fatigued to make a good effort. It is likely that part of the effectiveness of the devices is due to the enforced deep inspiration that precedes the expiration. Here too lies the danger of the machines, because inflation of diseased lungs to 40 mm Hg pressure may cause alveolar rupture. It is true that much higher pressures exist in the alveoli during a natural cough and the lung does not rupture. But we must differentiate clearly between *absolute* intra-alveolar pressure and *transalveolar* pressure in the lung, just as we did for the pulmonary circulation (p. 78). During a cough, the *absolute* pressure in the alveoli may be well above 40 mm Hg but the *transmural* (transalveolar) distending pressure is very low. This is because the glottis is closed and the force generated by the expiratory muscles is applied to all the contents of the thorax, i.e., to *both* sides of the alveolar membrane. Alveoli rupture not because of increased *absolute* intra-alveolar pressure but because of overdistention, which is due to excessive *trans*alveolar pressure. Thus, when there is 40 mm Hg *trans*alveolar pressure, alveoli may tear, but if there is 80 mm Hg both *inside* and *outside* the alveoli, there is no transalveolar distending pressure and no danger of rupture.

Expectorants.—Iodides, ammonium chloride, ipecac and other drugs have been used for generations to increase bronchial tract secretions. The rationale of their use is the belief that viscid sputum is difficult to move upward by ciliary action or by coughing, but if thinned, lubricated or liquefied by fresh watery secretion it can be dislodged, mobilized and expelled. It is difficult to prove that expectorants do increase bronchial secretion, do produce thin watery secretion at the desired spot and do break up tenacious sputum. We hope that physicians will not have so much faith in the value of expectorants that they do not fully explore other therapeutic measures.

Alteration in physical properties of sputum.—Because enzymes can attack proteins and mucin and break these into simpler compounds, enzymes have been used in aerosol form in the treatment of pulmonary disease. Rational therapy with specific enzymes should require knowledge of the chemical composition of "sputum" in any patient, just as rational antibiotic therapy requires knowledge of the organism involved and its susceptibility to destruction.

Rational therapy with enzymes should also require knowledge of the optimal enzyme concentration, proper chemical environment and time necessary for effective splitting of the substrate. Unfortunately, sputum contains a variety of substances—mucus, white and red blood cells, plasma and tissue debris. Enzymes that split mucus do not split protein, and enzymes that split protein components of cell nuclei have no effect on mucus. Among enzymes used in aerosols are: (1) crystalline trypsin (Tryptar), a proteolytic enzyme especially effective in lysing fibrin; (2) desoxyribonuclease (streptodornase, pancreatic dornase), which splits desoxyribonucleoproteins in cell debris though not in living cells protected by intact cytoplasm; (3) streptokinase, an exotoxin from beta-hemolytic streptococci, which acts specifically as a fibrinolysin; (4) hyaluronidase, which acts on hyaluronic acid (a constituent of intercellular cement) but not on mucus or fibrin, and (5) lysozyme, which specifically dissolves mucus but does so rather slowly. Some investigators claim rapid thinning of sputum, increased volume of sputum and remarkable improvement in patients given aerosols containing one or more of these. Other investigators find no objective evidence of decreased viscosity or increased volume of sputum, and some report positive evidence of harm (irritation of eyes and respiratory tract, bronchoconstriction and hypersensitivity reactions). Clearing of the respiratory tract of mucus and cell debris with a mixture of specific, highly active enzymes is a desirable therapeutic goal; much research remains to be done before such therapy becomes acceptable to critically thinking physicians.

Detergents; wetting agents; surface tension reducers.—The well-established use of detergents to cleanse skin and wound surfaces inspired a search for agents that would combat the cohesive forces between mucus or sputum and the surfaces in the respiratory tract; cilia or cough might then function more effectively in moving upward the sputum mobilized by detergents. The most widely used of these is Superinone, the surface-active ingredient of Alevaire. Reports claim that inhalation of this as an aerosol produces dramatic benefit in many pulmonary disorders and is non-irritating, non-toxic and non-hemolytic. Unfortunately, the few scientific investigations of this detergent do not substantiate the clinical reports. Further objective studies are needed to determine the effectiveness of detergents in the human airway; it is particularly important to know whether these aerosols hamper ciliary activity, interfere with sensory nerve endings or alter or displace the phospholipid alveolar film that Clements believes is essential to prevent alveolar collapse.

Humidification.—Natural protective mechanisms operate better with a moist respiratory surface than with a dry one. Normally the upper respiratory tract warms and humidifies air so that tracheal or bronchial surfaces do not become dehydrated. When the patient's upper respiratory tract is by-passed by a tracheotomy tube or when he is hyperventilating, the lower respiratory surfaces may become dry, and mucus in the airway may become inspissated. Whenever this possibility exists, moisture should be added to the inspired air; a nebulizer that provides a mist of water droplets ("cold stream") is effective.

Avoidance of atropine-like drugs.—It is known that atropine and some antihistaminic drugs, in therapeutic doses, cause dryness of the mouth and throat, and it is assumed that these drugs also reduce normal bronchial secretion as well as that formed in response to irritant gases or foreign particles. On the one hand, this appears to be a desirable effect; the anesthesiologist regularly uses atropine-like drugs to decrease the patient's secretion and to prevent airway obstruction. On the other hand, the use of atropine is considered harmful, either because it is harder to move sputum already present when the volume of secretion (which acts as a diluent or lubricant) is reduced or because post-atropine secretion is gluelike and harder to move. It is difficult to get direct evidence on the quantity and composition of normal respiratory tract mucus and its alteration by drugs. Until we know more, we assume, rightly or wrongly, that increasing the secretion of normal mucus somehow loosens, thins or liquefies the sputum; that when a patient can cough effectively, more fluid is better than little fluid; that when a patient cannot cough (e.g., when anesthetized), little sputum, even though thicker, is better than larger amounts of thin fluid.

Postural drainage.—Material in larger airways can be drained by gravity; this means that tubes in the lower lobes empty better when the patient is head down, but the upper lobe bronchi empty better when he is head up. In effect, frequent change in position may result in faster travel of sputum into the trachea; once there it can be coughed up readily. Fluid in fine airways, like fluid in capillary glass tubes, is not influenced by gravity.

B. CORRECTION OF DECREASED COMPLIANCE

Specific correction of decreased thoracic or pulmonary compliance should improve alveolar ventilation. For example, the removal of pleural or large pericardial effusion or ascites or the correction of pulmonary congestion or interstitial edema should enable the patient to achieve normal alveolar ventilation with less effort. Surgical decortication of lung restricted by fibrous or calcified pleura, removal of intrathoracic masses that compress healthy lung tissues, shrinking of inflammatory tissue by cortisone and surgical correction of kyphoscoliosis (to prevent later complications of the disease) are additional examples.

C. DIRECT INCREASE IN ALVEOLAR VENTILATION

DECREASE IN RESPIRATORY ANATOMIC DEAD SPACE.—When movement of the lungs or thorax is seriously limited, tracheotomy increases the fraction of the tidal volume that enters the alveoli. It by-passes about 50 ml of upper respiratory tract dead space and can convert alveolar hypoventilation into adequate ventilation, if total ventilation is maintained. New problems created by a tracheotomy are discussed on page 283.

Tracheal fenestration is a surgical procedure that results in a permanent opening with liplike valves. If the patient presses properly on the flaps, he can breathe and even cough and expectorate through normal channels. If he opens them, he can pass a semirigid catheter of reasonably wide bore into his lower airway and suck out bronchial secretion. When the flaps are open, the anatomic dead space is decreased by about 50 ml.

IMPROVEMENT IN RESPIRATORY MUSCLE ACTION.—1. *Improvement of diaphragmatic action.*—The thorax of some patients with chronic pulmonary emphysema is enlarged toward the full inspiratory position and the diaphragm is low and flat. Contraction of such a diaphragm either is ineffective or may actually pull the thorax in during inspiration. Abdominal belts and binders, pneumoperitoneum and breathing exercises have been used to raise the diaphragm and increase its usefulness. It is possible to push a diaphragm higher in the thorax by increasing the intra-abdominal pressure, but the diaphragm must then do additional work during inspiration to overcome the additional force. Subjective improvement after pneumoperitoneum in patients with emphysema has been claimed, but careful physiologic studies have rarely shown objective improvement.

Barach believes that the head-down position improves ventilation, since the abdominal contents push the diaphragm toward its normal position. A cycling device that would increase intra-abdominal pressure only during expiration would offer theoretical advantages but would probably be complex and expensive.

2. *Breathing exercises.*—Two goals have been set for breathing exercises: (*a*) To strengthen the respiratory muscles. One of the curious gaps in our knowledge is that we do not know whether increased work

by the respiratory muscles—known to occur in many patients with chronic respiratory disease—leads to their hypertrophy. This is in sharp contrast to our specific knowledge of the effect of stress on cardiac muscle and its consequent hypertrophy and possible failure. Some physicians, however, advocate breathing exercises because they assume that these strengthen the respiratory muscles and that strong muscles provide better ventilation. (b) To change the *pattern* of breathing. The first step is to determine the patient's pattern and see whether it is in fact ineffective. This of course requires knowledge of the patient's pulmonary function and particularly of abnormal mechanical factors in his breathing. The therapist then devises a cycle which does improve alveolar ventilation or maintains the same ventilation with less effort. For example, if an emphysematous patient has increased expiratory resistance owing to airway collapse, he should learn to breathe out slowly and less forcefully; if deeper inspiration improves distribution of air to the alveoli, it should be encouraged. Some therapists claim that the breathing pattern can be changed permanently so that it operates even during sleep.

MECHANICAL VENTILATORS.—We have discussed the use of these in the treatment of the completely apneic patient (p. 285). They are occasionally useful in the management of patients with chronic hypoventilation and respiratory acidosis. Positive-pressure breathing performs no feats of magic and accomplishes no more than natural breathing of the same tidal volume. Its use is limited to patients who cannot maintain an adequate tidal volume because they are unresponsive or unconscious or because their respiratory muscles are fatigued.

When a patient is still breathing and positive pressure is used to assist his breathing, there are technical problems not encountered in a completely apneic patient. A breathing patient may be breathing rapidly or irregularly, and the cycle provided by the apparatus may not synchronize with his cycle. If the patient is breathing *in* when the machine is breathing *out* and vice versa, the alveolar ventilation may be less when the breathing machine is used than when the patient breathes on his own. Devices in which the inspiratory phase is triggered by the patient's own inspiratory effort may avoid this asynchrony.

Positive pressure applied to the airway through a face mask may result in gaseous distention of the stomach and intestine. The increased intra-abdominal pressure may push the diaphragm higher into the thorax, may hinder venous return of blood to the heart or may initiate vagal reflex effects. A cuffed endotracheal tube avoids these disadvantages of the face mask.

DRUGS THAT STIMULATE RESPIRATION.—*Carbon dioxide.*—This should never be used to treat a patient with hypoventilation resulting from cardiopulmonary disease, since one goal of therapy is to correct respiratory acidosis and the CO_2 tension of arterial blood is already high.

Aminophylline.—The bronchodilating action of aminophylline is discussed on page 294. It can also produce central stimulation of respiration, probably as part of its excitatory effect on the central nervous system. The subjective improvement described by patients after the use of aminophylline may be partly due to such stimulation. The side effects of adequate doses of aminophylline taken orally (gastrointestinal irritation) usually prevent its administration over long periods.

Salicylates.—Large doses of salicylates stimulate respiration and increase respiratory minute volume, probably by direct stimulation of the medullary respiratory centers. The hyperventilation that results in healthy man from toxic doses of salicylates may be severe enough to cause marked lowering of alveolar and arterial CO_2 tension and tetany. In patients with pulmonary insufficiency, such hyperventilation is impossible owing to mechanical difficulties, but salicylates may cause some increase in breathing. The dose required to do this is large and may cause petechial hemorrhages in the brain.

Analeptics. Metrazol and Coramine (see p. 290) are occasionally used as respiratory stimulants in patients with chronic pulmonary insufficiency. However, these drugs are not *specific* respiratory stimulants and the dose required to increase breathing is very close to the amount that produces widespread central nervous system stimulation, twitching and convulsions.

DECREASE IN CEREBROSPINAL FLUID PRESSURE.—Patients with pulmonary insufficiency who have both anoxemia and CO_2 retention are apt to have high intracranial pressure and papilledema. This has been attributed by some to the vasodilator action of anoxia and elevated CO_2 acting on the cerebral vessels (cerebral blood flow is increased markedly without significant increase in driving pressure). If this is the sole cause of the increased intracranial pressure, one cannot attribute depression of the respiratory center to a decrease in cerebral blood flow. Indeed, patients with pulmonary insufficiency have the highest values for cerebral blood flow recorded in man. This suggests that diminished responsiveness of the respiratory center may be caused by increased intracranial pressure operating through some obscure mechanism or that there is cerebral edema due to the high cerebral capillary pressure.

Measures to reduce intracranial pressure would probably also reduce edema of the medullary respiratory centers and thereby improve ventilation. Correction of anoxemia and respiratory acidosis should restore cerebral arteriolar tone to normal and permit reabsorption of edema fluid. Diamox, through its diuretic action, may improve pulmonary insufficiency by reducing cerebral edema.

D. OXYGEN THERAPY

EFFECTS OF INHALATION OF OXYGEN

Let us first discuss some of the effects of inhalation of O_2 on healthy man.

1. EFFECT ON BLOOD O_2.—Table 24 shows the changes in a healthy, resting man when he breathes 100% O_2 instead of air. If the total

TABLE 24.—CHANGES IN HEALTHY, RESTING MAN BREATHING 100% O_2*

| | DURING INHALATION OF | |
	Air	100% O_2
Gas		
Inspired, Po_2, mm Hg	159	760
Alveolar, Po_2, mm Hg	104	673
Blood		
End of pulmonary capillary, Po_2, mm Hg	104⁻	673⁻
Arterial		
Po_2, mm Hg	100	640
O_2 saturation, %	97	100
Dissolved O_2, ml/100 ml	0.30	1.92
O_2 combined with Hb, ml/100 ml	19.50	20.1
Total O_2 content, ml/100 ml	19.8	22.02
Mixed venous		
Po_2, mm Hg	40	53.5
O_2 saturation, %	75	85.5
Dissolved O_2, ml/100 ml	0.12	0.16
O_2 combined with Hb, ml/100 ml	15.07	17.19
Total O_2 content, ml/100 ml	15.19	17.35

* These values apply to man at sea level with Hb concentration of 15.0 gm/100 ml and ventilation-blood flow O_2 consumption and R values given in Figure 15 (p. 46). The O_2 consumption and A-V O_2 difference (4.6 ml O_2/100 ml) are the same during inhalation of O_2 and air.

atmospheric pressure is 760 mm Hg, alveolar Pco_2 40 mm Hg and alveolar PH_2O 47 mm Hg, the alveolar Po_2 must be 673 mm Hg once tissue, blood and alveolar gas N_2 are "washed out."* The Po_2 of arterial

* Since some N_2 can be absorbed through the skin, this maximal Po_2 can be obtained only if the man is living in an environment of pure O_2.

blood (640 mm Hg) is less than alveolar gas Po_2 only because some venous blood from the bronchial and thebesian circulations normally empty into the left heart without first passing through alveolar capillaries. Because inhalation of O_2 increases the arterial O_2 saturation to 100% (and so adds about 0.6 ml O_2 to each 100 ml of blood) and increases the dissolved O_2 to almost 2 ml (and so adds 1.6 ml O_2 to each 100 ml of blood), the total increment of O_2 is 2.2 ml and the total increase in arterial blood Po_2 is about 540 mm Hg.

2. EFFECTS ON BODY N_2.—Inhalation of pure O_2 decreases the inspired N_2 to zero. As a result, the P_{N_2} of alveolar gas decreases promptly, N_2 passes from the mixed venous blood into the alveolar gas and from the tissues into mixed venous blood; eventually N_2 is completely eliminated from the body. The rate of its elimination is slower if there are many poorly ventilated regions of the lung or if a considerable fraction of body tissues has poor blood flow (e. g., fat depots).

3. EFFECTS ON P_{CO_2}.—The effects of inhalation of O_2 on P_{CO_2} are frequently misunderstood. Tissue, blood and alveolar gas *nitrogen* originates in the air we breathe, but *carbon dioxide* is derived from the metabolic activity of our tissues. Inhalation of O_2, therefore, cannot eliminate CO_2 from alveolar gas, blood or tissues. It can of course affect P_{CO_2} if it causes hypo- or hyperventilation. Theoretically, inhalation of O_2 can interfere with CO_2 transport. Normally some oxyhemoglobin is changed to reduced hemoglobin when the blood passes through the tissue capillaries. Reduced hemoglobin is a stronger base than oxyhemoglobin and accepts more CO_2 per unit of blood. When man breathes pure O_2, less oxyhemoglobin is dissociated, less reduced hemoglobin is formed in tissue capillaries and less CO_2 is combined with hemoglobin. This can result in an increased transport of CO_2 in dissolved form and therefore an increase in P_{CO_2}. This effect is unimportant when man breathes O_2 at 1 atm. At 3 atm, however, there is 6.0 ml of dissolved O_2 in 100 ml of arterial blood, and this more than meets the tissues' need for O_2; therefore no oxyhemoglobin would be changed to reduced hemoglobin, the uptake of CO_2 from tissues would be hampered, and tissue P_{CO_2} would rise.

4. EFFECTS ON RESPIRATION.—The immediate effect of inhalation of O_2 on respiration of healthy man is a slight decrease in respiratory rate, tidal volume and minute volume. The effect is slight (about 3% decrease) and temporary (2–3 min). It is probably due to the abrupt increase in arterial blood Po_2, which abolishes any reflex respiratory stimulation caused by arterial blood Po_2 less than 673 mm Hg. (Presum-

ably, some of the chemoreceptors of the carotid and aortic bodies are tonically active and react to even a normal arterial P_{O_2} of 100 mm Hg as to an anoxic stimulus.) This causes hypoventilation and a consequent increase in arterial P_{CO_2} which, by stimulation of medullary respiratory centers, causes breathing to return toward normal.

The minute volume of healthy man then increases about 10% above control values. The reasons for this are not clear. Several possibilities are: (1) the P_{CO_2} of cells in the respiratory center may increase because of the failure of normal quantities of oxyhemoglobin to dissociate to reduced hemoglobin; (2) O_2, acting as an irritant, may stimulate receptors in the lower respiratory tract; and (3) high arterial blood P_{O_2} may cause vasoconstriction in the region of the respiratory center, a decrease in local blood flow and a consequent increase in P_{CO_2} of these cells (assuming that their metabolism remains the same).

5. EFFECTS ON CIRCULATION.—Inhalation of O_2 usually decreases the heart rate about 5% and cardiac output 10–15%, probably because of a physiologic denervation of carotid and aortic bodies. There are no consistent changes in blood pressure. Oxygen may cause constriction of certain vascular beds, such as the cerebral, coronary and pulmonary. The effect of O_2 on pulmonary vessels is complex—relief of pre-existing anoxia may result in pulmonary vasodilatation, but a change from normal to very high P_{O_2} may cause vasoconstriction.

6. EFFECTS ON BLOOD FORMATION.—It is well known that anoxemia stimulates the formation of new red blood cells. For this reason it is reasonable to believe that high P_{O_2} might depress the bone marrow. When pure O_2 is breathed by normal subjects for 2–3 days, there is no change in the red blood cell count. However, this is not conclusive evidence; even if bone marrow activity stopped completely during this period, the effect could not be detected by measurements of circulating red blood cells if these have a life span of 120 days. The red blood cells of patients with sickle cell anemia have a very short life span, and inhalation of O_2 by these patients is followed by a measurable decrease in the number of circulating erythrocytes.

INDICATIONS FOR INHALATION OF OXYGEN

1. CORRECTION OF ANOXEMIA OR ANOXIA.—Table 25 shows clearly that O_2 therapy is not required by some patients with anoxemia *if* they can breathe air adequately or can be properly ventilated with air. Further, there are some patients (Class 3; large venous-to-arterial shunts) in

TABLE 25.—O$_2$ THERAPY IN ANOXEMIA AND ANOXIA

CAUSE OF ANOXEMIA OR ANOXIA	THERAPY
1. Inadequate oxygenation of normal lung	
a) Deficiency of O$_2$ in atmosphere	Restore Po$_2$ of inspired gas to 159 mm Hg
b) Airway obstruction; neuromuscular disorders	Adequate ventilation with air
2. Inadequate oxygenation of abnormal lung	
a) Hypoventilation	Adequate ventilation with air
b) Uneven alveolar ventilation/pul. capillary blood flow	Hyperventilation with air; inhalation of O$_2$
c) Impaired diffusion	Hyperventilation with air; inhalation of O$_2$
3. Venous-to-arterial shunts	Close shunt; O$_2$ inhalation corrects anoxemia only partially
4. Inadequate circulatory transport of O$_2$	
a) anemia; abnormal Hb	Increase amount of active Hb
b) General circulatory deficiency	Increase systemic blood flow
c) Localized circulatory deficiency	Increase local blood flow
5. Inadequate tissue oxygenation	
a) Tissue edema	Inhalation of O$_2$ (?)
b) Abnormal tissue demand	Inhalation of O$_2$ (?)
c) Poisoning of cellular enzymes	Inhalation of O$_2$ of no value

whom O$_2$ therapy cannot correct anoxemia and some (Classes 4, *a-c*, and 5, *c*) in whom O$_2$ therapy does not correct the basic deficiency. For example, when patients with ischemic peripheral, coronary or cerebral vascular disease inhale O$_2$, arterial Po$_2$ is raised to very high levels, O$_2$ diffuses further from nearby vessels into ischemic tissues and tissue Po$_2$ increases. But this does not correct the ischemia, because tissues do not live on O$_2$ alone. All cells in the body require metabolites such as glucose, amino acids and lipids for their energy. Metabolically, O$_2$ acts only on a hydrogen acceptor after dehydrogenation. If there is little or no blood flow to tissues, there will soon be insufficient metabolites available for cellular activity; O$_2$ itself will then have no metabolic role or usefulness.

In what anoxemic patients is O_2 therapy useful?

a) In some patients it is the only means of prolonging life. For example, a patient was kept alive for more than a year solely by inhalation of O_2 by nasal catheter. If this was stopped, his arterial O_2 saturation decreased to 30%, but it increased to 95% within a minute when oxygen was provided at a flow of 6 L/min. This patient was, of course, tied to an O_2 tank to the end of his life, but this necessity should not contraindicate O_2 therapy in similar patients.

b) Oxygen seems to restore some patients to a better state of health than other methods of treatment. This is particularly true of patients with pulmonary heart disease in whom the predominant problem is congestive heart failure initiated or aggravated by serious anoxemia of pulmonary disease. For example, a patient had severe edema of the ankles, thighs and abdomen which failed to respond to conventional treatment; the edema cleared after two days of inhalation of O_2 by nasal catheter.

If pulmonary disease has reduced the pulmonary arteriolar or capillary bed and consequently increased pulmonary vascular resistance, right ventricular strain and hypertrophy will result. Increased work of the right ventricle does not necessarily lead to right ventricular failure, any more than left ventricular failure inevitably follows hypertension in the systemic circulation. However, when anoxemia is also present, the right ventricle is apt to fail because anoxemia increases the work of the heart further, both reflexly and by causing polycythemia and increased blood viscosity; at the same time, the amount of O_2 in the coronary blood is reduced.

Oxygen given to patients with these complications of pulmonary disease relieves the anoxemia, removes the reflex stimulation of the cardiovascular system caused by arterial anoxemia and permits the heart to produce an adequate output with less work per minute. In addition, it may produce some pulmonary arteriolar dilatation, though there is disagreement on this point. Long-term correction of anoxemia also removes the anoxic stimulus to the bone marrow, polycythemia disappears and the work of the right ventricle is further reduced. For these reasons O_2 therapy either is more effective than other means of correcting right heart failure or permits other measures, such as digitalis, diuretics and salt restriction, to become maximally effective.

c) Oxygen administration is sometimes essential for patients with severe chronic pulmonary disease and respiratory acidosis to keep them alive until antibiotic therapy can be fully effective and for patients with pulmonary edema until other therapy (p. 319) can be instituted.

d) Oxygen administration may permit a non-breathing newborn infant to survive until natural breathing starts.

e) Inhalation of O_2 permits patients with mild or moderate anoxemia to travel by air at cabin pressures equivalent to 6000–8000 ft above sea level. Planes have the equipment to provide O_2 for patients, though some airlines prefer not to use it because of the unfavorable psychologic effect on other passengers. An anoxemia test, in which the patient breathes O_2 at a partial pressure comparable to that which will be encountered in the plane, can be done before air travel to identify patients who require O_2.

2. DIAGNOSIS OF ANOXEMIA.—Oxygen inhalation is useful as a diagnostic test of the presence, severity and type of anoxemia, using the change in arterial O_2 saturation, oximeter reading, pulse rate or cutaneous color (in decreasing order of precision) as an index (Chapter 6).

3. ELIMINATION OF GAS FROM BODY CAVITIES.—Inhalation of 100% O_2 hastens the absorption of gas from any closed* body space, such as subcutaneous spaces, the gastrointestinal tract, cerebral ventricles, peritoneal cavity, pleural cavity, paranasal sinuses and alveoli not in free communication with their airway.

Let us take a subcutaneous gas pocket as an example. The sum of the partial pressures of gases in the pocket must equal 760 mm Hg (at sea level) because the total barometric pressure is transmitted directly to this pocket and maintains its pressure at 760 mm Hg until the last molecules of gas are absorbed into the blood. The subcutaneous gas is in contact with tissues and tissue capillaries and will be absorbed into the capillary blood if the sum of the partial pressures there is less than in the pocket.

The partial pressures of the end-capillary blood of tissues are given in Table 26.

No matter what the initial composition of gas in the subcutaneous pocket is, the gas will be absorbed more rapidly if O_2 is inhaled, because the difference in total gas pressure is $760 - 146.5$, or 613.5 mm Hg, during inhalation of O_2 and $760 - 706$, or 54 mm Hg, during inhalation of air. It is difficult for some physicians to grasp the concept that body tissues and capillary or venous blood never have gas tensions which add up to total atmospheric pressure. When O_2 is breathed, this is largely because O_2 utilization by the tissues has decreased the partial pressure of O_2 from 640 mm Hg in the arterial blood to 53.5 mm Hg at the end of the tissue capillary. Table 26 shows that the total partial pressure of gases in mixed venous blood does not equal 760, even when the patient

---

* "Closed" is used in the relative sense, i.e., that the gas in the space is not replenished faster than it is being absorbed.

TABLE 26.—GAS TENSIONS AT END OF A TISSUE CAPILLARY*

	DURING INHALATION OF	
	Air	100% O_2
P_{O_2}, mm Hg	40	53.5
P_{CO_2}, mm Hg	46	46.0
P_{H_2O}, mm Hg	47	47.0
P_{N_2}, mm Hg	573	0.0
Sum, mm Hg	706	146.5

* The gas pressures in any *actual* capillary will differ from these, according to local blood flow and tissue metabolic rate.

breathes air; in this case the partial pressure of O_2 decreases 60 mm Hg (from 100 to 40) as blood flows through the tissue capillary, but at the same time the partial pressure of CO_2 increases only 6 mm Hg (from 40 to 46); P_{N_2} and P_{H_2O} remain the same.

METHODS FOR ADMINISTERING OXYGEN

1. MASK OR CUFFED ENDOTRACHEAL TUBE.—When it is necessary to administer 100% O_2, a face mask or a cuffed endotracheal tube is required. An adequate flow of O_2 to the mask or tube can be supplied by a demand regulator or by a reservoir bag. A face mask is usually uncomfortable and annoying to the patient when worn for long periods and makes speaking, eating or coughing up secretions difficult. It is not indicated for patients with cardiopulmonary disease, even for those with severe impairment of diffusion, since maximal oxygenation of the arterial blood can be attained with lower concentrations of O_2 (unless there is an anatomic venous-to-arterial shunt or continued blood flow to nonventilated alveoli).

2. OXYGEN TENT.—There are many modifications of the full-bed oxygen tent that supply O_2 only to the patient's head or merely to the nose and mouth. The full oxygen tent is the most uneconomical of these; it must contain a motor blower and cooling unit to keep the temperatures of the enclosure from rising, and it wastes O_2.

A great initial flow of O_2 is required to attain an O_2 concentration of 40–60% within the fairly large enclosure. Thereafter, the flow should be reduced to maintain the concentration at the desired level. However, the concentration rapidly falls toward 21% whenever the tent is opened, and rapid flow is necessary after closure to boost it quickly to 40–50%.

Oxygen concentration in tents fluctuates markedly on this account and the mean Po_2 throughout the day may be quite low. Frequent O_2 analyses are desirable. An inexpensive and simple device is the 5 ml Scholander analyzer; one merely draws a 5 ml sample of air from the tent into a syringe, injects this into an analyzer filled with O_2 absorbent and notes the change in volume. A more expensive but even simpler device is the Pauling paramagnetic oxygen analyzer; a sample of tent gas is drawn into the apparatus, which measures O_2 tension directly. The Pauling analyzer is light, portable and self-contained.

Because no tent is leak-proof, there need be no provision for absorption of CO_2. A flow of O_2 of 12 L/min into the enclosure means that almost 12 L/min must escape around the edges of the tent, since only 250 ml of O_2/min is removed for body metabolism and only 200 ml of CO_2/min is excreted into the tent.

3. NASOPHARYNGEAL CATHETER.—This is an inexpensive and simple means of providing 35–40% O_2 in the inspired air. A catheter is passed through the nose to the oropharyngeal cavity and is taped in place; a flow of 5–7 L/min of O_2 is provided. The inspired O_2 must be humidified, since it is dry and by-passes the normal warming and moistening apparatus of the nose and mouth. Even so, the pharyngeal mucosa on which the O_2 stream impinges is apt to become dry; the catheter location should be changed occasionally to prevent this (a nasal cannula is often used instead of the oropharyngeal catheter).

A small catheter is sometimes placed near the bifurcation of the trachea and O_2 is passed through it to provide a high alveolar O_2 concentration in unconscious, non-breathing patients. This "tracheal insufflation" of O_2 (introduced by Meltzer and Auer) has recently been called "diffusion" respiration because it was thought that the O_2 diffused to the alveoli because of its higher partial pressure in the trachea. This, of course, cannot be true because gas molecules do not traverse such great distances quickly by diffusion alone. What actually occurs is this: In a non-breathing patient, 250 ml of O_2 continues to leave the alveoli and enter the pulmonary capillary blood each minute, but considerably less CO_2 enters the alveoli at the same time; therefore the total alveolar gas pressure must fall and there is an actual flow of air toward the alveoli. This form of O_2 administration should be used only in an emergency and for brief periods, since it makes no provision for CO_2 elimination; the flow of gas is always downward, with no "expiratory" phase.[†]

[†] Tracheal insufflation is effective in maintaining oxygenation only if alveolar N_2 is first "washed out."

4. INTERMITTENT POSITIVE-PRESSURE BREATHING WITH O_2.—Positive-pressure breathing apparatus may be used with O_2. The chief advantages of positive-pressure breathing are (*a*) that it might result in greater ventilation than the patient can achieve by his own voluntary effort and (*b*) it can be used to replace his own inspiratory effort, rest fatigued respiratory muscles and lower his O_2 consumption.

SUMMARY.—In general, we advise using the lowest concentration of O_2 that will relieve anoxemia. If an oximeter is available, there is a simple way to determine this: Allow the patient to breathe pure O_2 and note the maximal level of arterial saturation achieved. Then find the lowest concentration of inspired O_2 which will produce this maximal level. Usually, inhalation of 35–50% O_2 will result in maximal saturation of the arterial blood, and this concentration can be inhaled indefinitely without causing O_2 toxicity.

Oxygen therapy may be used repeatedly for short periods throughout the day or night for patients who require O_2 but cannot be restricted to an oxygen tank. Although O_2 cannot be stored in the body, inhalation for short periods will relieve anoxemia and improve the function of some organs (heart, kidneys), at least temporarily.

POSSIBLE HARM FROM OXYGEN INHALATION

1. CESSATION OF RESPIRATION.—This is the most dramatic side effect following the inhalation of O_2. In our experience, it is rare and occurs only when O_2 is given to a severely anoxic patient whose respiratory center is not responsive to CO_2 and whose only important drive to maintain respiration is the chemoreceptor reflex.‡ Examples of this combination of factors are: (*a*) a patient whose respiration has been severely depressed by large doses of barbiturates or morphine; (*b*) a patient with cerebral trauma, and (*c*) a patient with severe anoxia and hyperventilation at high altitude.

When a patient is severely anoxic and the partial pressure of O_2 in arterial blood is 30–60 mm Hg, practically all of his carotid and aortic chemoreceptors are maximally stimulated. His ventilation may stop when he inhales O_2 and his arterial blood Po_2 changes suddenly from 40 to more than 600 mm Hg.

---

‡ The cells of the carotid and aortic bodies, their pathways and central synapses appear to resist depression by narcotics, anoxia, etc., more than do central chemoreceptors and other reflex paths.

2. DEPRESSION OF VENTILATION.—Depression of breathing after the inhalation of O_2 is more common than apnea and may be even more serious because it is more likely to be overlooked. In some patients with chronic pulmonary disease and respiratory acidosis, the inhalation of O_2 is followed by depression of breathing and somnolence or even coma. In our experience, this is uncommon; among 66 patients with mild to severe chronic anoxemia who were treated with O_2 therapy, this reaction developed in nine, one of whom died as a result.

Table 27 gives the data obtained in a patient with pulmonary emphysema and severe respiratory insufficiency before and during inhalation of O_2. Marked decrease in ventilation was associated with maximal saturation of hemoglobin with O_2 but with increasing respiratory acidosis.

TABLE 27.—EFFECT OF INHALATION OF O_2 IN PATIENT
WITH PULMONARY INSUFFICIENCY

	AIR	O_2
Art. O_2 sat., %	69	100
Art. P_{CO_2}, mm Hg	125	150
Art. pH	7.12	7.06
Resp. MV, L/min	4.6	2.2
Resp. TV, ml	191	120

Are the somnolence and coma due simply to the depression of breathing and consequent increase in arterial CO_2 tension? Possibly. Normal men given 10% CO_2 to breathe may become unresponsive; inhalation of 30% CO_2 causes surgical anesthesia. There is, however, no knowledge of the level of CO_2 or the amount of change that is required in healthy persons or in patients with respiratory acidosis to produce this effect. For example, the patient in Table 27 was not unconscious with an arterial P_{CO_2} of 125 mm Hg but did become unconscious when the arterial P_{CO_2} was 150. A change of 25 mm Hg in CO_2 tension does not normally induce mental changes in healthy persons or even in patients with pulmonary disease.

Possible mechanisms for "oxygen coma" other than "carbon dioxide narcosis" should be mentioned:

a) By relieving anoxemia, inhalation of pure O_2 might lead to spasm of cerebral blood vessels and thus precipitate coma. Most patients with emphysema and pulmonary insufficiency have an *unusually* high cerebral blood flow because of the combined effect of low arterial P_{O_2} and high

P_{CO_2} on cerebral vessels, and there are no striking changes while they inhale pure O_2.

b) Anoxemia reflexly stimulates the cerebral cortex as well as the respiratory and vasomotor centers. The restlessness and delirium associated with anoxemia are probably manifestations of this effect. Inhalation of high concentrations of O_2 may result in sudden withdrawal of this cortical stimulation and so lead to coma.

c) Patients with chronic pulmonary insufficiency may have high cerebrospinal fluid pressure and papilledema, presumably because of the marked vasodilatation of cerebral vessels. Some investigators have noted that cerebrospinal fluid pressure rises even higher in these patients when they inhale O_2. How increased intracranial pressure produces coma is obscure. It cannot be due to ischemia because over-all cerebral blood flow is greater than normal.

d) Patients with chronic anoxemia may have compensatory alterations in cerebral metabolism. Sudden removal of these may lead to inability to utilize O_2 at normal or even high pressures, and coma results.

In our experience no patient given O_2 to breathe became comatose unless (1) initial arterial P_{CO_2} was 50 mm Hg or more, (2) arterial O_2 saturation was below 90%, and (3) the O_2 therapy relieved anoxemia. Because coma is an uncommon reaction and the prompt use of mechanical ventilators can correct hypoventilation when it occurs, patients with anoxemia should not be denied the possible benefits of O_2 therapy.

However, since there is no way of predicting whether coma will develop, it appears best to begin O_2 therapy with 30–40% O_2 and to watch patients for the first few hours of O_2 therapy. Some patients, sleepless for many nights because of anoxemia and dyspnea, may simply fall asleep as soon as the anoxemia is relieved; they can be easily aroused and should continue to inhale O_2. If true coma occurs, the physician should increase the patient's ventilation mechanically to ensure elimination of CO_2; he should provide extra O_2 if needed to correct anoxemia.

3. PULMONARY IRRITATION.—Animals exposed continuously to concentrations of O_2 between 80 and 100% invariably die of pulmonary congestion, exudation and edema. Normal men breathing 100% O_2 continuously for 24 hours may experience substernal distress that is aggravated by deep breathing; their vital capacity may decrease by 500–800 ml. Symptoms disappear after a few hours of breathing air. Inhalation of 50% O_2 for long periods does not result in this syndrome.

4. ATELECTASIS.—Inhalation of high concentrations of O_2 leads to absorption of gases from closed body cavities. In the middle ear, if the

eustachian tube is blocked, gas absorption causes the drum to be drawn in. In the paranasal sinuses, if the ostia are blocked, it leads to congestion and pain. Postoperative atelectasis is more apt to occur if alveoli contain gas rich in O_2; its incidence can be decreased by making sure that the alveoli contain 80% N_2 and that the patient is breathing air in the recovery room.

5. RETROLENTAL FIBROPLASIA.—Inhalation of 100% O_2 is believed to be the cause of retrolental fibroplasia and blindness in infants. Inhalation of 40% O_2 appears to be safe.

6. OXYGEN TOXICITY occurring at 3–4 atm is entirely different in nature; it is not discussed here because it cannot occur in the ordinary therapeutic use of O_2.

E. TREATMENT OF DISORDERS OF THE PULMONARY CIRCULATION

1. VENOUS-TO-ARTERIAL SHUNTS; PULMONARY HEMANGIOMAS

When these are in one region of the lung and not scattered diffusely throughout both lungs, they may be corrected by excision. Even though the anoxemia is not severe and the heart has not failed, surgical removal of pulmonary hemangiomas may still be proper because these patients are susceptible to serious pulmonary hemorrhage.

2. RIGHT VENTRICULAR AND PULMONARY ARTERIAL HYPERTENSION

This occurs either because of left ventricular failure, which increases the pressure in the left atrium into which the pulmonary blood must flow, or because of an increased resistance to pulmonary blood flow at one or more points in the pulmonary circulation. This resistance may be caused by mitral stenosis, by obstruction in the pulmonary veins, by reduction of the pulmonary capillary bed, by obstruction or obliteration of pulmonary arterioles, by narrowing of the pulmonary artery or pulmonary conus or by stenosis of the pulmonic valves. If the obstruction is sharply localized (pulmonic or mitral valvular stenosis), surgical procedures may eliminate the increased resistance.

We know little about the production and relief of vasoconstriction in the pulmonary vascular bed. Spasm of pulmonary arterioles is believed to follow a rise in the left atrial pressure, as in patients with severe mitral stenosis, but there is no easy, consistent way of reducing pulmonary vascular resistance, either by drugs or by surgical procedures. Injections of acetylcholine or isoproterenol into the pulmonary artery are often followed by a reduction in pulmonary artery pressure and pulmonary vascular resistance if these were initially increased. This reduction has diagnostic significance because it indicates that spasm had been present. Unfortunately it is of no practical therapeutic importance because the injection, to be effective, must be into the pulmonary artery. Nitrites may occasionally lower pulmonary vascular resistance. Oxygen inhalation sometimes results in reduction of pulmonary artery pressure and calculated vascular resistance, but this may be appreciable only in patients who had previous anoxemia.

Surgical correction of mitral stenosis might be expected to reduce pulmonary vascular resistance immediately, if the increased resistance had been produced reflexly. However, vascular resistance may not decrease until several weeks to several months later; presumably this change represents regression of hypertrophic or sclerotic change in the arterioles rather than delayed vasodilatation.

3. PULMONARY EMBOLISM

Pulmonary embolism is a special kind of obstruction of the pulmonary circulation. Some physiologists believe that impaction of a *blood clot* in pulmonary vessels is followed by the release of such chemical substances as serotonin, histamine and bradykinin and by the initiation of vagal or axonal reflexes that cause bronchoconstriction, systemic arterial hypotension, coronary vasoconstriction or even constriction of non-embolized vessels in the pulmonary circulation. There is insufficient evidence at present to justify the use of specific chemical antagonists or drugs that block reflexes in the pulmonary circulation.

4. POLYCYTHEMIA SECONDARY TO ANOXEMIA

Patients with severe polycythemia have two additional problems: (*a*) increased viscosity of the blood, which can lead to further cardiac work, and (*b*) a tendency to thrombosis. There are no satisfactory data relating red blood cell count or packed cell volume to actual pulmonary vascular resistance, but it is believed that resistance to pulmonary blood flow increases sharply when the packed cell volume is between 60 and 70%. Reduction of red cell count is ordinarily a simple matter, but when the polycythemia is due to anoxemia and is presumably a compensatory mechanism to provide additional Hb for the carriage of O_2, the physician must decide whether the patient can tolerate right ventricular strain better than decreased O_2 transport. As a rule, anoxemia is not severe except in patients with congenital heart disease or pulmonary hemangiomas, and the decision is to reduce the packed cell volume; it is not necessary to decrease it to a normal level to achieve the desired hemodynamic effect.

5. PULMONARY CONGESTION

Except for patients with mitral stenosis, pulmonary vein obstruction or large patent ductus arteriosus, the treatment of pulmonary congestion is essentially the management of left ventricular failure. This means therapy with digitalis, diuretics, low-salt diet and O_2, usually combined.

6. PULMONARY EDEMA

Electron microscope studies have shown that the initial disturbance in experimental pulmonary edema is a thickening of the capillary and alveolar membranes and an increase in the distance between gas and blood; fluid does not pass into the alveoli until the alveolar-capillary membranes are about 10 times their normal thickness. In the early stages of pulmonary edema, diffusion of O_2 may be impaired without any excess fluid in the alveoli or airways and hence without any of the clinical signs of râles. Fluid that has leaked from capillaries into tissue spaces makes no noise; only when fluid mixes with air in the air spaces can râles be heard. Therefore it is difficult to diagnose early pulmonary edema clinically and to distinguish it from simple pulmonary congestion. Further, dyspnea and roentgenographic evidence of fine, diffuse haziness of the lungs are common in both conditions.

After intra-alveolar edema has begun to form, fluid may well up into the airways and block them. Then the problem is no longer one of impaired diffusion but one of hypoventilated or nonventilated alveoli.

CAUSES.—1) *Increase in pulmonary capillary pressure.*—Pulmonary edema of cardiac origin is usually due to the development of a pulmonary capillary pressure greater than the colloidal osmotic pressure of the plasma proteins. The Starling hypothesis for fluid exchange between capillaries and tissues states that fluid leaves the capillaries and enters tissues when the transcapillary hydrostatic pressure is greater than the transcapillary colloidal osmotic pressure; hydrostatic pressure tends to force fluid out of the capillaries into the tissues and colloidal osmotic pressure tends to pull it back into the capillaries. In a "typical" capillary in the systemic circulation, the transcapillary hydrostatic pressure is greater than the transcapillary osmotic pressure at the beginning of the capillary and lower at the end of the capillary. This system promotes fluid exchange so that fluid, electrolytes and metabolites may enter the tissues and waste material may enter the capillary. The pulmonary capillary, however, appears to be organized for gas exchange; the pressure at both its beginning and its end is normally far lower than colloidal osmotic pressure of the plasma proteins; therefore the direction of fluid flow is from alveoli to capillary and the alveolar membrane is normally "dry." In 1873, long before Starling's work, Colin demonstrated this principle in a dramatic way by administering 21 liters of water over a 3½ hour period into the trachea of a horse without causing any harm to the animal.

Other things being equal, the pulmonary *capillary* (*not* the pulmonary *arterial*) blood pressure must exceed the plasma colloidal osmotic pressure for pulmonary edema fluid to form. The capillary pressure may exceed colloidal osmotic pressure in patients with mitral stenosis, left ventricular failure or large patent ductus arteriosus. Capillary pressure may rise abruptly when a patient with left ventricular failure, mitral stenosis or aortic stenosis exercises or when he is given large amounts of fluid intravenously in a short time. It may rise when a patient with only one lung engages in severe exercise.

When pulmonary edema is due to an increase in pulmonary capillary pressure, treatment must be directed promptly to decreasing it. Measures which may be effective are:

(*1*) Venesection. Rapid venesection helps by removing blood rapidly from the total vascular system so that there is less blood available for all vascular beds, including the pulmonary circulation.

(*2*) Measures which redistribute blood so that there is less in the pulmonary circulation and more in the systemic. (*a*) Digitalis increases the force of contraction of the left ventricle and shifts blood out of the pulmonary circulation into the systemic circulation. However, even the rapidly acting digitalis preparations may not act quickly enough to achieve this in a patient with acute fulminating pulmonary edema. (*b*) Tourniquets placed around all four extremities at pressures less than arterial permit the left ventricle to pump blood from the pulmonary circulation into the limbs, where it is trapped in the veins. (*c*) Compression of the inferior vena cava may trap blood in the lower extremities. This requires an increase in intra-abdominal pressure, which may be produced by binding the abdomen or by a forceful, sustained contraction of the abdominal muscles (as in grunting). (*d*) Standing leads to accumulation of extra blood in the veins of the lower parts of the body and a loss of blood from the pulmonary circulation. (*e*) Pressure breathing increases intrapulmonary and intrathoracic pressure and compresses the inferior and superior venae cavae where they enter the thorax; as a result, venous return to the right heart is reduced temporarily and pulmonary congestion is decreased. Compensatory mechanisms soon restore the pressure difference between the extremities and the thorax, and venous flow returns to normal. (*f*) Procedures which dilate peripheral arterioles in the systemic circulation are often effective because they have little effect on the pulmonary vessels. They are: carotid sinus pressure; intravenous anesthesia; spinal anesthesia; small doses of amyl nitrite or nitroglycerin; morphine; ganglionic blocking agents such as hexamethonium; aminophylline. A reflex initiated by increased pulmonary vascular pressure also aids in redistribution by dilating systemic arterioles.

2) *Decrease in intrathoracic pressure.*—Whenever the intrathoracic pressure decreases (becomes more subatmospheric), the pulmonary transcapillary pressure rises. If a patient has severe obstruction on inspiration and continues to make vigorous inspiratory efforts, the intrathoracic pressure may decrease to 60–70 mm below atmospheric pressure. Under these conditions, the capillary pressure will rise abruptly and pulmonary edema fluid will form; pleural effusions may also occur at this time. In massive atelectasis, the diaphragm may be pulled up, the mediastinum drawn over and the soft tissues of the thorax pulled in, but negative pressure in the thorax may still be such that pulmonary edema forms. This is probably the cause of edema in the "drowned atelectatic lung."

The treatment here is to raise the intrathoracic pressure toward normal values by relief of airway obstruction or by pressure breathing.

3) *Decrease in plasma colloidal osmotic pressure.*—This is rarely the sole cause of pulmonary edema. Even in severe nephrosis there may be edema fluid in practically every other tissue in the body but none in the lungs. This is because the pulmonary capillary pressure is normally below 11 mm Hg and the colloidal osmotic pressure rarely falls below 14 mm Hg. However, the rapid intravenous administration of large volumes of saline solution will increase pulmonary capillary pressure, simultaneously decrease plasma colloidal osmotic pressure, and can result in edema formation.

Pulmonary edema associated with a decrease in colloidal osmotic pressure presents a therapeutic problem. Correction of the low colloidal osmotic pressure by giving hypertonic plasma will draw edema fluid from tissues into the circulating blood, but this will increase blood volume rapidly and aggravate congestive heart failure, particularly in patients whose renal blood flow and glomerular filtration rate are reduced and who cannot eliminate fluids quickly. In such patients it seems wise to keep the blood volume normal by venesection while fluid is entering the circulation rapidly as a result of increase in plasma colloidal osmotic pressure.

4) *Increased pulmonary capillary permeability.*—Some believe that capillary permeability increases whenever pulmonary edema fluid forms, no matter what its cause, because they find that the protein content of pulmonary edema fluid is always high. The reasons for this are uncertain: possibly congestion of the pulmonary capillaries stretches their walls and enlarges their pores; possibly the pulmonary edema fluid displaces the surface-active layer lining pulmonary alveoli and so alters capillary permeability.

Increased capillary permeability is an important cause of the pulmonary edema of infections such as pneumonia and bronchopneumonia, trauma, burns of the respiratory tract, inhalation of irritant gases such as phosgene, chlorine and nitrous fumes, prolonged inhalation of O_2, inhalation of regurgitated stomach contents and the ingestion of chemicals such as kerosene and ANTU (alpha-naphthol thiourea). Approximately two thirds of patients who die of cerebral hemorrhage or a fractured skull have pulmonary edema and the fluid has a high protein content. The same condition, produced experimentally by injecting fibrinogen and thrombin into the cerebral ventricles, has been explained on a hemodynamic basis; i.e., intense stimulation of the sympathetic nervous system leads to abrupt systemic arterial hypertension, left ventricular failure and high pulmonary capillary blood pressure. Since it is known that alveolar cells secrete a phospholipid that lines the alveoli, it is possible that this secretion is regulated by nervous activity and that nervous impulses or their absence may have an important influence on the formation of pulmonary edema.

There is no specific treatment for increased capillary permeability. Oxygen therapy and adequate ventilation with mechanical resuscitators may arterialize the mixed venous blood until the lung damage is repaired. Suction is helpful in removing edema fluid from the larger airways, and bronchodilators might be helpful in aiding the expulsion of fluid from the lower airways.

There are several other ways in which excess fluid may appear in the alveoli and air space. One is by the deliberate injection of radiopaque materials into the lungs during roentgen examination. Another is by drowning in fresh or in sea water (in the latter the high concentration of electrolytes in the alveolar fluid draws additional fluid into the air space). Again, O_2 therapy may tide the patient over until the fluid is reabsorbed or expelled.

PART THREE

Appendix

Useful Data, Equations and Calculations

I. GENERAL

A. Typical Values for Pulmonary Function Tests

THESE ARE values for a healthy, resting, recumbent young male (1.7 M^2 surface area) breathing air at sea level, unless other conditions are specified. They are presented merely to give approximate figures. These values may change with position, age, size, sex and altitude; there is variability among members of a homogeneous group under standard conditions. For predicted values, see the next section.

Lung Volumes (btps)

Inspiratory capacity, ml	3600
Expiratory reserve volume, ml	1200
Vital capacity, ml	4800
Residual volume (RV), ml	1200
Functional residual capacity, ml	2400
Thoracic gas volume, ml	2400
Total lung capacity (TLC), ml	6000
RV/TLC × 100, %	20

Ventilation (btps)

Tidal volume, ml	500
Frequency, respirations/min	12
Minute volume, ml/min	6000
Respiratory dead space, ml	150
Alveolar ventilation, ml/min	4200

DISTRIBUTION OF INSPIRED GAS

Single-breath test (% increase N_2 for 500 ml expired alveolar gas),
% N_2 .... $<$ 1.5
Pulmonary nitrogen emptying rate (7 min test), % N_2 .... $<$ 2.5
Helium closed-circuit (mixing efficiency related to perfect mixing), % .. 76

ALVEOLAR VENTILATION/PULMONARY CAPILLARY BLOOD FLOW

Alveolar ventilation (L/min)/blood flow (L/min) 0.8
Physiologic shunt/cardiac output × 100, % .... $<$ 7
Physiologic dead space/tidal volume × 100, % .... $<$ 30

PULMONARY CIRCULATION

Pulmonary capillary blood flow, ml/min 5400
Pulmonary artery pressure, mm Hg 25/8
Pulmonary capillary blood volume, ml 90
Pulmonary "capillary" blood pressure (wedge), mm Hg 8

ALVEOLAR GAS

Oxygen partial pressure, mm Hg 104
CO_2 partial pressure, mm Hg 40

DIFFUSION AND GAS EXCHANGE

O_2 consumption (STPD), ml/min 240
CO_2 output (STPD), ml/min 192
Respiratory exchange ratio, R (CO_2 output/O_2 uptake) 0.8
Diffusing capacity, O_2 (STPD) resting, ml O_2/min/mm Hg .... $>$ 15
Diffusing capacity, CO (steady state (STPD) resting,
   ml CO/min/mm Hg 17
Diffusing capacity, CO (single-breath) (STPD) resting,
   ml CO/min/mm Hg 25
Diffusing capacity, CO (rebreathing) (STPD) resting,
   ml CO/min/mm Hg 25
Fractional CO uptake, resting, % 53
Maximal diffusing capacity, O_2 (exercise) (STPD), ml O_2/min/mm Hg. 60

ARTERIAL BLOOD

O_2 saturation (% saturation of Hb with O_2), % 97.1
O_2 tension, mm Hg 95
CO_2 tension, mm Hg 40
Alveolar-arterial PO_2 difference, mm Hg 9
Alveolar-arterial PO_2 difference (12–14% O_2), mm Hg 10
Alveolar-arterial PO_2 difference (100% O_2), mm Hg 35
O_2 saturation (100% O_2), % (+1.9 ml dissolved O_2/100 ml blood)... 100
O_2 tension (100% O_2), mm Hg 640
pH 7.4

Mechanics of Breathing

Maximal voluntary ventilation (BTPS), L/min....................	170
Forced expiratory volume, % in 1 sec..........................	83
% in 3 sec..........................	97
Maximal expiratory flow rate (for 1 L) (ATPS), L/min.............	>400
Maximal inspiratory flow rate (for 1 L) (ATPS), L/min.............	>300
Compliance of lungs and thoracic cage, L/cm H$_2$O................	0.1
Compliance of lungs, L/cm H$_2$O.................................	0.2
Airway resistance, cm H$_2$O/L/sec................................	1.6
Pulmonary resistance, cm H$_2$O/L/sec............................	1.9
Work of quiet breathing, kgM/min................................	0.5
Maximal work of breathing, kgM/breath........................	10
Maximal inspiratory and expiratory pressures, mm Hg..............	60–100

B. Predicted and Normal Values for Pulmonary Function Tests

TABLE 28.—Prediction of Lung Volumes from Age, Sex, Height and Weight

Division of Lung Volume (ml, BTPS)	Subjects	Formula	Normal Range (2 SD)
VC*	Men	$(- 38 \times age) + (121 \times height) - 2100$	± 970
	Women	$(- 22 \times age) + (110 \times height) - 2980$	± 790
ERV	Men	$(- 15 \times age) + (88 \times height) - (9 \times weight) - 2650$	± 680
	Women	$(- 8 \times age) - (29 \times weight) + (3850 \times SA) - 1340$	± 480
TLC	Men	$(- 11 \times age) + (176 \times height) + (1650 \times SA) - 4630$	± 1500
	Women	$(- 11 \times age) + (121 \times height) - 2400$	± 1190
RV	Men	$(26 \times age) + (110 \times height) - (11 \times weight) - 4570$	± 900
	Women	$(10 \times age) + 1320$	± 790
FRC	Men	$(11 \times age) + (198 \times height) - (20 \times weight) - 7220$	± 1300
	Women	$(- 44 \times weight) + (5500 \times SA) - 580$	± 990
RV/TLC ratio	Men	$(0.50 \times age) + (0.66 \times height) - (0.13 \times weight) - 7.8$	± 9.7
	Women	$(0.37 \times age) - (0.08 \times weight) + 34.4$	± 11.9

From Needham, C. D., et al.: Thorax 9:313, 1954. Lung volumes have been increased 10% to convert them from ATPS to BTPS. Age is in years, height in inches, weight in pounds, and body surface area (SA) in square meters.

* Alternate formulae (Baldwin, E. de F., et al.: Medicine 27:243, 1948):
   VC   Adult men   [27.63 − (0.112 × age in yr)] × height in cm
           Adult women   [21.78 − (0.101 × age in yr)] × height in cm
   NOTE: ERV can be calculated approximately as ⅓ of VC (patient sitting) or ¼ to ⅕ of VC (patient supine). TLC can be calculated approximately from VC by dividing VC by 0.8 (16–34 yr age group), 0.766 (35–49 yr age group) or 0.692 (50–69 yr age group).

TABLE 29.—NORMAL LUNG VOLUMES IN YOUNG AND OLDER SUBJECTS

	50 YOUNG MEN* (RECUMBENT)		50 YOUNG WOMEN* (RECUMBENT)		11 MEN > 50 YR† (SEMIRECUMBENT)	
	Mean	SD	Mean	SD	Mean	SD
Age (yr)	22.9	3.3	23.1	3.4	61.5	6.8
Height (cm)	176.2	5.1	163.4	4.2	169	4.8
Weight (kg)	72.5	11.2	57.2	9.4	65.9	12.4
Inspiratory capacity (L)........	3.79	0.52	2.42	0.36	2.61	0.61
Expiratory reserve volume (L)...	0.98	0.26	0.73	0.19	1.01	0.38
Vital capacity (L).............	4.78	0.59	3.14	0.41	3.48	0.48
Residual volume (L)..........	1.19	0.35	1.10	0.30	2.43	0.50
Functional residual capacity (L).	2.18	0.50	1.82	0.39	3.44	0.74
Total lung capacity (L)........	5.97	0.81	4.24	0.57	5.92	0.57
RV/TLC × 100 (%)..........	19.8	4.4	25.9	5.0	40.9	7.1

* From Kaltreider, N. L., et al.: Am. Rev. Tuberc. 37:662, 1938.
† From Greifenstein, F. E., et al.: Appl. Physiol. 4:641, 1952.

TABLE 30.—EFFECT OF POSTURAL CHANGE ON LUNG VOLUMES

DIVISION OF LUNG VOLUME	MEAN VALUES (L)		MEAN DIFF., SITTING MINUS LYING (L)
	Sitting	Lying	
40 male subjects			
Total lung capacity................	5.788	5.483	+ 0.305
Vital capacity	4.098	4.018	+ 0.080
Inspiratory capacity	2.708	3.027	− 0.319
Expiratory reserve volume..........	1.389	0.991	+ 0.398
Functional residual capacity........	3.080	2.456	+ 0.624
Residual volume	1.691	1.465	+ 0.226
16 female subjects			
Total lung capacity................	4.659	4.320	+ 0.339
Vital capacity	3.107	3.109	− 0.002
Inspiratory capacity	2.094	2.451	− 0.357
Expiratory reserve volume..........	1.013	0.659	+ 0.354
Functional residual capacity........	2.565	1.869	+ 0.696
Residual volume	1.553	1.211	+ 0.342

From Whitfield, A. G. W., et al.: Brit. J. Soc. Med. 4:90, 1950.

TABLE 31.—PREDICTION OF VITAL CAPACITY IN CHILDREN FROM AGE OR HEIGHT

SUBJECTS	BASED ON	RANGE	FORMULA* (ml, BTPS)	RANGE OF NORMAL (ml, BTPS)
Boys	Age (yr)	4–9	VC = (193 × age) + 88'	± 30%
		10–12	VC = (194 × age) + 83	± 30%
		13–19	VC = (338 × age) − 1720	± 34%
Girls	Age (yr)	4–11	VC = (191 × age) − 62	± 30%
		12–16	VC = (200 × age) − 121	± 30%
		17–18	VC = (154 × age) + 608	
Boys	Height (cm)	98–118	VC = (27.4 × height) − 1770	± 25%
		123–148	VC = (40 × height) − 3330	± 23%
		153–173	VC = (63 × height) − 6730	± 21%
		178–188	VC = (30 × height) − 1050	
Girls	Height (cm)	98–113	VC = (27.8 × height) − 1900	± 26%
		118–138	VC = (32.2 × height) − 2400	± 22%
		143–163	VC = (43.2 × height) − 3970	± 24%
		168–173	VC = (26.5 × height) − 1200	

From Stewart, C. A.: Am. J. Dis. Child. 24:451, 1922. Additional tables of normal values for vital capacity in children are given in: Helliesen, P. J., et al.: Pediatrics 22:80, 1958; Ferris, B. G., Jr., et al.: Pediatrics 9:659, 1952; Ferris, B. G., Jr., et al.: Pediatrics 12:341, 1953; Needham, C. D., et al.: Thorax 9:313, 1954.
* Values in the table have been increased by 10% to convert them from ATPS to BTPS.

TABLE 32.—PREDICTION OF MINUTE VOLUME OF VENTILATION, BASAL CONDITIONS

AGE RANGE (yr)	MINUTE VOLUME (L/min, BTPS)	
	Males	Females
16–34	3.6 × SA (SD 0.3 × SA)	3.2 × SA (SD 0.4 × SA)
35–49	3.1 × SA (SD 0.5 × SA)	3.2 × SA (SD 0.4 × SA)
50–69	3.9 × SA (SD 0.45 × SA)	3.4 × SA (SD 0.4 × SA)

From Baldwin, E. de F., et al.: Medicine 27:243, 1948.

NOMOGRAM FOR PREDICTING STANDARD (BASAL) VENTILATION
FROM BREATHING FREQUENCY, WEIGHT AND SEX

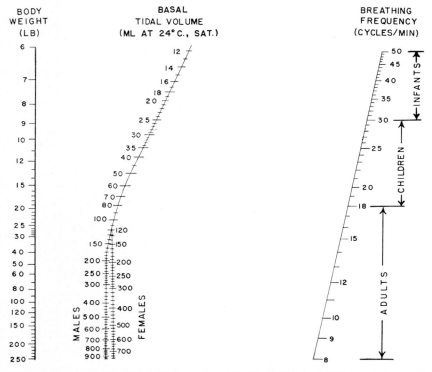

From Radford, E. P. Jr.: New England J. Med. 251:877, 1954, and J. Appl. Physiol. 7:451, 1955.

To determine tidal volume required of mechanical ventilator, connect body weight of patient and cycles/min of the device with a straight line and determine where it crosses the Basal Tidal Volume Line. Corrections to be applied as required: *daily activity,* add 10%; *fever,* add 5% for each degree F above 99° (rectal); *altitude,* add 5% for each 2000 ft above sea level; *metabolic acidosis during anesthesia,* add 20%; *tracheotomy and endotracheal intubation,* subtract a volume equal to ½ the body weight; *added dead space with anesthesia apparatus,* add volume of apparatus and mask dead space. Tidal volumes are adequate only in patients with uniform (or matched) alveolar ventilation and capillary blood flow and no impairment of diffusion; in patients with abnormal lungs, measurement of arterial O_2 saturation and end-tidal P_{CO_2} may be necessary.

TABLE 33.—Normal Values for Maximal Mid-Expiratory Flow

Subjects	Age Range	Average Value (L/min)	Normal Range
Men	20–29	282	148–414
	30–39	263	143–383
	40–49	262	130–395
	50–59	223	103–342
	60–79	187	91–283
Women	17–29	216	111–322
	30–45	226	121–332
	46–62	178	107–250

From Leuallen, E. C., *et al.*: Am. Rev. Tuberc. 72:783, 1955.

TABLE 34.—Normal Values for Lung Compliance

Subjects	Formula (L/cm H_2O)	Range of Normal
Young adults	$C = (0.00343 \times \text{height in cm}) - 0.425$	65–145% of C
Adults	$C = 0.05 \times \text{FRC in L}$	$0.070 \times \text{FRC}$ to $0.038 \times \text{FRC}$
Age 50–89	$C = 0.13$	0.08 to 0.23

From Frank, N. R., *et al.*: J. Appl. Physiol. 9:38, 1956; Marshall, R.: Clin. Sc. 16:507, 1957; Frank, N. R., *et al.*: J. Clin. Invest. 36:1680, 1957.

TABLE 35.—Pulmonary and Airway Resistance

Subjects	Pulmonary Resistance* (cm H_2O/L/sec)		Airway Resistance (cm H_2O/L/sec)
	Mean	Range of Normal	Formula
Age 18–47	1.9	1.2 to 3.4	
Age 9–44	2.3	1.2 to 3.4	$\dfrac{4.2}{\text{lung volume}}$†
Age 50–89	2.8	1.3 to 4.4	

* From Frank, N. R., *et al.*: J. Clin. Invest. 36:1680, 1957, and Marshall, R.: Clin. Sc. 16:507, 1957.

† From Briscoe, W. A., *et al.*: J. Clin. Invest. 37:1279, 1958. "Lung volume" is the volume of gas (L) in the lungs at the time airway resistance is measured (body plethysmograph, subject panting).

C. Symbols and Abbreviations Used by Pulmonary Physiologists
(Based on report in Federation Proc. 9:602-605, 1950)

Before 1950, each pulmonary physiologist had developed a jargon of his own. In 1950 a group of American pulmonary physiologists, in order to lessen confusion, agreed to use a standard set of symbols and abbreviations. The symbols below are used in equations in this book and in most original articles published since 1950; they cannot be applied to earlier articles.

Special Symbols

— Dash above any symbol indicates a *mean* value.
. Dot above any symbol indicates *a time derivative.*

For Gases

Primary Symbols (Large Capital Letters)		Examples	
V	= gas volume	V_A	= volume of alveolar gas
$\dot{V}$	= gas volume/unit time	$\dot{V}_{O_2}$	= O_2 consumption/min
P	= gas pressure	$P_{A_{O_2}}$	= alveolar O_2 pressure
$\bar{P}$	= mean gas pressure	$\bar{P}_{C_{O_2}}$	= mean capillary O_2 pressure
F	= fractional concentration in dry gas phase	$F_{I_{O_2}}$	= fractional concentration of O_2 in inspired gas
f	= respiratory frequency (breaths/unit time)		
D	= diffusing capacity	D_{O_2}	= diffusing capacity for O_2 (ml O_2/min/mm Hg)
R	= respiratory exchange ratio	R	= $\dot{V}_{CO_2}/\dot{V}_{O_2}$

Secondary Symbols (small capital letters)		Examples	
I	= inspired gas	$F_{I_{CO_2}}$	= fractional concentration of CO_2 in inspired gas
E	= expired gas	V_E	= volume of expired gas
A	= alveolar gas	$\dot{V}_A$	= alveolar ventilation/min
T	= tidal gas	V_T	= tidal volume
D	= dead space gas	V_D	= volume of dead space gas
B	= barometric	P_B	= barometric pressure
STPD	= 0°C, 760 mm Hg, dry		
BTPS	= body temperature and pressure saturated with water vapor		
ATPS	= ambient temperature and pressure saturated with water vapor		

For Blood

PRIMARY SYMBOLS
(Large Capital Letters)

EXAMPLES

Q   = volume of blood

Qc   = volume of blood in pulmonary capillaries

$\dot{Q}$ = volume flow of blood/unit time

$\dot{Q}c$ = blood flow through pulmonary capillaries/min

C   = concentration of gas in blood phase

Ca_{O_2} = ml O_2 in 100 ml arterial blood

S   = % saturation of Hb with O_2 or CO

$S\bar{v}_{O_2}$ = saturation of Hb with O_2 in mixed venous blood

SECONDARY SYMBOLS
(small letters)

EXAMPLES

a   = arterial blood

Pa_{CO_2} = partial pressure of CO_2 in arterial blood

v   = venous blood

$P\bar{v}_{O_2}$ = partial pressure of O_2 in mixed venous blood

c   = capillary blood

Pc_{CO} = partial pressure of CO in pulmonary capillary blood

For Lung Volumes

VC = Vital Capacity = maximal volume that can be expired after maximal inspiration

IC   = Inspiratory Capacity = maximal volume that can be inspired from resting expiratory level

IRV = Inspiratory Reserve Volume = maximal volume that can be inspired from end-tidal inspiration

ERV = Expiratory Reserve Volume = maximal volume that can be expired from resting expiratory level

FRC = Functional Residual Capacity = volume of gas in lungs at resting expiratory level

RV = Residual Volume = volume of gas in lungs at end of maximal expiration

TLC = Total Lung Capacity = volume of gas in lungs at end of maximal inspiration

D. The Gas Laws

A gas, or mixture of gases, behaves not as a continuous fluid but rather as an enormous number of tiny particles. These particles (molecules) are separated by distances large in comparison to their own dimensions and are in a continual state of random motion. They exert no forces on one another except when they collide. During collisions with other molecules or with the walls of the containing vessel, energy is conserved, and there is no chemical reaction; therefore the collisions may be regarded as perfectly elastic. The gas laws describe how the gases behave in or out of the lungs, during various conditions of pressure, temperature, flow and diffusion.

BOYLE'S LAW.—At a constant temperature, the volume of any gas varies inversely as the pressure to which the gas is subjected. For a perfect gas, changing from pressure P_1 and volume V_1 to pressure P_2 and V_2 without change of temperature, $P_1V_1 = P_2V_2$. The basis for this relationship is that gas molecules in a container produce pressure by colliding with the walls of the container; if the volume is compressed, the molecules become more crowded so that collisions are more frequent, and the pressure on the walls is greater. For adiabatic compression (non-isothermal), a different relationship must be used.

CHARLES' LAW.—The volume of a gas at constant pressure increases proportionately to the absolute temperature. If V_1 and V_2 are volumes of the same mass of gas at absolute temperatures, T_1 and T_2,

$$\frac{V_1}{V_2} = \frac{T_1}{T_2}$$

The basis for this is that at absolute zero ($-273\,°C$), molecular motion ceases. At warmer temperatures, molecular velocity is proportional to the square root of the absolute temperature. By heating a gas, the molecules rebound more following collisions, so that either the pressure in the container must rise or the space between the molecules of gas must increase (i.e., increased gas volume) if the pressure is kept constant.

DALTON'S LAW.—The pressure exerted by each component in a gaseous mixture is independent of other gases in the mixture, and the total pressure of the mixture of gases is equal to the sum of the separate pressures which each gas would exert if it alone occupied the whole volume. For example, the gases in the lung are CO_2, O_2, N_2 and H_2O. Each of these behaves in the alveoli as if it were independent of the others present, and yet the partial pressures of all together add up to the atmospheric pressure in the lungs:

$$P_{CO_2} + P_{O_2} + P_{N_2} + P_{H_2O} = P_B$$

The independent action can be explained on the basis that CO_2 molecules, on the average, colliding with O_2 molecules behave as they do when they collide with other CO_2 molecules.

PARTIAL PRESSURE OF A GAS IN A LIQUID.—The O_2, CO_2, N_2 or H_2O molecules which are in physical solution in a liquid, such as plasma, continually escape through the liquid surface into the gas phase and may also return from the gas phase into solution. When the partial pressure of a particular gas tending to come out of solution is equal to the partial pressure of the same gas tending to go back into solution, the system is in equilibrium for that particular gas. Therefore, a liquid may also have a partial pressure of O_2, CO_2, CO or N_2. A common way of measuring this is to mix a very small bubble of gas with a very large volume of blood until the gas pressures in the two are equal. The partial pressure of the gas in the equilibrated gas bubble can then be measured. (The terms "partial pressure" and "tension" are interchangeable here.)

PARTIAL PRESSURE OF WATER VAPOR.—This obeys similar laws. H_2O molecules tend to leave or enter the aqueous medium, and equal exchange occurs when the partial pressure of water vapor equals the "vapor pressure" of the liquid water. The warmer the liquid, the greater the vapor pressure. Water vapor in a gas in contact with a liquid phase maintains a partial pressure of 47 mm Hg (at 37°C) regardless of changes in barometric pressure. Some water vapor pressures covering the range encountered in physiologic conditions are given in Table 36.

EXAMPLES OF USE OF THE GAS LAWS

1. CALCULATION OF PARTIAL PRESSURE OF CO_2 IN ALVEOLAR GAS.— Most chemical and electrical gas analyzers yield data in terms of "per cent of dry gas." To calculate the partial pressure at body temperature, saturated with water vapor, the fraction of dry gas must be multiplied by (B — 47). For example: Alveolar gas, on analysis, contained 5.6% CO_2. Then $F_{CO_2} = 0.056$. Barometric pressure was 760 mm Hg. $P_{CO_2} = 0.056 (760 — 47) = 40$ mm Hg.

2. CORRECTION OF VOLUMES OF GASES COLLECTED AND MEASURED AT ROOM TEMPERATURE.—A subject has just exhaled into a spirometer. Correct the volume to BTPS. After exhalation, the change of volume in the spirometer is 4.0 liters. The temperature of the gas under the bell is 25°C. The barometric pressure is 750 mm Hg.

Air inside the spirometer is assumed to be saturated with water vapor at the spirometer temperature (T = 25° C; $P_{H_2O} = 24$ mm Hg), whereas air in the lungs is assumed to be saturated at body temperature (T = 37° C; $P_{H_2O} = 47$ mm Hg). The volume of gas in the spirometer must be increased by a factor $\dfrac{750 — 24}{750 — 47}$, in order to correct for the effect of a change in temperature on water vapor. Since the temperature of the gas in the body was greater than in the spirometer, the volume must also be increased by another factor $\dfrac{273° + 37°}{273° + 25°}$ to correct for the temperature change itself. Therefore, combined corrections on the volume in the spirometer are

$$V \text{ (BTPS)} = (4.0) \left(\frac{273 + 37}{273 + 25} \right) \left(\frac{750 - 24}{750 - 47} \right)$$

or $V = 4.3$ liters

Table 36 gives correction factors so calculated.

TABLE 36.—FACTORS TO CONVERT GAS VOLUMES FROM ROOM TEMPERATURE, SATURATED, TO 37° C, SATURATED

FACTOR TO CONVERT VOL. TO 37° C SAT.	WHEN GAS TEMPERATURE (C) IS	WITH WATER VAPOR PRESSURE (MM HG) * OF
1.102	20	17.5
1.096	21	18.7
1.091	22	19.8
1.085	23	21.1
1.080	24	22.4
1.075	25	23.8
1.068	26	25.2
1.063	27	26.7
1.057	28	28.3
1.051	29	30.0
1.045	30	31.8
1.039	31	33.7
1.032	32	35.7
1.026	33	37.7
1.020	34	39.9
1.014	35	42.2
1.007	36	44.6
1.000	37	47.0

* H_2O vapor pressures from *Handbook of Chemistry and Physics* (34th ed.; Cleveland: Chemical Rubber Publishing Co., 1952), p. 1981.

NOTE: These factors have been calculated for barometric pressure of 760 mm Hg. Since factors at 22° C, for example, are 1.0904, 1.0910 and 1.0915, respectively, at barometric pressures 770, 760 and 750 mm Hg, it is unnecessary to correct for small deviations from standard barometric pressure.

II. ALVEOLAR VENTILATION AND PULMONARY BLOOD FLOW

Quantitative analysis of the exchange of gas between alveoli and blood requires knowledge of the quantity of alveolar ventilation and pulmonary capillary blood flow and of the gaseous composition of alveolar gas and capillary blood. Representative samples of alveolar gas and pulmonary capillary blood cannot be obtained, but gas entering and leaving the alveoli (inspired and expired gas) and blood entering the pulmonary capillaries (mixed venous) and arterial blood can be obtained and analyzed.

By means of a series of equations, the desired relationships can be calculated. These equations permit:

1. Calculation of the respiratory dead space.
2. Calculation of the composition of alveolar gas.
3. Calculation of alveolar ventilation.
4. Calculation of the alveolar ventilation/blood flow ratio.
5. Calculation of the physiologic shunt.
6. Calculation of uneven ventilation with respect to blood flow.

A. BOHR'S EQUATION FOR RESPIRATORY DEAD SPACE

Bohr's equation as it applies to a particular gas x is developed as follows:

Total vol. of expired gas (V_E) = vol. of alv. gas portion (V_A)
$$+ \text{ vol. of dead space portion } (V_D) \qquad (1)$$

Expired gas is defined as the total volume of gas which leaves the nose and mouth between the onset and end of a single expiration. V_A is used here to denote the volume of alveolar gas contributed to the expired gas and does not refer to the total volume of gas in the alveoli.

The amount of gas x in V_E, V_A or V_D is its fractional concentration, F_x, times the total gas volume in which gas x is contained. Therefore, as in (1)

$$F_{E_x} V_E = F_{A_x} V_A + F_{D_x} V_D \qquad (2)$$

The gas in the dead space at the beginning of expiration is inspired gas; therefore, $F_{D_x} = F_{I_x}$ and

$$F_{E_x} V_E = F_{A_x} V_A + F_{I_x} V_D \qquad (3)$$

Since the volume of the alveolar gas portion (V_A) = volume of expired gas (V_E) — volume of dead space gas (V_D), equation (3) becomes

$$F_{E_x} V_E = F_{A_x} (V_E - V_D) + F_{I_x} V_D \qquad (4)$$

Rearranging

$$V_D = \frac{[F_{A_x} - F_{E_x}] V_E}{[F_{A_x} - F_{I_x}]} \qquad (5)$$

When the gas in question is CO_2, equation (5) is simplified because inspired air contains practically no CO_2 and $F_{I_{CO_2}} = 0$

$$V_D = \frac{[F_{A_{CO_2}} - F_{E_{CO_2}}] V_E}{F_{A_{CO_2}}} \qquad (6)$$

A sample calculation may be made from the data in Figure 14 (p. 43), where the fraction of CO_2 in alveolar gas ($F_{A_{CO_2}}$) is 0.056 (5.6%), the fraction of CO_2 in dead space gas is 0.0, the volume of a single expiration (V_E) is 450 ml, and the fraction of CO_2 in expired gas (F_{ECO_2}) is 0.0373 (3.73%). Then

$$V_D = \frac{(0.056 - 0.0373)}{0.056} \times 450 = 150 \text{ ml}$$

The same calculation may be applied to a single breath (as above) or to multiple breaths, in which case the expired gas is collected over a period of several minutes.

B. SINGLE-BREATH MEASUREMENT OF ANATOMIC DEAD SPACE

This technique for measuring the respiratory dead space requires a continuous analysis of the concentration of a gas in the expired breath plus simultaneous measurement of the expired volume flow rate. A typical record is shown in Figure 60, in which N_2 concentration and flow rate at the mouth are recorded during expiration following a single inspiration of N_2-free gas (O_2) (see Fig. 12, p. 40).

If a square front (Fig. 9, p. 32) were maintained during expiration between the dead space gas (0% N_2) and alveolar gas (in this example, about 60% N_2, because of dilution by O_2), the expired N_2 concentration would remain zero until a volume equal to the dead space had been expired, at which point the expired N_2 concentration would suddenly rise (thin vertical line in Figure 60) to the N_2 concentration of alveolar gas. In this hypothetical case, the dead space volume would simply be the volume expired up to the point where the alveolar gas suddenly appeared. However, alveolar gas does mix with dead space gas during expiration (see Fig. 9), so that the exact point at which a volume equal to the anatomic dead space has been expired is not immediately apparent. However, it is possible to construct a "square front" on the record by numerical methods. It is only necessary to place a vertical line (the thin vertical line in Fig. 60) so that the amount of N_2 in shaded area A exactly equals the N_2 that could be contained in the non-shaded area B. (The amount of N_2 equals the concentration of N_2 times the total volume of expired gas; in the example in Figure 60, where the expiratory volume flow rate is constant, equal amounts of N_2 are contained in equal areas of the N_2 meter record.) Once the square front is constructed, the dead space volume is simply the volume expired up to that point.

Bohr's equation (5) can also be applied to these data.

$$V_D = \frac{[F_{A_x} - F_{E_x}] V_E}{[F_{A_x} - F_{I_x}]}$$

RESPIRATORY DEAD SPACE

(SINGLE BREATH ANALYSIS)

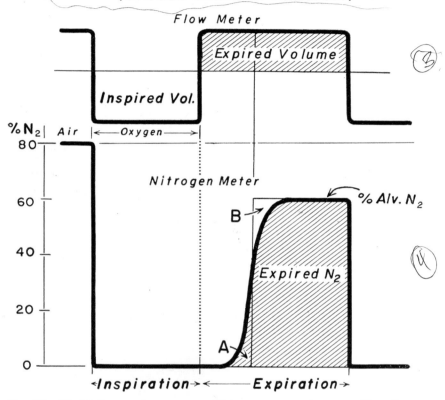

FIG. 60.—SINGLE BREATH ANALYSIS FOR MEASUREMENT OF ANATOMIC DEAD SPACE
Above: Volume flow of inspired and expired gas. A constant flow rate is pictured
for ease of measurement, though this would not be obtained in actual practice.
Below: Nitrogen concentration of inspired and expired gas following a single breath
of O_2. For further explanation, see text.

337

In this case, N_2 is measured instead of CO_2. At the end of the single breath of O_2 the dead space is filled with O_2, a N_2-free gas. Therefore, $FI_{N_2} = 0$, and the equation is simplified to

$$VD = \frac{[FA_{N_2} - FE_{N_2}] \, VE}{FA_{N_2}} \qquad (7)$$

FA_{N_2} is read directly from the nitrogen meter record of expired alveolar gas. VE is computed from the flow meter record. FE_{N_2} equals the volume of N_2 expired (obtained from measuring the area under the curve of N_2 concentration) divided by the total volume of expired gas (VE).

C. "PHYSIOLOGIC" DEAD SPACE

In Bohr's equation (6) for respiratory dead space, FE_{CO_2} and VE can be measured easily, but the *alveolar* CO_2 concentration (FA_{CO_2}) is difficult to obtain (see p. 64), and VD cannot be calculated without knowing the correct value for FA_{CO_2}. The controversy between Krogh and Haldane about the size of VD centered largely on what constituted representative alveolar gas. This has been resolved by the following reasoning.

There is almost always complete equilibrium between the alveolar PCO_2 and end-pulmonary capillary PCO_2. Therefore, in patients who do not have significant venous-to-arterial shunts, the arterial PCO_2 represents a mean alveolar PCO_2 over several respiratory cycles if the arterial blood is drawn over this period of time. Thus, arterial PCO_2 can be used to replace alveolar PCO_2. When this is done and F is changed to P ($P = F \times 713$ mm Hg), equation (6) becomes

$$\underset{\text{(physiologic)}}{VD} = \frac{[Pa_{CO_2} - PE_{CO_2}] \, VE}{Pa_{CO_2}} \qquad (8)$$

In the "ideal" case (p. 88), the anatomic dead space equals the physiologic dead space. However, in patients with uneven ventilation/blood flow ratios throughout the lung, the "physiologic dead space" is larger than the anatomic dead space (Fig. 10, p. 36). This is because regions with a high alveolar ventilation in relation to blood flow may be considered to be partly respiratory dead space regions.

A calculation of anatomic and physiologic dead spaces in an extreme case will make this point clear:

One pulmonary artery has been ligated but the lung has been left in situ (Fig. 33, p. 106). As a result of hyperventilation, the normal lung, *B,* receives 4 liters of alveolar ventilation/min and so is able to arterialize the entire cardiac output (5 L/min) and maintain an arterial P_{CO_2} of 40 mm Hg (equivalent to 5.6% CO_2 in alveolar gas). Frequency of breathing is 20/min. Total expired volume is 11 L/min, and the expired CO_2 (all of which comes from alveoli B) is 224 ml/min, or 2.04% CO_2 $\left[\dfrac{224}{11,000} \times 100 = 2.04\%\right]$; the P_{CO_2} of expired gas is 2.04% of 713, or 14.5 mm Hg. *Expired alveolar gas contains not 5.6% CO_2 but only 2.8% CO_2 since the gas from alveoli B is diluted equally with CO_2-free gas from alveoli A.* Tidal volume (V_E) is 11,000/20 or 550 ml.

According to equation (6)

$$\underset{\text{(anatomic)}}{V_D} = \frac{[0.028 - 0.0204]\,550}{[0.028]} = 150 \text{ ml}$$

According to equation (8)

$$\underset{\text{(physiologic)}}{V_D} = \frac{[40 - 14.5]\,550}{40} = 350 \text{ ml}$$

Since expired volume = tidal volume, some express equation (8) as

$$\frac{V_D}{V_T} = \frac{P_{A_{CO_2}} - P_{E_{CO_2}}}{P_{A_{CO_2}}}$$

The fraction V_D/V_T is considered to be normal if it does not exceed 0.3.

D. Calculation of Composition of Alveolar Air (Alveolar Air Equation)

It was stated earlier that the determination of alveolar P_{O_2} and P_{CO_2} from analyses of a spot sample of expired alveolar gas is subject to considerable error, but that mean alveolar P_{O_2} can be *calculated* with reasonable accuracy. The basis for the calculation, stated in words, is given on page 125. The precise formula (assuming that inspired P_{CO_2} is zero) is

$$\underset{\text{(unknown)}}{P_{A_{O_2}}} = \underset{\text{(known)}}{P_{I_{O_2}}} - \underset{\text{(measured)}}{P_{A_{CO_2}}} \underset{\text{(correcting factor)}}{\left[F_{I_{O_2}} + \frac{1 - F_{I_{O_2}}}{R}\right]}$$

---

* This is not strictly true since some end-expiratory dead space gas (2.8% CO_2) does enter alveoli A during inspiration. Further, the flow of blood through the bronchial arteries supplying alveoli A does contribute some CO_2 to the expired gas. Further, it does not allow for bronchiolar constriction on the vascularly occluded side (p. 97).

PI_{O_2} is inspired O_2 tension (moist); at sea level, this is 20.93% of $(760 - 47) = 149$ mm Hg. PA_{CO_2} is alveolar CO_2 tension. It is assumed to be equal to arterial PCO_2; the latter is measured. The *"correcting" factor* introduces no correction when R, the respiratory exchange ratio $\dot{V}CO_2/\dot{V}O_2$, is 1.0.

If $R = 1$, the correcting factor is

$$\left[FI_{O_2} + \frac{1 - FI_{O_2}}{R} \right] = 0.2093 + \frac{1 - 0.2093}{1} = 1$$

Usually, R is less than 1.0 (the volume of O_2 absorbed exceeds the CO_2 excreted), so that the volume of expired gas is slightly less than the volume of inspired air. In Chapter 3, Pulmonary Ventilation, this slight difference was ignored; here it cannot be, if great accuracy is desired.

For example, if $R = 0.8$, the correcting factor is

$$\left[FI_{O_2} + \frac{1 - FI_{O_2}}{R} \right] = 0.2093 + \frac{1 - 0.2093}{0.8} = 1.2$$

If $R = 1$, $PA_{CO_2} = 40$ and the correcting factor is 1.0, $PA_{O_2} = 109$ mm Hg. If $R = 0.8$, $PA_{CO_2} = 40$ and the correcting factor is 1.2, $PA_{O_2} = 101$ mm Hg.

The actual derivation of the alveolar air equation follows:

It is based on the knowledge that N_2 is not metabolized in the body and that, under steady-state conditions, the quantity of N_2 entering the alveoli per minute in inspired gas must equal the quantity of N_2 leaving the alveoli each minute in expired gas.

$$\dot{V}AI (1 - FI_{O_2} - FI_{CO_2}) = \dot{V}AE (1 - FA_{O_2} - FA_{CO_2}) \qquad (1)$$

This equation is based on the fact that when O_2, N_2 and CO_2 are the only gases present in the lungs (the gases here are measured as dry gases), the sum of their fractional concentrations must add up to 1.0. Therefore, $1 - FO_2 - FCO_2$ must equal FN_2. Note that the volumes of alveolar ventilation on inspiration and on expiration are given different symbols ($\dot{V}AI$ and $\dot{V}AE$ respectively) because these volumes differ when R is $<$ or >1.0. Since the *number of N_2 molecules* must be the same in inspired and expired gas but the total volume of gas in which they are contained may change on expiration, it is obvious that FN_2 may be different in inspired and expired gas.

If we rearrange this equation, considering FI_{CO_2} negligible when the patient breathes air,

$$\frac{\dot{V}AI}{\dot{V}AE} = \frac{1 - FA_{O_2} - FA_{CO_2}}{1 - FI_{O_2}} \qquad (2)$$

The correction factor requires knowledge of $\dot{V}_{O_2}$ and $\dot{V}_{CO_2}$. O_2 consumption ($\dot{V}_{O_2}$) equals the quantity of O_2 entering the alveoli in inspired gas less the quantity leaving the alveoli in expired gas.

$$\dot{V}_{O_2} = \dot{V}_{AI}F_{IO_2} - \dot{V}_{AE}F_{AO_2} \tag{3}$$

CO_2 production ($\dot{V}_{CO_2}$) equals the quantity expired since no appreciable amount of CO_2 is inspired while the patient breathes air.

$$\dot{V}_{CO_2} = \dot{V}_{AE}F_{ACO_2} \tag{4}$$

Respiratory exchange ratio (R) =

$$\frac{\dot{V}_{CO_2}}{\dot{V}_{O_2}} \tag{5}$$

Substituting equations (3) and (4) in equation (5)

$$R = \frac{\dot{V}_{AE}F_{ACO_2}}{\dot{V}_{AI}F_{IO_2} - \dot{V}_{AE}F_{AO_2}} = \frac{F_{ACO_2}}{\left[\dfrac{\dot{V}_{AI}F_{IO_2}}{\dot{V}_{AE}}\right] - F_{AO_2}} \tag{6}$$

Substitute equation (2) in equation (6)

$$R = \frac{F_{ACO_2}}{\left[\dfrac{1 - F_{AO_2} - F_{ACO_2}}{1 - F_{IO_2}}\right]F_{IO_2} - F_{AO_2}} \tag{7}$$

Clearing and solving for F_{AO_2}

$$F_{AO_2} = F_{IO_2} - F_{ACO_2}\left[F_{IO_2} + \frac{1 - F_{IO_2}}{R}\right] \tag{8}$$

If P_{AO_2} is desired, the equation becomes

$$P_{AO_2} = F_{IO_2}(713) - P_{ACO_2}\left[F_{IO_2} + \frac{1 - F_{IO_2}}{R}\right] \tag{9}$$

In some circumstances it is more convenient to calculate P_{AO_2} directly from the experimental data and use the form of alveolar air equation given on page 353.

E. Calculation of Alveolar Ventilation

The derivation of the equation in Figure 14 (p. 43) is as follows: The CO_2 in expired gas must all come from alveolar gas. The volume of CO_2 leaving the alveoli and entering the expired gas per unit time ($\dot{V}_{CO_2}$)

must equal the volume of alveolar ventilation in that same time ($\dot{V}A$) $\times$ the fractional concentration of CO_2 in the alveolar gas (FA_{CO_2}). Thus

$$\dot{V}_{CO_2} = \dot{V}A \times FA_{CO_2}$$

or

$$\dot{V}A = \frac{\dot{V}_{CO_2}}{FA_{CO_2}}$$

$$FA_{CO_2} = \frac{\%\ \text{alveolar}\ CO_2}{100}$$

Therefore

$$\dot{V}A = \frac{\dot{V}_{CO_2}}{\%\ \text{alveolar}\ CO_2} \times 100$$

This equation is correct only when $\dot{V}A$ and $\dot{V}_{CO_2}$ are corrected to BTPS. $\dot{V}A$ is usually corrected to BTPS, but $\dot{V}_{CO_2}$ to STPD. If this is the case, the right-hand side of the above equation must be multiplied by a factor of 1.21, or the left by 0.83.

The equation is often used with alveolar P_{CO_2} instead of % alveolar CO_2. This requires the use of a new factor to include the above correction and to convert % CO_2 into mm Hg pressure. The equation then becomes

$$\dot{V}A\ (ml) = \frac{\dot{V}_{CO_2}\ (ml) \times 0.863}{\text{alv.}\ P_{CO_2}}$$

F. Relationship of Alveolar Ventilation to Pulmonary Blood Flow

This mathematical equation is very helpful in displaying the factors which determine the adequacy of alveolar ventilation. The equation is based on the fact that, in any steady state, the quantity of CO_2 which leaves the venous blood to enter the alveoli must equal the amount of CO_2 which leaves the alveoli to enter the expired gas.

The CO_2 leaving the pulmonary capillary blood each minute equals the pulmonary capillary blood flow in ml/min $\times$ the A–V difference in ml of gas/ml of blood.

$$\dot{V}_{CO_2} = \dot{Q}c\ (C\bar{v}_{CO_2} - C\dot{c}_{CO_2}) \tag{1}$$

where $\dot{Q}c$ is pulmonary capillary blood flow and $C\bar{v}_{CO_2}$ and $C\dot{c}_{CO_2}$ refer to the concentration of CO_2 in mixed venous and end-pulmonary capillary blood respectively.

The quantity of CO_2 washed out of the alveoli by alveolar ventilation equals

$$\dot{V}_{CO_2} = \dot{V}A FA_{CO_2}\ 0.83\ {}^* \tag{2}$$

---

* See footnote, p. 343.

Since equations (1) and (2) are equal

$$0.83 \, \dot{V}_A F_{A_{CO_2}} = \dot{Q}_C (C\bar{v}_{CO_2} - C\acute{c}_{CO_2}) \tag{3}$$

This can be rearranged to give

$$\frac{\dot{V}_A}{\dot{Q}_C} = \frac{(C\bar{v}_{CO_2} - C\acute{c}_{CO_2})}{F_{A_{CO_2}} \, 0.83} \tag{4}$$

If it is desired to express $F_{A_{CO_2}}$ as $P_{A_{CO_2}}$, equation (4) becomes

$$\frac{\dot{V}_A}{\dot{Q}_C} = \frac{863 \, (C\bar{v}_{CO_2} - C\acute{c}_{CO_2})}{P_{A_{CO_2}}} \tag{5}$$

Substituting normal values (concentrations expressed in ml of CO_2/ml of blood)

$$\frac{\dot{V}_A}{\dot{Q}_C} = \frac{863 \, (0.530 - 0.493)}{40} = 0.8$$

Since in any individual, the mixed venous blood distributed to all the pulmonary capillaries has the same CO_2 concentration, and since end-pulmonary capillary blood has the same P_{CO_2} as alveolar gas, the alveolar P_{CO_2} is determined by the ratio $\dot{V}_A/\dot{Q}_C$.

An analogous equation can be derived for O_2, but is considerably more complex because of the necessity for correcting for the change in volume between inspired tidal volume and expired tidal volume (see p. 340).

The *uncorrected* equation for O_2 is

$$\frac{\dot{V}_A}{\dot{Q}_C} = \frac{(C\acute{c}_{O_2} - C\bar{v}_{O_2})}{(F_{I_{O_2}} - F_{A_{O_2}})}$$

G. Calculation of Quantity of a Venous-to-Arterial Shunt

When a patient has a venous-to-arterial shunt, his arterial blood contains some mixed venous blood that by-passed the lungs and some well oxygenated blood that had passed through the pulmonary capillaries. The equation that expresses this relationship for blood is quite analogous to Bohr's equation for the calculation of respiratory dead space.

---

* Since $\dot{V}_A$ is expressed in ml (BTPS) and $\dot{V}_{CO_2}$ is in ml (STPD)/min, $\dot{V}_A$ must be multiplied by $\frac{B - 47}{B}$ to convert to a dry gas volume, multiplied by $\frac{B}{760}$ to convert to standard pressure (760 mm Hg), and multiplied by $\frac{273}{273 + 37}$ to convert to standard temperature (0°C). The combined factor equals

$$\frac{760 - 47}{760} \times \frac{760}{760} \times \frac{273}{310} = 0.83$$

when ambient pressure is sea level (760 mm Hg).

Amt. of O_2 in arterial blood = amt. of O_2 in blood that has
traversed the pulmonary capillaries + amt. of O_2 in   (1)
shunted blood

Since the amount of $O_2 = Co_2 \times \dot{Q}$, therefore

$$Ca_{O_2} \dot{Q} = C\dot{c}_{O_2} \dot{Q}c + C\bar{v}_{O_2} \dot{Q}s \qquad (2)$$

where $\dot{Q}$ = total blood flow, $\dot{Q}c$ = blood flow through pulmonary capillaries, and $\dot{Q}s$ = blood flow (of mixed venous blood) through shunt.

$$\dot{Q}c = \dot{Q} - \dot{Q}s$$

Therefore, equation (2) becomes

$$Ca_{O_2} \dot{Q} = C\dot{c}_{O_2} (\dot{Q} - \dot{Q}s) + C\bar{v}_{O_2} \dot{Q}s$$

Rearranging

$$\dot{Q}s = \frac{Ca_{O_2} - C\dot{c}_{O_2}}{C\bar{v}_{O_2} - C\dot{c}_{O_2}} \times \dot{Q} \qquad (3)$$

If $\dot{Q}$ has been measured, $\dot{Q}s$ can be calculated in absolute quantities; if not, $\dfrac{\dot{Q}s}{\dot{Q}}$ can be calculated as the fraction of the total cardiac output that flows through the shunt

$$\frac{\dot{Q}s}{\dot{Q}} = \frac{Ca_{O_2} - C\dot{c}_{O_2}}{C\bar{v}_{O_2} - C\dot{c}_{O_2}}$$

Arterial and mixed venous blood can be obtained so that Ca_{O_2} and $C\bar{v}_{O_2}$ may be measured. End-pulmonary capillary blood cannot be obtained for direct analysis of $C\dot{c}_{O_2}$ but its Po_2 and hence its Co_2 can be estimated by the procedure described on page 356. The final value for $\dfrac{\dot{Q}s}{\dot{Q}}$ is that of the "physiologic shunt," which includes not only anatomic shunts but also a quantity of blood coming from regions with a low ventilation/blood flow ratio. The latter is included because the calculated "end-capillary" Po_2 is really a *contrived* end-capillary Po_2 which deliberately eliminates any component due to variations in ventilation/blood flow ratios.

The quantity of blood flowing through the anatomic shunt can be revealed by giving the patient 100% O_2 to breathe for a long enough period to wash all of the N_2 from the alveoli. Alveolar Po_2 will then be $760 - P_{A_{H_2O}} - P_{A_{CO_2}}$, or approximately 673 mm Hg. With such a high alveolar Po_2, there will be no alveolar to end-capillary gradient and end-capillary blood can be assumed to contain an amount equal to the O_2 capacity of Hb plus 2.0 ml of dissolved $O_2/100$ ml.

For example, if during inhalation of 100% O_2, O_2 capacity $= 20$ vol%, O_2 content of end-pulmonary capillary blood $= 22$ vol%, O_2 content of arterial blood $= 21$ vol%, and O_2 content of mixed venous blood $= 17.5$ vol%, then

$$\frac{\dot{Q}s}{\dot{Q}} = \frac{21-22}{17.5-22} = \frac{-1}{-4.5} = 22\% \text{ shunt}$$

NOTE: Under these conditions (22% shunt), the arterial blood is 100% saturated with O_2 and contains 1.0 ml of dissolved O_2. Unless very precise measurements of O_2 content and capacity are made, such a shunt may be overlooked completely since arterial blood is fully saturated when the patient is breathing 100% O_2. Direct measurements of arterial Po_2 (by polarography) are much more sensitive in a case such as this since the decrease in dissolved O_2 below maximal possible values ($22.0 - 21$ ml $= 1.0$ ml) would result in a fall in Po_2 from the theoretical maximal value of 673 mm Hg to 343 mm Hg. The normal amount of blood flowing through anatomic shunts (2% of the cardiac output) would result in a decrease in O_2 *content* of only 0.1 ml of $O_2/100$ ml of blood but a fall in Po_2 of 35 mm Hg below the theoretic maximal values for arterial O_2 when the patient is breathing pure O_2.

H. THE O_2-CO_2 DIAGRAM (RAHN AND FENN)

A slide rule appears to be an extremely complicated instrument at first sight, but once one becomes accustomed to using it, one can solve many complex mathematical problems with it without ever knowing how and why the rule works. Similarly, the O_2-CO_2 diagram appears to be formidable at first glance, but with very little practice one can use it to solve quickly many difficult problems dealing with pulmonary gas exchange without knowing how the diagram was constructed.

Two graphs are included: Figure 61 is the basic diagram, and Figure 62 is this same diagram with additional lines, much more complex but also more useful.

FIGURE 61.—The conventional coordinates are Po_2 and Pco_2. On this grid have been placed isopleths for O_2 saturation and CO_2 content (lines of equal O_2 saturation and lines of equal whole blood CO_2 concentration). This graph thus combines all of the O_2 and CO_2 dissociation curves (as these vary with changing Pco_2 and O_2 saturation respectively) in Figures 41 (p. 142) and 42 (p. 154) into one. The O_2 saturation isopleths do not run vertically because of the effect of changing Pco_2 (Bohr effect); the CO_2 content isopleths do not run horizontally because of the effect of changing O_2 saturation (Haldane effect).

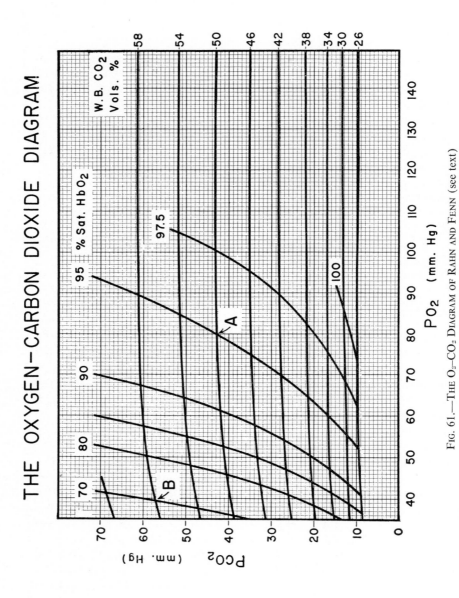

THE OXYGEN–CARBON DIOXIDE DIAGRAM.

Fig. 61.—The O_2–CO_2 Diagram of Rahn and Fenn (see text)

HOW TO USE FIGURE 61

Example 1.—Alveolar Po_2 is 80 mm Hg and alveolar Pco_2 is 43 mm Hg. Assuming that no difference exists between Po_2 and Pco_2 in alveolar gas and in arterial blood, determine arterial O_2 saturation and whole blood CO_2. *A* is the point where Po_2 of 80 and Pco_2 of 43 meet. This coincides with an arterial O_2 saturation of 95% and CO_2 content of 50 volumes %.

Example 2.—Analysis of arterial blood in a patient with hypoventilation shows that the O_2 saturation is 70% and the whole blood CO_2 is 58 volumes %. What is the equivalent Po_2 for this saturation and CO_2 content and what is the equivalent Pco_2 for this CO_2 content and degree of anoxemia? *B* is the point at which saturation = 70% and CO_2 content = 58 volumes %. Po_2 = 39.4 mm Hg and Pco_2 = 57.5 mm Hg.

FIGURE 62.—The conventional coordinates are the same as in Figure 61, and again lines of equal O_2 saturation have been placed on this grid; however, the O_2 isopleths (equal volume lines) are incomplete and the CO_2 isopleths are deleted so that additional lines may be clearly visible. The latter include:

1. A group of lines of equal R (respiratory exchange ratio) radiating from the moist inspired gas point (Po_2 = 149 and Pco_2 = 0 mm Hg). These are analogous to lines of equal barometric pressure on a weather map. These were calculated from the alveolar air equation. Every point on any one of these lines could represent an alveolus which is exchanging O_2 and CO_2 in the same *ratio,* though the absolute quantities may be different. Thus an alveolus at *A* on the 0.5 R line might have a Po_2 of 110 and a Pco_2 of 22 mm Hg, whereas another alveolus at *B* on the same 0.5 R line might have a Po_2 of 80 and a Pco_2 of 39. In both, the ratio is the same. These R lines permit ready determination of PA_{co_2}, PA_{o_2} or R if two of the three values are known. If PA_{o_2} = 110 and R = 0.7, PA_{co_2} must be 30 mm Hg. If PA_{co_2} is 40 and R = 0.8, PA_{o_2} must be 102 mm Hg.

2. A series of parallel lines of alveolar ventilation expressed as L/min of alveolar ventilation for every 100 ml of O_2 consumed.

3. A curved "distribution line" ($\dot{V}A/\dot{Q}c$), which represents all of the possible combinations of Po_2 and Pco_2 which could occur in alveolar gas and pulmonary capillary blood after mixed venous blood has equilibrated with alveolar gas at all possible ventilation/blood flow ratios. This particular line applies only when venous blood and inspired air have the composition indicated at the two extremes of the line.

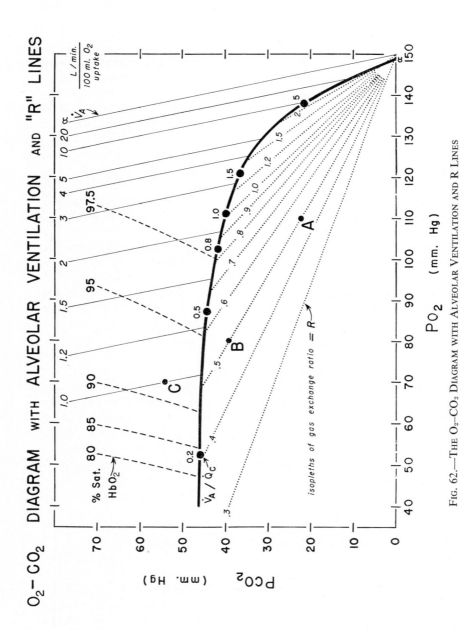

FIG. 62.—THE O_2–CO_2 DIAGRAM WITH ALVEOLAR VENTILATION AND R LINES

348

It will be seen that one end of the distribution line terminates at the inspired gas point and the other terminates at the venous blood point. An alveolus at point 0.8 has an alveolar ventilation of 4 units and pulmonary capillary blood flow of 5 units. An alveolus at point 0.2 has an alveolar ventilation of 1 unit and blood flow of 5 units; this approaches a shunt and is very close to the mixed venous point. An alveolus at point 5.0 has alveolar ventilation of 5 units and blood flow of 1.0 unit; this approaches ventilation of the dead space volume and so is very close to the inspired gas point.

HOW TO USE FIGURE 62

A patient has an alveolar P_{O_2} of 70 and P_{CO_2} of 54. What is his alveolar ventilation? C marks the intersection of $P_{A_{O_2}}$ 70 and $P_{A_{CO_2}}$ 54. This point lies on the $\dot{V}_A$ 1.0 line. Therefore, $\dot{V}_A$ is 1.0 L/min for each 100 ml of O_2 consumed. If there is no impairment of diffusion, arterial O_2 saturation would be 91%.

The same information could be obtained if one knew that $P_{A_{CO_2}}$ was 54 mm Hg and R (determined from analysis of expired gas) was 0.6.

III. ALVEOLAR-CAPILLARY DIFFUSION

A. Diffusion of Gases

The molecules of gas are constantly in motion and moving in random direction. Consequently, if there is a greater concentration of molecules of a particular gas in one region than in another, the laws of statistics permit us to predict the time required to abolish this difference in concentration. The conservation of energy is such that two different gases having an equal number of molecules in an equal volume possess the same mo-

---

◄———◀ Fig. 62.—This diagram is identical with Figure 61, and one may be superimposed on the other. It differs in that the graph lines, lower part of the O_2 saturation isopleths and all of the CO_2 isopleths have been omitted to permit inclusion of new lines. The latter are: (1) The heavy curved $\dot{V}_A/\dot{Q}_C$ line which originates at the left with mixed venous blood (no ventilation) and passes through ratios labeled 0.2, 0.5, 0.8, 1.0, 1.5, and 5 to infinity at the moist inspired gas point (no pulmonary capillary blood flow). (2) The dotted isopleths of gas exchange ratio (R lines) which radiate from the moist inspired gas point (P_{O_2}, 149 mm Hg; P_{CO_2}, 0 mm Hg); R lines from 0.3 to 2.0 are included on this graph. (3) The alveolar ventilation lines ($\dot{V}_A$), which range from 1.0 to 20 or more liters/min for every 100 ml O_2 uptake. For further explanation, see text.

lecular energy. Light molecules, since they possess the same molecular energy as heavier molecules, will travel faster, collide more frequently and diffuse faster than heavy molecules.

GRAHAM'S LAW.—The relative rates of diffusion of gases under the same conditions are inversely proportional to the square root of the densities of those gases.

HENRY'S LAW.—When a gas diffuses between a gaseous phase and a liquid phase, the solubility of the gas in the liquid must also be considered. This is expressed by Henry's law, which states that the weight of a slightly soluble gas that dissolves in a definite weight of a liquid at a given temperature is very nearly directly proportional to the partial pressure of that gas. This holds for gases which do not unite chemically with the solvent. At the surface of the liquid or tissue the gas tension will be equal to that in the gas phase, but immediately below the surface it will be less. The solubility of CO_2 in water is high and therefore its concentration in the surface layer will be higher. Thus, for CO_2, there will be a large *concentration* gradient between the surface and deeper layers of the fluid or tissues. Since the diffusion rate within a liquid is dependent upon its *concentration* gradient, the greater the solubility of a gas in a liquid, the more rapid its rate of diffusion will be in the liquid.

When the laws of diffusion and solubility are combined, the relative rates of diffusion of two different gases between a gaseous and a liquid phase is found to be proportional to the ratio of solubilities of the gases in the liquid, and inversely proportional to the ratio of the square roots of the molecular weights of the gases. For example

$$\frac{D_{O_2}}{D_{CO}} = \frac{\text{Sol. } O_2}{\text{Sol. } CO} \times \frac{\sqrt{MW_{CO}}}{\sqrt{MW_{O_2}}} = \frac{0.0244}{0.0185}\sqrt{\frac{28}{32}} = 1.23$$

Another gas, CO_2, is much more soluble than oxygen in water and

$$\frac{D_{CO_2}}{D_{O_2}} = \frac{0.592}{0.0244}\sqrt{\frac{32}{44}} = 20.7$$

There are two types of diffusion that are important in pulmonary physiology.

1. *Diffusion in a gas medium.*—This is the process by which a gas diffuses from one point within an alveolus to another or from an alveolus along the bronchial tree to the mouth (when there is no mass movement of air, i.e., alveolar ventilation). The alveolus is so small that any difference between the partial pressure of a gas at one point and another in the alveolus will be eliminated by gaseous diffusion within a fraction of a

second. However, when a gas must diffuse over longer distances, e.g., from an alveolus to the mouth, the rate of diffusion is much too slow to permit any useful gas exchange. This is well illustrated by the accumulation of CO_2 that occurs in the alveoli, blood and tissues during a period of respiratory arrest. (The process by which arterial O_2 saturation may be maintained for a while by supplying O_2 to the nose and mouth, during a period of complete respiratory arrest, is really not "diffusion respiration"; the saturation is maintained in part by a very high initial P_{O_2} in the alveoli and in part by mass movement of O_2 from mouth to alveoli caused by an R of <1.0, so that the alveolar gas volume shrinks slightly and lowers the total pressure of gases in the alveoli below atmospheric pressure.)

2. *Diffusion across a membrane.*—This has been discussed in Chapter 5; certain special problems relating to this process are discussed below.

B. Pulmonary Diffusing Capacity Measured by Single-Breath CO Method

In this technique, starting from residual volume, the subject inspires maximally a gas mixture containing a low concentration (0.3%) of CO and 10% helium. He holds this breath for about 10 sec, then rapidly expires an alveolar gas sample. If the lung is considered a closed bag of volume V_A (STPD) from which CO disappears at a rate proportional to its concentration, the alveolar CO concentration ($F_{A_{CO}}$) at any time is given by the equation of Krogh

$$F_{A_{CO}} = F_{A_{CO_0}}\, e^{-\frac{D713}{V_A}\frac{t}{60}} \tag{1}$$

where $F_{A_{CO_0}}$ is the alveolar CO concentration before any absorption into the blood has occurred, 713 is the total pressure of dry gases, D is the diffusing capacity, and 60 is the number of seconds in a minute. This can be rearranged to solve for D

$$D = \frac{V_A 60}{713\, t}\, \ln^* \left[\frac{F_{A_{CO_0}}}{F_{A_{CO}}} \right] \tag{2}$$

$F_{A_{CO}}$ can be measured in the expired sample. t is 10 seconds. V_A is the total alveolar volume which can be calculated from the volume inspired plus the residual volume. The initial alveolar CO concentration $F_{A_{CO}}$ is calculated from the concentration of He in the expired alveolar sample

---

* ln = naperian logarithm.

($F_{A_{He}}$); because He is relatively insoluble, its dilution in the expired sample equals the dilution of the inspired CO *before* any of it had been absorbed by the blood. Therefore

$$\frac{F_{A_{He}}}{F_{I_{He}}} = \frac{F_{A_{CO}}}{F_{I_{CO}}} \text{ or } F_{A_{CO}} = \frac{F_{A_{He}}}{F_{I_{He}}} F_{I_{CO}} \tag{3}$$

Since inspired CO ($F_{I_{CO}}$) and inspired He ($F_{I_{He}}$) are known, as well as expired alveolar He ($F_{A_{He}}$), the initial alveolar CO ($F_{A_{CO_0}}$) can be calculated. All the unknowns in equation (1) are then available, and D can be calculated. In a typical example

Inspired CO concentration ($F_{I_{CO}}$) $= 0.300\%$
Inspired He concentration ($F_{I_{He}}$) $= 10\%$
Expired alveolar CO ($F_{A_{CO}}$) $= 0.159\%$ after 10 sec breath-holding
Expired alveolar He ($F_{A_{He}}$) $= 8\%$

Total alveolar volume during breath-holding equals 4930 ml STPD; inspired volume is 4000 ml STPD and residual alveolar volume 930 ml STPD. Substituting in equation (3)

$$F_{A_{CO_0}} = \frac{8\%}{10\%} \times 0.300\% = 0.240\% \, CO$$

Substituting in equation (2)

$$D = \frac{4930 \times 60}{713 \times 10} \ln\left(\frac{0.240}{0.159}\right) = 41.4 \times 0.415 = 17 \text{ ml CO/min/mm Hg}$$
$$\text{pressure difference}$$

C. ALVEOLAR CO TENSION CALCULATED FOR STEADY-STATE METHOD

The object of this method is to calculate the alveolar P_{CO}, knowing expired CO_2 concentration ($F_{E_{CO_2}}$), expired CO concentration ($F_{E_{CO}}$), arterial P_{CO_2} (Pa_{CO_2}) and inspired CO concentration ($F_{I_{CO}}$) under steady-state conditions, when the patient is breathing a gas mixture containing a low percentage of CO. We can rearrange Bohr's equation to give

$$\frac{V_D}{V_E} = \frac{F_{A_{CO_2}} - F_{E_{CO_2}}}{F_{A_{CO_2}}} \tag{1}$$

We can calculate V_D/V_E for CO_2, as on page 339. If we rearrange equation (5) under Bohr's equation and consider the unknown gas x to be CO

$$\frac{V_D}{V_E} = \frac{F_{A_{CO}} - F_{E_{CO}}}{F_{A_{CO}} - F_{I_{CO}}} \tag{2}$$

We assume that V_D/V_E is the same for CO. Therefore we can solve equation (2) for the desired $F_{A_{CO}}$ because we know V_D/V_E, $F_{E_{CO}}$ and

F_{ICO}. These two operations have been combined into one by Filley by equating (1) and (2).

$$\frac{V_D}{V_E} = \frac{F_{ACO_2} - F_{ECO_2}}{F_{ACO_2}} = \frac{F_{ACO} - F_{ECO}}{F_{ACO} - F_{ICO}} \tag{3}$$

This is now solved for alveolar CO concentration

$$F_{ACO} = F_{ICO} - \frac{F_{ACO_2}}{F_{ECO_2}} (F_{ICO} - F_{ECO}) \tag{4}$$

It is of interest to point out that if O_2 were substituted for CO in this equation, it would become another form of the alveolar air equation given on page 341.

In a typical example, arterial P_{CO_2} is 40 mm Hg (40/713 equals 5.6%), expired CO_2 concentration is 3.7%, inspired CO concentration is 0.2%, and expired CO concentration is 0.102%.
Substituting in equation (4)

$$F_{ACO} = 0.2 - \frac{5.6}{3.7} [0.2 - 0.102] = 0.2 - 0.148 = .052\% \text{ CO}$$

This value, converted to P_{ACO}, can be used to calculate D_{CO}.

D. Bohr's Integration Procedure for Calculation of Mean P_{O_2} of Pulmonary Capillary Blood

In measurements of pulmonary diffusing capacity, it is necessary to know the mean pressure gradient driving O_2 across the alveolar-capillary membranes. Under certain conditions (see lower part of Fig. 39, p. 128), the mean gradient is very close to the $\dfrac{\text{initial gradient} - \text{final gradient}}{2}$, but it is often far removed from the latter value (see upper part of Fig. 39). The mean gradient can be determined precisely only if the P_{O_2} gradient from gas to blood is known at every instant along the pulmonary capillary. This can be determined by Bohr's integration procedure, which requires knowledge of (1) alveolar P_{O_2}, (2) mixed venous P_{O_2}, (3) end-pulmonary capillary P_{O_2} and (4) the interrelationship between blood P_{O_2} and O_2 saturation (the oxyhemoglobin dissociation curve).

Table 37 shows each step in the integration procedure. The subject is a normal man breathing 14% O_2. Alveolar P_{O_2} is calculated to be 57 mm Hg. The P_{O_2} of his mixed venous blood is 32 mm Hg and the O_2 saturation is 58%; the P_{O_2} of end-pulmonary capillary blood is 51 mm Hg (obtained by the "trial and error" procedure), and the O_2 saturation is

TABLE 37.—CALCULATION OF THE OXYGEN TENSION ALONG THE PULMONARY CAPILLARY IN A NORMAL MAN BREATHING 14% O_2

	A PUL. CAP. HbO₂ % SAT. S_{O_2}	B PUL. CAP. O₂ TENSION P_{CO_2} MM HG	C ALV.-CAP. GRADIENT AT EACH POINT $57 - P_{CO_2}$ MM HG	D RECIPROCAL OF EACH GRADIENT $\frac{1}{57 - P_{CO_2}}$	E SUM OF RECIPROCALS TO EACH POINT $\sum \frac{1}{57 - P_{CO_2}}$	F % OF TOTAL (1.7661) TO EACH POINT	G TIME (SEC) TO EACH POINT
Mixed venous blood →	58	32			0.000	0.0	0.0
	59	32.5	24.5	0.0409	0.0409	2.3	0.017
	60	33	24	0.0416	0.0825	4.7	0.035
	61	33.5	23.5	0.0425	0.1250	7.1	0.053
	62	34	23	0.0435	0.1685	9.6	0.072
	63	34.5	22.5	0.0445	0.2130	12.0	0.090
	64	35	22	0.0455	0.2585	14.6	0.110
	65	35.5	21.5	0.0465	0.3050	17.3	0.130
	66	36.0	21	0.0475	0.3525	20.0	0.150
	67	37	20	0.0500	0.4025	22.8	0.172
	68	37.5	19.5	0.0513	0.4538	25.7	0.194
	69	38	19	0.0526	0.5064	28.7	0.215
	70	38.5	18.5	0.0540	0.5604	31.8	0.237
	71	39	18	0.0556	0.6160	35.0	0.263
	72	40	17	0.0588	0.6748	38.2	0.287
	73	40.5	16.6	0.0606	0.7354	41.6	0.313
	74	41.5	15.5	0.0645	0.7999	45.4	0.340
	75	42	15	0.0666	0.8665	49.0	0.367
	76	43	14	0.0715	0.9380	53.2	0.400
	77	43.5	13.5	0.0740	1.0120	57.2	0.430
	78	44	13	0.0770	1.0890	61.6	0.462
	79	45	12	0.0834	1.1724	66.3	0.496
	80	46	11	0.0910	1.2634	71.4	0.535
	81	47	10	0.1000	1.3634	77.0	0.577
	82	48	9	0.1110	1.4744	83.5	0.626
	83	49	8	0.1250	1.5994	90.5	0.680
End-pulmonary capillary blood →	84	51	6	0.1667	1.7661	100.0	0.750

354

84%. In column A is listed each 1% increase in HbO_2 saturation between mixed venous blood (58%) and end-pulmonary capillary blood (84%). In column B is listed the blood Po_2 which corresponds to each saturation value.

Although this presents all the increments in Po_2 and O_2 saturation that the blood must experience in changing from venous to arterialized blood, it gives no information as to the *time* that is required for each of these unit changes in saturation. When the saturation (So_2) is 60 per cent (see Table 37) and the driving pressure is 24 mm Hg, O_2 diffuses across the alveolar-capillary membranes twice as fast as when the saturation has risen to 79 per cent and the driving pressure is only 12 mm Hg. Thus it takes twice as long for the saturation to rise from 79 to 80 per cent as it does to rise from 60 to 61 per cent. The relative time (t) required for each increment in So_2 (ΔSo_2) can be determined as follows:

$$\text{Rate of diffusion of } O_2 = \text{change in } O_2 \text{ saturation/time}$$
$$\therefore \text{Rate of diffusion of } O_2 = \frac{\Delta So_2}{t}$$

This rate is proportional to the Po_2 gradient between alveolar gas and pulmonary capillary blood.

$$\therefore \frac{\Delta So_2}{t} \propto (P_{A_{O_2}} - P_{C_{O_2}})$$

$$\text{or } \frac{\Delta So_2}{t} = K (P_{A_{O_2}} - P_{C_{O_2}})$$

The time required for each increment in So_2 then becomes

$$t = \frac{\Delta So_2}{K (P_{A_{O_2}} - P_{C_{O_2}})}$$

Since, in our example (Table 37), each increment in So_2 is constant (1 per cent) and since K is a constant, the time required for each increment to occur is proportional to the reciprocal of the Po_2 gradient. Thus

$$t \propto \frac{1}{P_{A_{O_2}} - P_{C_{O_2}}}$$

$\dfrac{1}{P_{A_{O_2}} - P_{C_{O_2}}}$ is the reciprocal of the O_2 pressure gradient at each point along the pulmonary capillary and provides an index of time required to achieve each ΔO_2 saturation.

Column C is a tabulation of each $(P_{A_{O_2}} - P_{C_{O_2}}{}^*)$, or the alveolar-

---

* The Po_2 of pulmonary capillary blood at the *end* of each stepwise increase of saturation is used instead of the average. Actually, this procedure is inexact unless a very large number of steps is used.

capillary pressure gradient. Column D lists the reciprocal of each alveolar-capillary pressure gradient in column C; each reciprocal is proportional to the time needed to produce each 1% increase in saturation. Each figure in column E is the total of the reciprocals up to each point, and each is therefore proportional to the time needed to increase the blood O_2 saturation from the mixed venous value to the saturation at that point. The last number in column E (1.766) is proportional to the total time the capillary blood took to increase from the mixed venous saturation to the end-capillary saturation. Column F shows the percentage of the total time required for the transfer of O_2 to each point. The total time required for the blood to traverse the pulmonary capillary in a resting normal subject is about 0.75 sec. Using this value, column G shows the actual time required for the transfer of each unit of O_2 in the pulmonary capillary. In Figure 39 (p. 128), the capillary Po_2 values (column B) are plotted against time (column G).

CALCULATION OF MEAN CAPILLARY Po_2.—Once the capillary Po_2 is plotted as in Figure 39, the mean capillary Po_2 can be obtained graphically, by finding the value of Po_2 which is as often above as below the actual capillary Po_2. This mean capillary Po_2 (42 mm Hg) is shown as a dotted line in Figure 39; the two shaded areas between the mean capillary Po_2 and the actual capillary Po_2 must be equal.

If alveolar Po_2, mixed venous Po_2 and end-pulmonary capillary Po_2 are known, the mean capillary Po_2 can be determined. In fact, if any three of these four figures are known, the fourth can be determined without further measurement.

E. TRIAL-AND-ERROR ESTIMATION OF DIFFUSING CAPACITY OF LUNGS FOR OXYGEN*

$$Do_2 = \frac{\dot{V}o_2}{\overline{P}_{Ao_2} - \overline{P}_{Co_2}}$$

Where Do_2 = diffusing capacity of the lungs for O_2; $\dot{V}o_2$ = O_2 consumption/min; $\overline{P}_{Ao_2}$ = mean alveolar O_2 pressure (calculated; see p. 339), and $\overline{P}_{Co_2}$ = mean pulmonary capillary O_2 pressure. $\overline{P}_{Co_2}$ requires knowledge of the *end*-pulmonary capillary Po_2 ($P\acute{c}_{o_2}$). This cannot be

* See page 132.

measured directly but can be estimated by a trial-and-error method of Riley as follows:

Step 1: Patient breathing air

MEASURE	ESTIMATE	CALCULATE
1. Arterial Po_2 and O_2 content	5. End-pulmonary capillary Po_2 (see Fig. 38) and O_2 content	6. Physiologic shunt ($\dot{Q}s$) (from 1, 2 and 5 using the shunt equation)
2. Mixed venous Po_2 and O_2 content		
3. Mean alveolar Po_2		
4. O_2 consumption/min		

$$\frac{\dot{Q}s}{\dot{Q}} = \frac{Ca_{O_2} - C\dot{c}_{O_2}}{C\bar{v}_{O_2} - C\dot{c}_{O_2}}$$

Step 2: Patient breathing 14% O_2

MEASURE	ASSUME	CALCULATE
7. Arterial Po_2 and O_2 content	11. Physiologic shunt ($=$ 6, above)	12. *End*-pulmonary capillary O_2 content (from 7, 8, 11 and shunt equation) and corresponding Po_2 (from O_2 dissociation curve)
8. Mixed venous Po_2 and O_2 content		
9. Mean alveolar Po_2		13. *Mean* capillary Po_2 (from 8, 9, 12 using Bohr's integration procedure)
10. O_2 consumption/min		14. Do_2 (from 10, 9, and 13)

Step 3: Patient breathing air

MEASURE	ASSUME	CALCULATE
15. Use measured values 1, 2, 3 and 4 (above)	16. Do_2 ($=$ 14, above)	17. *Mean* pulmonary capillary Po_2 (from 16, 4 and 3)
		18. *End*-pulmonary capillary Po_2 (from 17, 2 and 3)

Steps 1 to 18 all depend on the accuracy of No. 5 (estimated value of end-pulmonary capillary Po_2), since No. 5 is used to calculate the physiologic shunt and the latter is necessary to calculate Do_2 (No. 14).

This value for Do_2 is the *true* one *only* if, when used with the *measured* values 2 and 3, it yields the estimated value for end-pulmonary capillary pressure. If it does not, the "trial" was in "error" and a new estimate of No. 5 must be made until compatible values are found which fit the values obtained both during the breathing of air and of 14% O_2. The process of trial and error is facilitated by the use of graphs prepared by Riley.

The method depends on the assumptions that the physiologic shunt and the Do_2 do not change when the patient breathes 12–14% O_2 instead of air.

IV. ALVEOLAR GAS-ARTERIAL BLOOD Po_2 AND Pco_2 DIFFERENCES

A. CAUSES OF $\Delta PA_{O_2} - Pa_{O_2}$

1. HYPOVENTILATION OF ALVEOLI.—Hypoventilation, in relation to blood flow, leads to a low alveolar Po_2 in the alveoli so affected. Because of this, complete equilibrium may not be reached between alveolar and end-capillary Po_2 in the time available, for the initial pressure gradient for diffusion of O_2 may be greatly reduced at the beginning of the pulmonary capillary (see lower part of Fig. 39, p. 128). This occurs without any increase in the thickness of the alveolar-capillary membranes or any decrease in their area but causes a ΔPo_2 between alveolar gas and end-capillary blood in individual alveoli.

2. UNEVEN VENTILATION IN RELATION TO PULMONARY CAPILLARY BLOOD FLOW.—This condition represents the most frequent cause of a decrease in Pa_{O_2} below PA_{O_2}. Except in cases in which alveoli are severely hypoventilated (see 1, above), there is no difference between the Po_2 of alveolar gas and that of *end*-pulmonary capillary blood for any single alveolus and its capillaries; the Po_2 difference is, in reality, between *mixed alveolar gas* and *mixed capillary blood*. Even though the patient hyperventilates sufficiently to maintain a normal arterial O_2 *saturation,* a Po_2 difference still exists between alveolar gas and arterial blood.

The Po_2 difference between gas and blood caused by variations in the ventilation/blood flow ratios can occur for several reasons:

a) In Figure 28, p. 94), the Po_2 obtained by averaging the values for Po_2 in alveoli *A* and *B* would be $\dfrac{116 + 66}{2} = 91$ mm Hg. But during expiration, alveoli *A* contribute 3.2 liters to expired alveolar gas and alveoli *B* only 0.8 liter; so the true mean Po_2 of expired alveolar gas is $\dfrac{(3.2 \times 116) + (0.8 \times 66)}{4.0} = 106$ mm Hg. Since the same volume of blood flows past alveoli *A* and alveoli *B,* it might be thought that mixed capillary blood from *A* and *B* would have a Po_2 of 91 mm Hg. Actually, it is even lower, because an increase in Po_2 above normal (to 116 mm Hg) in alveoli *A* adds little total O_2 to the blood, whereas the decrease in Po_2 to 66 in alveoli *B* lowers the content considerably; this is because of the shape of the O_2 dissociation curve. Thus, a Po_2 difference occurs between mixed alveolar gas and mixed capillary blood even though the gas in each alveolus comes into equilibrium with blood flowing past it.

B. Poiseuille's Law

Poiseuille's law illustrates the various factors which determine the flow of liquids* through a tube.

$$\dot{V} = \frac{P\,r^4}{8\,l\,N}$$

where l is the length of the tube (cm); r is the radius of the tube (cm); P is the difference in pressure between the two ends of the tube (dynes/cm^2); N is the coefficient of viscosity (poises), and $\dot{V}$ is the volume of flow/sec (cm^3/sec).

The value of N for air is about 1.9×10^{-4} poises (the poise has units which are dyne-seconds/cm^2).

A pressure of 1 cm H_2O is equivalent to 980 dynes/cm^2.

C. Effects of Density of a Gas on the Gas Flow

At rapid rates of air flow, the density of the gas produces certain definite effects that require pressure to maintain the air flow. For example, to maintain flow through a constricted region of the trachea, the gas molecules must accelerate. This requires pressure in proportion to the density of the gas and the square of the velocity (calculations are based on equating the potential energy with the kinetic energy of the gas).

Again, pressure is required to move the gas molecules when they become abruptly stopped by protrusions in the walls of the airways, or when they change their direction and form eddy currents or turbulence. These effects involve acceleration of molecules which have become "slowed down" with respect to the rest of the air stream, and require pressure in proportion to the density of the gas, as well as approximately the square of the average air flow (see Fig. 48, p. 180).

D. The Work of Expiration

The work of breathing equals the product of pressure and volume (Fig. 45, p. 168). It can be measured as the work performed during inspiration, during expiration or during the whole respiratory cycle. Some of this work is required to move the thorax and some to move the lungs and air. If the transpulmonary pressure is measured by determining intrathoracic or esophageal pressure, the work required to move the lungs and

---

* At low rates of flow, air behaves like a fluid of low viscosity.

air can be calculated. The work required to move the whole system (thorax + lungs + air) is more difficult to measure because the energy comes from the contraction of the respiratory muscles and there is no direct way of measuring this. However, if the patient's muscular force could be eliminated and a *measurable* force substituted for the contractile force of the muscles, the total work could be measured. This can be accomplished by placing the patient in a body respirator, requesting the patient to relax voluntarily all of his respiratory muscles, and then ventilating the lungs by the action of the respirator. Inspiration must always be accomplished by active work of the respirator pump and bellows just as inspiration by muscular effort must always be accomplished by active contraction of the inspiratory muscles. Expiration may be "passive" or "active." It is passive if a large valve is opened quickly so that the subatmospheric pressure in the box returns abruptly to atmospheric; this would be analogous to a sudden and complete relaxation of the inspiratory muscles at end-inspiration. Expiration may be "active" if the pump actually produces a positive (greater than atmospheric) pressure in the box; this is analogous to an active contraction of the expiratory muscles. There is a third possibility, namely, that the negative pressure around the thorax is brought back to atmospheric slowly; this is analogous to a continued contraction of some of the inspiratory muscles during part of expiration (i.e., slow relaxation of inspiratory tone).

In order to measure the total work of breathing it is necessary to use the body respirator. When this method is used, it is convenient to think in the following terms:

1. Subatmospheric pressure in box = active contraction of *inspiratory* muscles.
2. Greater than atmospheric pressure in box = active contraction of *expiratory* muscles.
3. Abrupt change from subatmospheric to atmospheric pressure = abrupt relaxation of inspiratory muscles (passive expiration).
4. Slow change from subatmospheric to atmospheric pressure = slow relaxation of inspiratory muscles.

(1) and (2) require mechanical work *and* metabolic work (O_2 consumption), (3) requires neither mechanical work nor metabolic work, (4) does not require mechanical work but does require metabolic work.

A. ACTIVE EXPIRATION.—At the end of inspiration, there is a subatmospheric pressure in the respirator and the lungs and thorax have been inflated to a certain volume; this pressure-volume point is *B* in Figure 63. Potential energy is now stored in the elastic tissues of the

WORK OF EXPIRATION

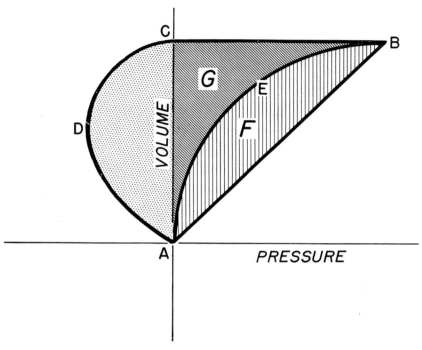

FIG. 63.—THE WORK OF EXPIRATION

Graphic representation of expiratory "pressure-volume loops" as visualized on the cathode ray oscilloscope using the method of DuBois and Ross. The inspiratory portion of the "loop" (shown on p. 192) is omitted. For explanation, see text.

lungs and thorax; this is numerically equal to the area of triangle *ABC,* and is sufficient to produce passive expiration. However, when very rapid expiration is required (as in exercise) or when expiration must be completed against obstruction in a limited time, active expiration (greater than atmospheric pressure in the box, or active contraction of the expiratory muscles) is required. This requires new energy (in addition to that represented by area *ABC*), and the pressure-volume points during expiration go outside *ABC,* and follow a path such as *BCDA.* The total energy used during expiration is therefore *BCDA,* but of this, *ABC* was potential energy created during inspiration and only *CDA* represents work of the expiratory muscles.

B. PASSIVE EXPIRATION.—The potential energy stored in the elastic tissues at end-inspiration, *BCA,* is sufficient to cause passive expiration. In these circumstances, the pressure-volume points during expiration may follow the path *BCA* or a path such as *BEA*.

1. Assume that, at end-inspiration, a large valve is opened so as to vent the respirator abruptly; this is equivalent to sudden and complete relaxation of the inspiratory muscles. Before the lungs have any time to change volume, the pressure in the box drops to zero and the pressure-volume point moves from *B* to *C*. Then, as the lungs begin to empty (pressure in the respirator remaining at zero), the pressure-volume points follow the path *CA*. Thus the expiratory path is *BCA*. The stored end-inspiratory energy was used in producing air flow and overcoming the tissue resistance of the lungs and thorax.

2. The respiratory pattern described above would produce a pneumotachogram in which air flow rose abruptly to a very high value and then decreased in a predictable manner during the remainder of expiration. However, since the *actual* pneumotachogram during "passive" expiration is not of this type, it appears that inspiratory tone does not cease abruptly at end-inspiration but tapers off more gradually. To simulate the latter pattern, it is only necessary to permit the subatmospheric pressure in the body respirator to return gradually to atmospheric pressure. In this case, the volume does not decrease so rapidly as the pressure (because of resistance to expiration). When the pressure-volume points are plotted during expiration, they move along a path such as *BEA*. At any moment, the pressure represented by the horizontal distance from line *CA* to a point on curve *BEA* is the pressure in the respirator, and the rest of the distance to *BA* is the elastic pressure required to overcome tissue resistance and produce air flow. The *work* in overcoming tissue resistance and airway resistance is equal to area *F,* and the work against the continuing subatmospheric pressure in the body respirator (continuing tone of the inspiratory muscles) is equal to area *G*. The continuing tone of the inspiratory muscles uses O_2 and so constitutes metabolic work but does not produce mechanical work.

3. *Work of moving the lungs and air.*—The work of ventilating the lungs alone (without the chest wall) has been measured by determining the transpulmonary pressure, using an intrapleural or esophageal balloon. The P–V diagram for this situation is similar in essentials to that obtained in a body respirator, but the chest wall now assumes the role of the respirator, whereas the lungs alone take the place of the lung-thorax system.

SELECTED REFERENCES

A. GENERAL

Macklin, C. C.: The musculature of the bronchi and lungs, Physiol. Rev. 9:1-60, 1929.

Miller, W. S.: *The Lung* (2d ed.; Springfield, Ill.: Charles C Thomas, Publishers, 1947).

Baldwin, E. de F.; Cournand, A., and Richards, D. W., Jr.: Pulmonary insufficiency, Medicine 27:243-278, 1948; 28:1-25, 1949; 28:201-237, 1949.

Comroe, J. H., Jr. (ed.): Pulmonary Function Tests, in *Methods in Medical Research* (Chicago: Year Book Publishers, Inc., 1950), Vol. 2, pp. 74-244.

Pappenheimer, J., *et al.*: Standardization of definitions and symbols in respiratory physiology, Fed. Proc. 9:602-605, 1950.

Seminars in pulmonary physiology, Am. J. Med. 10:77-90, 210-220, 356-374, 375-385, 481-496, 642-661, 719-738, 1951.

Comroe, J. H., Jr.: The functions of the lung, Harvey Lect. 48:110-144, 1952-53.

Arnott, W. M.: Order and disorder in pulmonary function, Brit. M. J. 2:279, 342, 1955.

Yerushalmy, J.: Reliability of chest radiographs in the diagnosis of pulmonary lesions, Am. J. Surg. 89:231, 1955.

Dittmer, D. S., and Grebe, R. M. (ed.): *Handbook of Respiration* (Philadelphia: W. B. Saunders Company, 1958).

Bartels, H., *et al.*: *Lungenfuntionsprüfungen* (Berlin: Springer Verlag, 1959).

Gordon, B. (ed.): *Clinical Cardiopulmonary Physiology* (2d ed.; New York: Grune & Stratton, Inc., 1960).

Rossier, P. H.; Bühlmann, A. A., and Wiesinger, K.: *Respiration: Physiologic Principles and Their Clinical Application* (tr. by Luchsinger, P. C., and Moser, K. M.) (St. Louis: C. V. Mosby Company, 1960).

Ciba Foundation Symposium: *Structure and Function of the Lung,* to be published, 1962.

Cunningham, D. J. C., and Lloyd, B. B. (eds.): *J. S. Haldane Symposium* (Oxford: Blackwell Scientific Publications, Ltd., 1962).

B. LUNG VOLUMES

Davy, H.: *Researches, Chemical and Philosophical, Chiefly Concerning Nitrous Oxide or Dephlogisticated Air and Its Respiration* (2d ed.; London, 1839).

Hutchinson, J.: Lecture on vital statistics, embracing an account of a new instrument for detecting the presence of disease in the system, Lancet 1:567-570, 594-596, 1844.

Christie, R. V.: Lung volume and its subdivisions, J. Clin. Invest. 11:1099-1118, 1932.

McMichael, J.: A rapid method for determining lung capacity, Clin. Sc. 4:167-173, 1939.

Darling, R. C.; Cournand, A., and Richards, D. W., Jr.: Studies on the intrapulmonary mixture of gases: III. An open circuit for measuring residual air, J. Clin. Invest. 19:609-618, 1940.

Baldwin, E. de F.; Cournand, A., and Richards, D. W., Jr.: Pulmonary insufficiency: I. Methods of analysis, physiologic classification, standard values in normal subjects, Medicine 27:243-278, 1948.

Gilson, J. G., and Hugh-Jones, P.: Measurement of total lung volume and breathing capacity, Clin. Sc. 7:185-216, 1949.

Meneely, G. R., and Kaltreider, N. L.: Volume of the lung determined by helium dilution, J. Clin. Invest. 28:129-139, 1949.

Rahn, H.; Fenn, W. O., and Otis, A. B.: Daily variations of vital capacity, residual air and expiratory reserve including a study of the residual air methods, J. Appl. Physiol. 1:725-736, 1949.

Whitfield, A. G.; Waterhouse, J. A. H., and Arnott, W. M.: Subdivisions of lung volume: Normal standards, Brit. J. Soc. Med. 4:1-25, 1950.

Comroe, J. H., Jr.: Interpretation of commonly used pulmonary function tests, Am. J. Med. 10:356-374, 1951.

Hickam, J. B.; Blair, E., and Frayser, R.: An open-circuit helium method for measuring functional residual capacity and defective intrapulmonary gas mixing, J. Clin. Invest. 33:1277-1286, 1954.

Needham, C. D.; Rogan, M. C., and McDonald, I.: Normal standards for lung volumes, intrapulmonary gas-mixing, and maximum breathing capacity, Thorax 9:313-325, 1954.

DuBois, A. B.; Botelho, S. Y.; Bedell, G. N.; Marshall, R., and Comroe, J. H., Jr.: A rapid plethysmographic method for measuring thoracic gas volume: A comparison with a nitrogen washout method for measuring functional residual capacity in normal subjects, J. Clin. Invest. 35:322-326, 1956.

Helliesen, P. J.; Cook, C. D.; Friedlander, L., and Agathon, S.: Mechanics of respiration and lung volumes in 85 normal children 5 to 17 years of age, Pediatrics 22:80-93, 1958.

Kory, R. C.; Callahan, R.; Boren, H. G., and Syner, J. C.: Clinical spirometry in normal men, Am. J. Med. 30:243-258, 1961.

C. RESPIRATORY DEAD SPACE

Henderson, Y.; Chillingworth, F. P., and Whitney, J. L.: Respiratory dead space, Am. J. Physiol. 38:1-19, 1915.

Krogh, A., and Lindhard, J.: The volume of dead space in breathing and the mixing of gases in the lungs of man, J. Physiol. 51:59-90, 1917.

Fowler, W. S.: The respiratory dead space, Am. J. Physiol. 154:405-416, 1948.

Riley, R. L., and Cournand, A.: "Ideal" alveolar air and the analysis of ventilation-perfusion relationships in the lungs, J. Appl. Physiol. 1:825-847, 1949.

Rossier, P. H., and Bühlmann, A.: The respiratory dead space, Physiol. Rev. 35:860-876, 1955.

Severinghaus, J. W., and Stupfel, M.: Alveolar dead space as an index of distribution of blood flow in pulmonary capillaries, J. Appl. Physiol. 10:335-348, 1957.

Shepard, R. H.; Campbell, E. J. M.; Martin, H. B., and Enns, T.: Factors affecting the pulmonary dead space as determined by single breath analysis, J. Appl. Physiol. 11:241-244, 1957.

D. ALVEOLAR GAS AND ALVEOLAR VENTILATION

Riley, R. L.; Lilienthal, J. L.; Proemmel, D. D., and Franke, R. E.: On the determination of the physiologically effective pressures of O_2 and CO_2 in alveolar air, Am. J. Physiol. 147:191-198, 1946.

Fenn, W. O.; Rahn, H., and Otis, A. B.: A theoretical study of the composition of the alveolar air at altitude, Am. J. Physiol. 146:637-653, 1946.

Brown, E. B., Jr.: Physiological effects of hyperventilation, Physiol. Rev. 33:445-471, 1953.

Briscoe, W. A.; Forster, R. E., and Comroe, J. H., Jr.: Alveolar ventilation at very low tidal volumes, J. Appl. Physiol. 7:27-30, 1954.

Radford, E. P., Jr.: Ventilation standards for use in artificial respiration, J. Appl. Physiol. 7:451-460, 1955.

Cherniack, R. M., and Shepard, R. H.: The effect of obstruction to breathing on the ventilatory response to CO_2, J. Clin. Invest. 35:111-117, 1958.

Griggs, D. E.; Hackney, J. D.; Collier, C. R., and Affeldt, J. E.: The rapid diagnosis of ventilatory failure with the CO_2 analyzer, Am. J. Med. 25:31-36, 1958.

Kory, R. C.: Routine measurement of respiratory rate: An expensive tribute to tradition, J.A.M.A. 165:448-450, 1958.

Stead, E. A., Jr.: "Hyperventilation," Disease-A-Month (Chicago: Year Book Medical Publishers, Inc.), February, 1960.

E. REGULATION OF RESPIRATION

Haldane, J. S., and Priestley, J. G.: *Respiration* (London: Oxford University Press, 1935).

Comroe, J. H., Jr.: The hyperpnea of muscular exercise, Physiol. Rev. 24:319-339, 1944.

Pitts, R. F.: Organization of the respiratory center, Physiol. Rev. 26:609-630, 1946.

Dawes, G. S., and Comroe, J. H., Jr.: Chemoreflexes from the heart and lungs, Physiol. Rev. 34:167-201, 1954.

Dripps, R. D., and Severinghaus, J. W.: General anesthesia and respiration, Physiol. Rev. 35:741-777, 1955.

Heymans, C., and Neil, E.: *Reflexogenic Areas of the Cardiovascular System* (Boston: Little, Brown & Company, 1958).

Liljestrand, A.: Neural control of respiration, Physiol. Rev. 38:691-708, 1958.

Robin, E. D., et al.: Alveolar gas tensions, pulmonary ventilation and blood pH during physiologic sleep in normal subjects, J. Clin. Invest. 37:981-989, 1958.

De Jours, P.: La regulation de la ventilation au cours de l'exercise musculaire chez l'homme, J. physiol., Paris 51:163-261, 1959.

Brodovsky, D.; Macdonell, J. A., and Cherniack, R. M.: The respiratory response to carbon dioxide in health and in emphysema, J. Clin. Invest. 39:724-729, 1960.

Nahas, G. G., and Fink, B. R. (eds.): Regulation of respiration, Ann. New York Acad. Sci. (in press).

F. DISTRIBUTION OF INSPIRED GAS

Cournand, A., et al.: Studies on intrapulmonary mixture of gases: IV. Significance of pulmonary emptying rate, J. Clin. Invest. 20:681-689, 1941.

Darling, R. C.; Cournand, A., and Richards, D. W., Jr.: Studies on intrapulmonary mixture of gases: V. Forms of inadequate ventilation in normal and emphysematous lungs, analyzed by means of breathing pure oxygen, J. Clin. Invest. 23:55-67, 1944.

Rauwerda, P. E.: Unequal Ventilation of Different Parts of the Lung, Thesis, University of Groningen, Holland, 1946.

Carlens, E.: A new flexible double-lumen catheter for bronchospirometry, J. Thor. Surg. 18:742-746, 1949.

Fowler, W. S.: Uneven pulmonary ventilation, J. Appl. Physiol. 2:283-299, 1949.

Bates, D. V., and Christie, R. V.: Intrapulmonary mixing of helium in health and in emphysema, Clin. Sc. 9:17-29, 1950.

Wright, G. W., and Michelson, E.: Bronchospirometry, in Comroe, J. H., Jr. (ed.): *Methods in Medical Research* (Chicago: Year Book Publishers, Inc., 1950), Vol. 2, pp. 82-93.

Comroe, J. H., Jr., and Fowler, W. S.: Detection of uneven ventilation during a single breath of O_2, Am. J. Med. 10:408-413, 1951.

Briscoe, W. A.: Further studies on the intrapulmonary mixing of helium in normal and emphysematous subjects, Clin. Sc. 11:45-58, 1952.

Fowler, W. S.: Intrapulmonary distribution of inspired gas, Physiol. Rev. 32:1-20, 1952.

Fowler, W. S.; Cornish, E. R., and Kety, S. S.: Analysis of alveolar ventilation by pulmonary N_2 clearance curves, J. Clin. Invest. 31:40-50, 1952.

Otis, A. B., et al.: Mechanical factors in distribution of pulmonary ventilation, J. Appl. Physiol. 8:427-443, 1956.

Bouhuys, A., and Lundin, G.: Distribution of inspired gas in the lungs, Physiol. Rev. 39:731-750, 1959.

G. RELATION BETWEEN ALVEOLAR VENTILATION AND PULMONARY CAPILLARY BLOOD FLOW

Riley, R. L., and Cournand, A.: "Ideal" alveolar air and the analysis of ventilation-perfusion relationships in the lungs, J. Appl. Physiol. 1:825-847, 1949.

Rahn, H.: A concept of mean alveolar air and the ventilation-blood flow relationships during pulmonary gas exchange, Am. J. Physiol. 158:21-30, 1949.

Riley, R. L., and Cournand, A.: Analysis of factors affecting partial pressures of O_2 and CO_2 in gas and blood of lungs: Theory, J. Appl. Physiol. 4:77-101, 1951.

Riley, R. L.; Cournand, A., and Donald, K. W.: Analysis of factors affecting partial pressures of O_2 and CO_2 in gas and blood of lungs: Methods, J. Appl. Physiol. 4:102-120, 1951.

Riley, R. L.: Pulmonary gas exchange, Am. J. Med. 10:210-220, 1951.

Hanson, H. E.: Temporary unilateral occlusion of the pulmonary artery in man, Acta chir. scandinav., Supp. 187, pp. 1-55, 1954.

Rahn, H., and Fenn, W. O.: *A Graphical Analysis of the Respiratory Gas Exchange: The O_2–CO_2 Diagram* (Washington: American Physiological Society, 1955).

Fahri, L. E., and Rahn, H.: A theoretical analysis of the alveolo-arterial O_2 difference with special reference to the distribution effect, J. Appl. Physiol. 7:699-703, 1955.

West, J. B., et al.: Measurement of the ventilation-perfusion ratio inequality in the lung by the analysis of a single expirate, Clin. Sc. 16:529-547, 1957.

West, J. B., et al.: Measurement of the inequality of ventilation and of perfusion in the lung by the analysis of single expirates, Clin. Sc. 16:549-565, 1957.

Briscoe, W. A.: A method for dealing with data concerning uneven ventilation of the lung and its effects on blood gas transfer, J. Appl. Physiol. 14:291-298, 1959.

Colldahl, H.; Alväger, T., and Uhler, J.: A comparison between pulmonary elimination capacity of acetylene and radioactive argon and xenon injected intravenously dissolved in saline, Acta allergol. 15:406-416, 1960.

West, J. B.; Dollery, C. T., and Hugh-Jones, P.: The use of radioactive CO_2 to measure regional blood flow in the lungs of patients with pulmonary disease, J. Clin. Invest. 40:1-12, 1961.

Ball, W. C., et al.: Regional pulmonary function studied with xenon[133]*, J. Clin. Invest. 41:519-531, 1962.

H. PULMONARY CIRCULATION

Roughton, F. J. W.: The average time spent by the blood in the human lung capillary, Am. J. Physiol. 143:621-633, 1945.

Riley, R. L., *et al.*: Studies of the pulmonary circulation at rest and during exercise in normal individuals and in patients with chronic pulmonary disease, Am. J. Physiol. 152:372-382, 1948.

Hellems, H. K.; Haynes, F. W., and Dexter, L.: Pulmonary "capillary" pressure in man, J. Appl. Physiol. 2:24-29, 1949.

Cournand, A.: Some aspects of the pulmonary circulation in normal man and in chronic cardiopulmonary diseases, Circulation 2:641-657, 1950.

Donald, K. W., *et al.*: The effect of exercise on the cardiac output and circulatory dynamics of normal subjects, Clin. Sc. 14:37-73, 1955.

Lee, G., and DuBois, A. B.: Pulmonary capillary blood flow in man, J. Clin. Invest. 34:1380-1390, 1955.

Lochner, W., and Witzleb, E.: *Lungen und Kleiner Kreislauf* (Berlin: Springer Verlag, 1957).

Adams, W., and Veith, I. (ed.): *Pulmonary Circulation* (New York: Grune & Stratton, Inc., 1959).

Lloyd, T. C., and Wright, G. W.: Pulmonary vascular resistance and vascular transmural gradient, J. Appl. Physiol. 15:241-245, 1960.

deReuck, A. V. S., and O'Connor, M. (ed.): *Problems of the Pulmonary Circulation* (Boston: Little, Brown & Company, 1961).

Fishman, A. P.: Respiratory gases in the regulation of the pulmonary circulation, Physiol. Rev. 41:214-280, 1961.

Burton, A. C.: Physical Principles of Circulatory Phenomena, in *Handbook of Physiology: Circulation I* (Washington: American Physiological Society, 1962), pp. 85–106.

Permutt, S., *et al.*: Effect of lung inflation on static pressure-volume characteristics of pulmonary vessels, J. Appl. Physiol. 16:64-70, 1961.

Severinghaus, J. W., *et al.*: Unilateral hypoventilation produced in dogs by occluding one pulmonary artery, J. Appl. Physiol. 16:53-60, 1961.

Harris, P., and Heath, D.: *The Human Pulmonary Circulation* (Edinburgh: E. & S. Livingstone, Ltd., 1962).

I. DIFFUSION ACROSS THE PULMONARY ALVEOLAR CAPILLARY MEMBRANES

Krogh, M.: Diffusion of gases through the lungs of man, J. Physiol. 49:271-300, 1914-15.

Barcroft, J.: *The Respiratory Function of the Blood:* Part I. The Diffusion of O_2 through Pulmonary Epithelium, Vol. I. (Cambridge: Cambridge University Press, 1925), pp. 63-74.

Lilienthal, J. L., *et al.*: An experimental analysis in man of the O_2 pressure gradient from alveolar air to arterial blood, Am. J. Physiol. 147:199-216, 1946.

Kety, S. S.: Pulmonary Diffusion Coefficient, in Comroe, J. H., Jr. (ed.): *Methods in Medical Research* (Chicago: Year Book Publishers, Inc., 1950), Vol. 2, pp. 234-242.

Riley, R. L., and Cournand, A.: Analysis of factors affecting partial pressures of O_2 and CO_2 in gas and blood of lungs: Theory, J. Appl. Physiol. 4:77-101, 1951.

Riley, R. L.; Cournand, A., and Donald, K. W.: Analysis of factors affecting partial pressures of O_2 and CO_2 in gas and blood of lungs: Methods, J. Appl. Physiol. 4:102-120, 1951.

Bates, D. V.: Uptake of CO in health and emphysema, Clin. Sc. 11:21-32, 1952.

Filley, G. F.; MacIntosh, D. J., and Wright, G. W.: Carbon monoxide uptake and pulmonary diffusing capacity in normal subjects at rest and during exercise, J. Clin. Invest. 33:530-539, 1954.

Forster, R. E., et al.: The absorption of CO by the lungs during breath-holding, J. Clin. Invest. 33:1135-1145, 1954.

Riley, R. L., et al.: Maximal diffusing capacity of the lungs, J. Appl. Physiol. 6:573-587, 1954.

Kruhøffer, P.: Studies on the lung diffusion coefficient for carbon monoxide in normal subjects by means of $C^{14}O$, Acta physiol. scandinav. 32:106-123, 1954.

Forster, R. E.: Exchange of gases between alveolar air and pulmonary capillary blood: Pulmonary diffusing capacity, Physiol. Rev. 37:391-452, 1957.

Marks, A., et al.: Clinical determination of the diffusion capacity of the lungs: Comparison of methods in normal subjects and patients with "alveolar-capillary block" syndrome, Am. J. Med. 22:51-73, 1957.

Ogilvie, C. M., et al.: A standardized breath holding technique for the clinical measurement of the diffusing capacity of the lung for carbon monoxide, J. Clin. Invest. 36:1-7, 1957.

Forster, R. E., et al.: Apparent pulmonary diffusing capacity for CO at varying alveolar O_2 tensions, J. Appl. Physiol. 11:277-289, 1957.

McNeill, R. S.; Rankin, J., and Forster, R. E.: The diffusing capacity of the pulmonary membrane and the pulmonary capillary blood volume in cardiopulmonary disease, Clin. Sc. 17:465-482, 1958.

Rankin, J.; McNeill, R. S., and Forster, R. E.: Influence of increased alveolar CO_2 tension on pulmonary diffusing capacity for CO in man, J. Appl. Physiol. 15:543-549, 1960.

Rankin, J.: Evaluation of Alveolar Capillary Diffusion, in Clinical Cardiopulmonary Physiology (New York: Grune & Stratton, 1960), pp. 624–634.

J. ARTERIAL O_2, CO_2 AND pH

Van Slyke, D. D., and Neill, J. M.: Determination of gases in blood and other solutions by vacuum extraction and manometric measurement, J. Biol. Chem. 61:523-573, 1924.

Van Slyke, D. D., and Sendroy, J., Jr.: Line charts for graphic calculations by Henderson-Hasselbalch equation and for calculating plasma CO_2 content from whole blood content, J. Biol. Chem. 79:781-798, 1928.

Roughton, F. J. W.: The transport of carbon dioxide by the blood, Harvey Lect. 39:96-142, 1943-44.

Roughton, F. J. W.: Darling, R. D., and Root, W. S.: Factors affecting the determination of oxygen capacity, content and pressure in human arterial blood, Am. J. Physiol. 142:708-720, 1944.

Drabkin, D. L., and Schmidt, C. F.: Spectrophotometric studies: Direct determination of the saturation of hemoglobin in arterial blood, J. Biol. Chem. 157:69-83, 1945.

Riley, R. L.; Proemmel, D. D., and Franke, R. E.: Direct method for determination of O_2 and CO_2 tensions in blood, J. Biol. Chem. 161:621-633, 1945.

Comroe, J. H., Jr., and Botelho, S.: The unreliability of cyanosis in the recognition of arterial anoxemia, Am. J. M. Sc. 214:1-6, 1947.

Singer, R. B., and Hastings, A. B.: Improved clinical method for estimation of disturbances of acid base balance of human blood, Medicine 27:223-242, 1948.

Wood, E. H.: Normal oxygen saturation of arterial blood during inhalation of air and oxygen, J. Appl. Physiol. 1:567-574, 1949.

Davenport, H.: *The ABC of Acid Base Chemistry* (Chicago: University of Chicago Press, 1950).

Comroe, J. H., Jr., and Dripps, R. D.: *The Physiological Basis for Oxygen Therapy* (Springfield, Ill.: Charles C Thomas, Publishers, 1950).

Comroe, J. H., Jr., and Wood, E. H.: Measurement of the Oxygen Saturation of Blood by Filter Photometers (Oximeters), in Comroe, J. H., Jr. (ed.): *Methods in Medical Research* (Chicago: Year Book Publishers, Inc., 1950), Vol. 2, pp. 144-159.

Consolazio, C. F.; Johnson, R. E., and Marek, E.: *Metabolic Methods* (St. Louis: C. V. Mosby Company, 1951).

Filley, G. F.; Gay, E., and Wright, G. W.: The accuracy of direct determinations of O_2 and CO_2 tensions in human blood in vitro, J. Clin. Invest. 33:500-516, 1954.

Astrup, P.: A simple electrometric technique for the determination of carbon dioxide tension in blood and plasma, total content of carbon dioxide in plasma, and bicarbonate content in "separated" plasma at a fixed carbon dioxide tension (40 mm Hg), Scandinav. J. Clin. & Lab. Invest. 8:33-43, 1956.

Shepard, R. H., and Meier, P.: Analysis of the errors of a bubble method for estimation of Pco_2 and Po_2 in whole blood, J. Appl. Physiol. 11:250-259, 1957.

Riley, R. L.; Campbell, E. J. M., and Shepard, R. H.: A bubble method for estimation of Pco_2 and Po_2 in whole blood, J. Appl. Physiol. 11:245-249, 1957.

Kreuzer, F.; Watson, T. R., Jr., and Ball, J. M.: Comparative measurements with a new procedure for measuring the blood oxygen tension in vitro, J. Appl. Physiol. 12:65-70, 1958.

Hackney, J. D.; Sears, C. H., and Collier, C. R.: Estimation of arterial CO_2 tension by rebreathing technique, J. Appl. Physiol. 12:425-430, 1958.

Severinghaus, J. W., and Bradley, A. F.: Electrodes for blood Po_2 and Pco_2 determination, J. Appl. Physiol. 13:515-520, 1958.

Severinghaus, J. W.: Respiratory System: Methods; Gas Analysis, in Glasser, O. (ed.): *Medical Physics* (Chicago: Year Book Medical Publishers, Inc., 1960), Vol. 3, pp. 550-560.

Symposium: Carbon dioxide and man, Anesthesiology 21:585-766, 1960.

K. MECHANICS OF BREATHING

Rohrer, F.: Der Strömungswiderstand in den menschlichen Atemwegen und der Einfluss der unregelmässigen Verzweigung des Bronchialsystems auf den Atmungsverlauf verschiedenen Lungenbezirken, Arch. ges. Physiol. 162:225-299, 1915.

Neergaard, K., and Wirz, K.: Über eine Methode zur Messung der Lungenelastizität am lebenden Menschen, insbesondere beim Emphysem, Ztschr. klin. Med. 105:35-51, 1927.

Christie, R. V., and MacIntosh, C. A.: The measurement of the intrapleural pressure in man and its significance, J. Clin. Invest. 13:279-294, 1934.

Bayliss, L. E., and Robertson, G. W.: The visco-elastic properties of the lungs, Quart. J. Exper. Physiol. 29:27-47, 1939.

Dean, R. B., and Visscher, M. B.: The kinetics of lung ventilation, Am. J. Physiol. 134:450-468, 1941.

Vuilleumier, P.: Über eine Methode zur Messung des intra-alveolaren Druckes und der Strömungswiderstände in den Atemwegen des Mensches, Ztschr. klin. Med. 143:698-717, 1944.

Rahn, H., *et al.*: The pressure-volume diagram of the lung and thorax, Am. J. Physiol. 146:161-178, 1946.

Buytendijk, H. J.: Intraesophageal Pressure and Lung Elasticity, Thesis, University of Groningen, Holland. (Electrische Drukkerij I. Oppenheim N. V., 1949.)

Gilson, J. C., and Hugh-Jones, P.: The measurement of the total lung volume and breathing capacity, Clin. Sc. 7:185-216, 1949.

Gray, J. S., *et al.*: Ventilatory function tests: I. Voluntary ventilation capacity, J. Clin. Invest. 29:677-681, 1950.

Matheson, H. W., *et al.*: Ventilatory function tests: II. Factors affecting the voluntary ventilation capacity, J. Clin. Invest. 29:682-687, 1950.

Matheson, H. W., and Gray, J. S.: Ventilatory function tests: III. Resting ventilation, metabolism, and derived measures, J. Clin. Invest. 29:688-692, 1950.

Otis, A. B.; Fenn, W. O., and Rahn, H.: Mechanics of breathing in man, J. Appl. Physiol. 2:592-607, 1950.

DuBois, A. B., and Ross, B. B.: A new method for studying mechanics of breathing using a cathode ray oscillograph, Proc. Soc. Exper. Biol. & Med. 78:546-549, 1951.

Gaensler, E. A.: Analysis of the ventilatory defect by timed capacity measurement, Am. Rev. Tuberc. 64:256-278, 1951.

Fenn, W. O.: Mechanics of respiration, Am. J. Med. 10:77-90, 1951.

Dayman, H.: Mechanics of airflow in health and emphysema, J. Clin. Invest. 30:1175-1190, 1951.

Ferris, B. G., *et al.*: Maximal breathing capacity and vital capacity in male and female children and adolescents, Pediatrics 9:659-669, 1952; 12:341-352, 1953.

Fry, D. L., *et al.*: The mechanics of pulmonary ventilation in normal subjects and in patients with emphysema, Am. J. Med. 16:80-96, 1954.

Otis, A. B.: The work of breathing, Physiol. Rev. 34:449-458, 1954.

DuBois, A. B.; Botelho, S. Y., and Comroe, J. H., Jr.: A new method for measuring airway resistance in man using a body plethysmograph: Values in normal subjects and in patients with respiratory disease, J. Clin. Invest. 35:327-335, 1956.

Marshall, R., and DuBois, A. B.: Measurement of the viscous resistance of the lung tissues in normal man, Clin. Sc. 15:161-170, 1956.

Butler, J.: The adaptation of the relaxed lungs and chest wall to changes in volume, Clin. Sc. 16:421-433, 1957.

Campbell, E. J. M.; Martin, H. B., and Riley, R. L.: Mechanisms of airway obstruction, Bull. Johns Hopkins Hosp. 101:329-343, 1957.

Gandevia, B., and Hugh-Jones, P.: Terminology for measurements of ventilatory capacity, Thorax 12:290-293, 1957.

Briscoe, W. A., and DuBois, A. B.: Relationship between airway resistance, airway conductance and lung volume in subjects of different age and body size, J. Clin. Invest. 37:1279-1285, 1958.

Campbell, E. J. M.: *The Respiratory Muscles and the Mechanics of Breathing* (Chicago: Year Book Publishers, Inc., 1958).

McNeill, R. S.; Malcolm, G. D., and Brown, W. R.: Comparison of expiratory and inspiratory flow rates in health and in chronic pulmonary disease, Thorax 14:225-231, 1959.

Fry, D. L., and Hyatt, R. E.: Pulmonary mechanics, Am. J. Med. 29:672-689, 1960.

Mead, J.: Mechanical properties of lungs, Physiol. Rev. 41:281-330, 1961.

Clements, J.: Studies of surface phenomena in relation to pulmonary function, The Physiologist 5:11-28, 1962.

Teaching film: "Mechanics of Breathing," by Department of Physiology, Harvard School of Public Health (Radford, Mead and Whittenberger).

L. CLINICAL EVALUATION OF PULMONARY FUNCTION

1. In older patients

Greifenstein, F. E., et al.: Pulmonary function studies in healthy men and women 50 years and older, J. Appl. Physiol. 4:641-648, 1952.

Shock, N. W., and Yungst, M. J.: Age changes in basal respiratory measurements and metabolism in males, J. Gerontol. 10:31-40, 1955.

Tenney, S. M., and Miller, R. M.: Respiratory response in the aged, J. Am. Geriatrics Soc. 3:937-944, 1955.

Hemingway, A.; Pocock, D., and Short, J. J.: Variations of basal respiration with age, J. Chron. Dis. 3:301-310, 1956.

Richards, D. W.: The aging lung, Bull. New York Acad. Med. 32:407-417, 1956.

Frank, N. R.; Mead, J., and Ferris, B. G., Jr.: The mechanical behavior of the lungs in healthy elderly persons, J. Clin. Invest. 36:1680-1687, 1957.

Pierce, J. A., and Ebert, R. V.: The elastic properties of the lungs in the aged, J. Lab. & Clin. Med. 51:63-71, 1958.

Gilson, J. C.: Changes in Pulmonary Function with Age, in Orenstein, A. J. (ed.): Proc. Pneumoconiosis Conference, Johannesburg, 1959 (London, J. & A. Churchill, Ltd.), pp. 280-285.

2. In newborn infants

Cook, C. D., et al.: Studies of respiratory physiology in the newborn infant: I. Observations on normal, premature and full-term infants, J. Clin. Invest. 34:975-982, 1955.

Cook, C. D., et al.: Studies of respiratory physiology in the newborn infant: III. Measurements of mechanics of respiration, J. Clin. Invest. 36:440-448, 1957.

Stahlman, M. T.: Pulmonary ventilation and diffusion in the human newborn infant, J. Clin. Invest. 36:1081-1091, 1957.

Cook, C. D.; Barrie, H., and Avery, M. E.: Respiration and Respiratory Problems of the Newborn Infant, in Levine, S. L. (ed.): Advances in Pediatrics (Chicago: Year Book Publishers, Inc., 1960) vol. 11, pp. 11-80.

3. In pregnant women

Cugell, D. W., et al.: Pulmonary function in pregnancy, Am. Rev. Tuberc. 67:568-597, 755-778, 779-797, 1953.

Rubin, A.; Russo, N., and Goucher, D.: The effect of pregnancy upon pulmonary function in normal women, Am. J. Obst. & Gynec. 72:963-969, 1956.

4. In obese patients

Bedell, G. N.; Wilson, W. R., and Seebohm, P. M.: Pulmonary function in obese persons, J. Clin. Invest. 37:1049-1060, 1958.

Gilbert, R.; Sipple, J. H., and Auchincloss, J. H., Jr.: Respiratory control and work of breathing in obese subjects, J. Appl. Physiol. 16:21-26, 1961.

5. In hypoventilation

Ferris, B. J., et al.: Pulmonary function in convalescent poliomyelitic patients, New England J. Med. 246:919-924, 1952; 247:43-47, 390-393, 1952.

Poliomyelitis: Papers and discussion presented at the Fourth International Poliomyelitis Conference (Philadelphia: J. B. Lippincott Company, 1958).

Bedell, G. N.: Alveolar Hypoventilation, in Gordon, B. (ed.): Clinical Cardiopulmonary Physiology (2d ed.; New York: Grune & Stratton, Inc., 1960), pp. 859-865.

6. *In patients with obstruction—(a) Asthma*

Beale, H. D.; Fowler, W. S., and Comroe, J. H., Jr.: Pulmonary function studies in 20 asthmatic patients in the symptom-free interval, J. Allergy 23:1-10, 1952.

McIlroy, M. B., and Marshall, R.: The mechanical properties of the lungs in asthma, Clin. Sc. 15:345-351, 1956.

In patients with obstruction—(b) Pulmonary Emphysema

Meakins, J.: Observations on the gases in human arterial blood in certain pathological pulmonary conditions and their treatment with oxygen, J. Path. & Bact. 24:79-90, 1921.

Baldwin, E. de F.; Cournand, A., and Richards, D. W., Jr.: A study of 122 cases of chronic pulmonary emphysema, Medicine 28:201-237, 1949.

Baldwin, E. de F., *et al.*: A study of 16 cases of large pulmonary air cysts or bullae, Medicine 29:169-194, 1950.

West, J. R., *et al.*: Physiopathologic aspects of chronic pulmonary emphysema, Am. J. Med. 10:481-496, 1951.

Fry, D. L., *et al.*: Mechanics of pulmonary ventilation in normal subjects and in patients with emphysema, Am. J. Med. 16:80-97, 1954.

Curtis, J. K.; Rasmusen, H. K., and Mendenhall, J. T.: The detection of early emphysema, Am. Rev. Tuberc. 72:569-576, 1955.

Mead, J.; Lindgren, I., and Gaensler, E. A.: The mechanical properties of the lungs in emphysema, J. Clin. Invest. 34:1005-1016, 1955.

Campbell, E. J. M.: Disordered pulmonary function in emphysema, Postgrad. M. J. 34:30-38, 1958.

Hugh-Jones, P.: The functional pathology of emphysema, Brit. J. Anaesth. 30:106-128, 1958.

McLean, K. H.: The pathogenesis of pulmonary emphysema, Am. J. Med. 25:62-74, 1958.

Symposium on Emphysema and the "Chronic Bronchitis" Syndrome, Am. Rev. Resp. Dis. 80:1-213, 1959.

Summary of Third Conference on Research in Emphysema, Am. Rev. Resp. Dis. 82:402-431; 563-586, 1961.

In patients with obstruction—(c) Bronchitis and Obliterative Airway Disease

Becklake, M. R., *et al.*: Long term effects of exposure to nitrous fumes, Am. Rev. Tuberc. 76:398-409, 1957.

Renzetti, A. D., *et al.*: Physiologic defects in chronic bronchitis, Am. Rev. Tuberc. 78:191-202, 1958.

Fletcher, C. M.: Chronic bronchitis, Am. Rev. Resp. Dis. 80:483-494, 1959.

7. *In patients with impaired diffusion*

Austrian, R., *et al.*: The syndrome of "alveolar-capillary block," Am. J. Med. 11:667-685, 1951.

Eldredge, F.: Pulmonary infiltration with eosinophilia and the alveolar-capillary block syndrome, Am. J. Med. 25:796-802, 1958.

Marshall, R., *et al.*: Pulmonary function in sarcoidosis, Thorax 13:48-58, 1958.

Gaensler, E. A., *et al.*: Respiratory pathophysiology in chronic beryllium disease, A.M.A. Arch. Indust. Health 19:132-145, 1959.

Dickie, H. A., and Rankin, J.: Interstitial Diseases of the Lungs: The Alveolar-Capillary Block Syndrome, in *Clinical Cardiopulmonary Physiology* (New York: Grune & Stratton, 1960), pp. 810-829.

Svanborg, N.: Studies on cardiopulmonary function in sarcoidosis, Acta med. scandinav., Supp. 366, 1961.

8. *In patients with restrictive disease*

Baldwin, E. de F.; Cournand, A., and Richards, D. W., Jr.: A study of 39 cases of pulmonary fibrosis, Medicine 28:1-25, 1949.

Wright, G. W., and Filley, G. F.: Pulmonary fibrosis and respiratory function, Am. J. Med. 10:642-661, 1951.

Riley, R. L.; Riley, M. C., and Hill, H. McD.: Diffuse pulmonary sarcoidosis, Bull. Johns Hopkins Hosp. 91:345-370, 1952.

Rogan, M. C.; Needham, C. D., and McDonald, I.: The effect of ankylosing spondylitis on ventilatory function, Clin. Sc. 14:91-96, 1955.

Whitfield, A. G. W.; Bond, W. H., and Arnott, W. M.: Radiation reactions in the lung, Quart. J. Med. 25:67-86, 1956.

Bergofsky, E. H., Turino, G. M., and Fishman, A. P.: Cardiorespiratory failure in kyphoscoliosis, Medicine 38:263-317, 1959.

Travis, D. M., *et al.*: The lungs in rheumatoid spondylitis, Am. J. Med. 29:623-632, 1960.

Caro, C. G., and DuBois, A. B.: Pulmonary function in kyphoscoliosis, Thorax 16:282-290, 1961.

9. *In patients with pulmonary arteriovenous shunts*

Hultgren, H. N., and Gerbode, F.: Physiologic studies in a patient with a pulmonary arteriovenous fistula, Am. J. Med. 17:126-133, 1954.

10. *In patients with pulmonary vascular congestion*

Carroll, D.; Cohn, J. E., and Riley, R. L.: Pulmonary function in mitral valvular disease: Distribution and diffusion characteristics in resting patients, J. Clin. Invest. 32:510-525, 1953.

West, J. R.; Bliss, H. A.; Wood, J. A., and Richards, D. W., Jr.: Pulmonary function in rheumatic heart disease, Circulation 8:178-187, 1953.

Sharp, J. T., *et al.*: Ventilatory mechanics in pulmonary edema in man, J. Clin. Invest. 36:1680-1687, 1958.

Ebert, R. V.: The lung in congestive heart failure, A. M. A. Arch. Int. Med. 107:450-459, 1961.

11. *In patients with polycythemia vera*

Newman, W.; Feltman, J. A., and Devlin, B.: Pulmonary function studies in polycythemia vera, Am. J. Med. 11:706-714, 1951.

Lawrence, J. H.; Berlin, N. I., and Huff, R. L.: The nature and treatment of polycythemia, Medicine 32:323-388, 1953.

Ratto, O. R., *et al.*: Anoxemia secondary to polycythemia and polycythemia secondary to anoxemia, Am. J. Med. 14:958-965, 1955.

12. *In patients with pneumothorax, pneumoperitoneum or phrenic nerve section*

Cournand, A., and Richards, D. W., Jr.: The effect of various types of collapse therapy upon cardiopulmonary function, Am. Rev. Tuberc. 44:123-172, 1943.

Wright, G. W.; Place, R., and Princi, F.: The physiological effects of pneumoperitoneum upon the respiratory apparatus, Am. Rev. Tuberc. 60:706-714, 1949.

Gaensler, F. A., and Strieder, J. W.: Pulmonary function before and after extrapleural pneumothorax, J. Thoracic Surg. 20:774-797, 1950.

13. *In patients following surgical procedures on the lungs*

Cournand, A., and Berry, F. B.: The effect of pneumonectomy upon cardiopulmonary function in adult patients, Ann. Surg. 116:532-552, 1942.

Birath, G.; Crafoord, C., and Rudstrom, P.: Pulmonary function after pneumonectomy and lobectomy, J. Thoracic Surg. 16:492-511, 1947.

Cournand, A., et al.: Pulmonary circulation and alveolar ventilation-perfusion relationship after pneumonectomy, J. Thoracic Surg. 19:80-116, 1950.

Gaensler, E. A., and Strieder, J. W.: Progressive changes in pulmonary function after pneumonectomy, J. Thoracic Surg. 22:1-34, 1951.

Patton, W. E.; Watson, T. R., and Gaensler, E. A.: Pulmonary function before and at intervals after surgical decortication of the lungs, Surg., Gynec. & Obst. 95:477-496, 1952.

Etsten, B. E., et al.: Pulmonary function after segmental pulmonary resection for bronchiectasis, New England J. Med. 248:81-86, 1953.

Burroughs, B., et al.: The postpneumonectomy state, Am. J. Med. 28:281-297, 1960.

14. In patients with tuberculosis

Birath, G.: Lung volume and ventilation efficiency, Acta med. scandinav., Supp. 154, pp. 1-215, 1944.

Warring, F. C., Jr.: Ventilatory function: Its evaluation in patients with pulmonary tuberculosis, Am. Rev. Tuberc. 51:432-454, 1945.

15. In patients with bronchiectasis

Cherniack, N., et al.: Pulmonary function tests in 50 patients with bronchiectasis, J. Lab. & Clin. Med. 53:693-707, 1959.

16. In patients with industrial pulmonary disease

Kazantis, G., and Buxton, R. J.: Respiratory function in men casting cadmium alloys, Brit. J. Indust. Med. 13:30-40, 1956.

Gilson, J. C., and Hugh-Jones, P.: Lung Function in Coalworker's Pneumoconiosis (London: Her Majesty's Stationery Office, 1958).

McKerrow, C. B., et al.: Respiratory function during the day in cotton workers: A study in byssinosis, Brit. J. Indust. Med. 15:75-83, 1958.

Becklake, M. R.; Zwi, S., and Lutz, W.: Studies on the nature and aetiology of respiratory disability in Witwatersrand gold-miners free of radiologic silicosis, Brit. J. Indust. Med. 16:290-296, 1959.

Gilson, J. C.: Industrial Pulmonary Disease, in Schilling, R.S.F. (ed.): Modern Trends in Occupational Health (London: Butterworth & Co., Ltd., 1960), Chap. 4.

Leathart, G. L.: Clinical, bronchographic, radiological and physiological observations in ten cases of asbestosis, Brit. J. Indust. Med. 17:213-227, 1960.

17. In patients with systemic disease

Wilson, W. R., and Bedell, G. N.: The pulmonary abnormalities in myxedema, J. Clin. Invest. 39:42-55, 1960.

Stein, M.; Kimbel, P., and Johnson, R. L.: Pulmonary function in hyperthyroidism, J. Clin. Invest. 40:348-363, 1961.

Cudkowicz, L.; Madoff, I. M., and Abelmann, W. H.: Rheumatoid lung disease, Brit. J. Dis. Chest 55:35-40, 1961.

M. PULMONARY DISABILITY AND DYSPNEA

Peabody, F. W.: Cardiac dyspnea, Harvey Lect. 12:248-271, 1916-1917.

Means, J. H.: Dyspnoea, Medicine 3:309-416, 1924.

Christie, R. V.: Dyspnoea: A review, Quart. J. Med. 7:421-454, 1938.

Wright, G. W.: Disability evaluation in industrial pulmonary disease, J.A.M.A. 141:1218-1222, 1949.

Richards, D. W.: The nature of cardiac and of pulmonary dyspnea, Circulation 7:15-29, 1953.

Christie, R. V.: Dyspnoea in relation to the visco-elastic properties of the lung, Proc. Roy. Soc. Med. 46:381-386, 1953.

Wright, G. W., and Branscomb, D. V.: The origin of the sensations of dyspnea, Tr. Am. Clin. & Climatol. A. 66:116-126, 1954.

Marshall, R.; Stone, R. W., and Christie, R. V.: The relationship of dyspnoea to respiratory effort in normal subjects, mitral stenosis and emphysema, Clin. Sc. 13:625-631, 1954.

Fowler, W. S.: The breaking point of breath holding, J. Appl. Physiol. 6:539-545, 1954.

Comroe, J. H., Jr.: Dyspnea, Mod. Concepts Cardiovas. Dis. 25:347-349, 1956.

McIlroy, M. B.: Dyspnea and the work of breathing in diseases of the heart, Prog. Cardiovas. Dis. 1:284-297, 1959.

McKerrow, C. B., and Gilson, J. C.: Lung Function and Its Measurement in Industrial Pulmonary Disease, in Schilling, R. S. F. (ed.): *Modern Trends in Occupational Health* (London: Butterworth & Co., Ltd., 1960), Chap. 3.

Gaensler, E. A.: "Dyspnea: Diagnostic and Therapeutic Implications," Disease-A-Month (Chicago: Year Book Medical Publishers, Inc.), May, 1961.

Campbell, E. J. M.; Dinnick, O. P., and Howell, J. B. L.: The immediate effects of elastic loads on the breathing of man, J. Physiol. 156:260-273, 1961.

N. ANESTHESIA, RESPIRATION AND PULMONARY FUNCTION

Dripps, R. D., and Dumke, P. R.: Effect of narcotics on balance between central and chemoreceptor control of respiration, J. Pharmacol. & Exper. Therap. 77:290-300, 1943.

Volpitto, P. P., and Brown, J. M.: Choice of anesthesia for patients with pulmonary emphysema, J.A.M.A. 142:897-901, 1950.

Beecher, H. K., et al.: Effect of position and artificial respiration on the excretion of CO_2 during thoracic surgery, J. Thoracic Surg. 22:135-148, 1951.

Dripps, R. D., and Severinghaus, J. W.: General anesthesia and respiration, Physiol. Rev. 35:741-777, 1955.

Greene, N. M.: Anesthetic management of patients with respiratory disease, J.A.M.A. 162:1276-1281, 1956.

O. PHYSIOLOGIC THERAPY

Comroe, J. H., Jr.; Bahnson, E. R., and Coates, E. O.: Mental changes occurring in chronically anoxemic patients during O_2 therapy, J.A.M.A. 143:1044-1048, 1950.

Comroe, J. H., Jr., and Dripps, R. D.: *The Physiological Basis for Oxygen Therapy* (Springfield, Ill.: Charles C Thomas, Publisher, 1950).

Whittenberger, J. L., and Sarnoff, S. J.: Physiologic principles in the treatment of respiratory failure, M. Clin. North America 34:1335-1362, 1950.

Dautrebande, L.: Physiological and pharmacological characteristics of liquid aerosols, Physiol. Rev. 32:214-276, 1952.

Cornell Conference on Therapy: Treatment of cough, Am. J. Med. 14:87-98, 1953.

Stone, D. J., *et al.*: Precipitation by pulmonary infection of acute anoxia, cardiac failure and respiratory acidosis in chronic pulmonary disease, Am. J. Med. 14:14-22, 1953.

Becklake, M. R.; Goldman, H. I., and McGregor, M.: Effects of pneumoperitoneum on lung function in pulmonary emphysema, Thorax 9:222-225, 1954.

Becklake, M. R.; McGregor, M., and Goldman, H. I.: A study of the effects of physiotherapy in chronic hypertrophic emphysema using lung function tests, Dis. Chest 26:180-191, 1954.

Boyd, E. M.: Expectorants and respiratory tract fluid, Pharmacol. Rev. 6:521-542, 1954.

Collier, C. R., and Affeldt, J. E.: Ventilatory efficiency of the cuirass respirator in totally paralyzed chronic poliomyelitis patients, J. Appl. Physiol. 6:531-538, 1954.

Campbell, E. J. M., and Friend, J.: Action of breathing exercises in pulmonary emphysema, Lancet 1:325-329, 1955.

Whittenberger, J. L.: Artificial respiration, Physiol. Rev. 35:611-628, 1955.

Suker, H. O., and Hickam, J. B.: Carbon dioxide intoxication: The clinical syndrome, its etiology and management with particular reference to the use of mechanical respirators, Medicine 35:389-423, 1956.

Forbes, J., and Wise, L.: Expectorants and sputum viscosity, Lancet 2:767-770, 1957.

Bucher, K.: Pathophysiology and pharmacology of cough, Pharmacol. Rev. 10: 43-58, 1958.

Mayer, E.; Rappaport, I., and Blazsik, C. F.: Indications and contraindications for tracheal fenestration, J.A.M.A. 168:169-173, 1958.

Miller, W. F.: Physical therapeutic measures in the treatment of chronic bronchopulmonary disorders, Am. J. Med. 14:929-940, 1958.

Symposium: Mouth to mouth resuscitation (expired air inflation), J.A.M.A. 167: 317-341, 1958.

Arnott, W. M.: Respiratory failure, Lancet 1:1-7, 1960.

Head, J. M.: Tracheostomy in the management of respiratory problems, New England J. Med. 264:587-591, 1961.

Tyler, J. M.: Failure to improve effective ventilation on shifting from mouth to tracheostomy breathing in clinically stable emphysema, New England J. Med. 265:414-418, 1961.

Whittenberger, J. L. (ed.): *Artificial Respiration: Theory and Applications* (New York: Hoeber Medical Division, Harper & Bros., 1962).

Index

An asterisk (*) indicates reference to an illustration; n. indicates footnote.

A

Abbreviations in pulmonary physiology, 330–331
Acid-base balance, and CO_2, 158–161
Acidosis
 diabetic and renal, Kussmaul breathing in, 56
 metabolic
  from anoxemia, 148
  causing hyperventilation, 49
 respiratory, 28
  during anesthesia (case), 279–280
  and blood CO_2 content, 160–161
  effect on respiration, 52*
  from hypoventilation, 45–47, 48*
  oxygen therapy in, 309
Aging: pulmonary function changes with, 212–213
Air flow, 178
 types, 180*, 181
Air trapping, 187, 196*, 197
Air velocity index, 203
Airway
 conducting, in ventilation process, 28, 31
 obstruction
  expiratory problems in, 296
  natural mechanism of clearing, 297
  treatment measures, 282–284, 291–301
 oropharyngeal, 283, 285
 resistance, *see* Resistance to breathing
Alkalosis: blood CO_2 with, 160–161
Alveolar air equation, 125, 339–341, 353

Alveoli
 in pulmonary gas exchange, 3, 4–5*
 surface film lining, 174
Alveolo-capillary block, 111, 114–115, 238
 diffusing capacity with, 137
Anemia: diffusing capacity with, 138
Anesthesia, general
 anoxemia in, 147, 148
 and CO_2 retention, 147, 278, 279–280
 in emphysema—mechanical problems with, 187
 hypoventilation in, 45, 49, 147
 respiratory problems in, 276–280
 ventilation/blood flow ratio in, 100*
Anoxemia
 see also Arterial blood
 causes, 146–150
  hypoventilation, 44–48, 46*, 147
  uneven ventilation/blood flow ratios, 90, 95–99
  venous-to-arterial shunt, 103–104
 definition, 146
 diagnosis by O_2 inhalation, 310
 differentiation of type, 142
 disability from, 150–151
 effect on respiration, 53–55
 in evaluation of pulmonary function, 147–150
 oxygen therapy in, 307–310
 with polycythemia—therapy, 317–318
Anoxia
 causes of, 149–150
 definition, 146
 effects of, 49, 150–151
 oxygen therapy in, 307–310

379